MALIFAUX

Malifaux

Wyrd Miniatures, LLC

malifaux.com
wyrd-games.net

Customer Service Email - support@wyrd-games.net

Second printing: September 2011. Printed in South Korea.

MALIFAUX: Twisting Fates
ISBN 978-0-9841509-3-9
WYR 6015

WYRD MINIATURES PRESENTS

MALIFAUX

TWISTING FATES

CREDITS

Creator of MALIFAUX
Nathan Caroland

Creative Direction
Miniature Direction
Nathan Caroland
Eric Johns

Managing Editor
Casey Jones

Game Creation and Design
Graphic Design
Photography
Eric Johns

Rules Development Lead
Drew Littell

Rules Development
Dave Bowen
Zafar Tejani
Dan Weber

Writers
Dave Bowen
Nathan Caroland
Lenny Glower
Casey Jones
Dave McGuire
Dan Weber

Illustration, Logo, Concept, and 3D Artists
Alexandur Alexandrov
Melvin de Voor
Lino Drieghe
Stéphane Enjoralas
Hardy Fowler
Christophe Madaru
Karla Ortiz
Pablo Quiligotti

Painting
Jessica Rich
Thomas Schadle
James Wappel

Office Administrator
Victoria Caroland

Webmaster
Matt Kutchins

Playtester Lead
Drew Littell
Dan Weber

Playtesters

Michael Akridge	Martin Hakenesch	Job Schumacher
Clint Ammenhauser	Max Hardenbrook	Charles Schweppe
Dan'O Amonette	Steve Henderson	Adrian Scott
David Amos	Tyler Herrick	Dan Seeley
Bill Anderson	Cory Hockman	Chris Seibert
Eric Appel	Mike Kelmelis	Alex Shelton
Will Ash	Benjamin Kiemle	Gary Seibel
Mike Austin	Gero Kieslich	Chis Slazinski
Ray Bannon	Andrew Kirschbaum	Ben Smith
David Barfield	Matt Kutchins	Gordon Snellgrove
Edd Barfield	Josh Leak	Anna Clara Soares
Jens Becker	Drew Littell	Dan Sulin
Matt Belmont	Johnathan Loveday	Richard Tate
Dave Bowen	Lauri Marx	Zafar Tejani
David Brown	Sascha Masterlertz	Sebastian Theisen
Tim Brown	Bjˆrn Mayer	Dixon Thiru
Aaron Brueckman	Patrick McCade	Andrew Timm
Alexander Cairns	Jeremy McDowell	Ruth Toomey
Travis Camara	Justin McDowell	Ransom Trimble
David Cattoir	Tyrone McElvenny	Dave Troxell
Marty Clemment	David B. McGuire	Christoph Van der Schoot
James Cook	Jelle Meersman	Joshua Vannelli
Tracy Cook	Ben Misky	Paul Vigar
Bart Corley	Bryan Moore	Adrian Wain
Bryan Creehan	Ryan Moore	Chris Walsh
Ashley Dennis	Mervyn Murphy	Dan Weber
Brett Dennis	James Naegele	David Webster
Eric Dietsch	Charles Oldbaugh	Ben Weller
Michael Edwards	Jay Powell	Jay Whisler
Mark Elwood	Josh Powers	Corey Wilke
Ron Fitzpatrick	Joshua Prielipp	John Wilson
Jeffery Frederick	Sebastiaan Raats	Nathan Wolf
Glenn Getyina	Scott Reid	Matt Younger
Evan Gibbs	Bret A. Rice	Steven Zukowski
Justin Gibbs	Ryan Rockett	
Jack Gibson	Jason Rollins	
Stefan Gˆrlitz	Adam Rosenblum	
Merlin Goss	Paul Schipitsch	
Jim Graham	Nick Schneider	

Wyrd Miniatures would like to thank everyone for their hard work and dedication in completing this latest book. We owe a special thanks to the creativity of the writers for excelling in their efforts. Game developers, artists, sculptors, painters, playtesters - we appreciate everything you've done for us. And to our families and all those whose personal friendship and support has helped us through some stressful times, you have our heartfelt love and gratitude for just being who you are and helping in all the little ways.

TABLE OF CONTENTS

Still A Character-Based Skirmish Game, but Now, Even Shirmishier (and bigger)

As anyone involved in the first few go-rounds of Malifaux playtesting could tell you, there were a lot of ideas come and go. By now, you know all about the Fate Deck, and Cheating Fate, and the Duel mechanic. One concept we liked but couldn't squeeze into that first release was the Avatars (they're big). We always knew it had to come, it was part of the story line and already part of the game, we just didn't know how to squeeze it into that first book.

Now, the world of Malifaux has reached a place where we think it's time to introduce the Avatars to you. (I'm sure those first alpha testers are happy that they finally get to talk about Avatars, 2.5 years later.) Not to mention, you might find them to be a great way to up-the-ante and make games more challenging.

Avatars are new (and big) manifestations of Malifaux Masters. Their stories, rules, and stats expand what it means to be a Master. There's more strategy, more ways to win (and lose!), and more choices for players during the game. Basically, it's just some new fun added to your Malifaux.

I think you'll also really enjoy the story. We think the people, the history, and the world of Malifaux are amazing and interesting, and we wanted to put the effort into detailing that for everyone. So we've taken time to give you the stories of some of the characters that have only been on the periphery in the first two books. And we've also provided a lot more information on what happens to those making their lives in this world. It should provide you with a great background for your Encounters, let you know what it feels like to live and grow there, so you can join in the experiences.

We also have a lot of rad new artwork. But there's more! Each faction also gets a collection of new Minions to play with, including the introduction of Effigies - (not big) physical embodiments of Malifaux's power.

We know everyone's been waiting to find out what happened to Justice. Alive? Dead? Undead? Well, a building did fall on her. What did you expect? ... So get reading, and you'll see whether she made it out, became one of Seamus' risen beauties, or maybe, if in her death, her powers changed her into some sort of hybrid creature. Nightmares aside, I hope you enjoy watching the characters evolve (and get bigger) as much as I do.

Eric Johns

Eric Johns
Game Designer

Twisting Fates

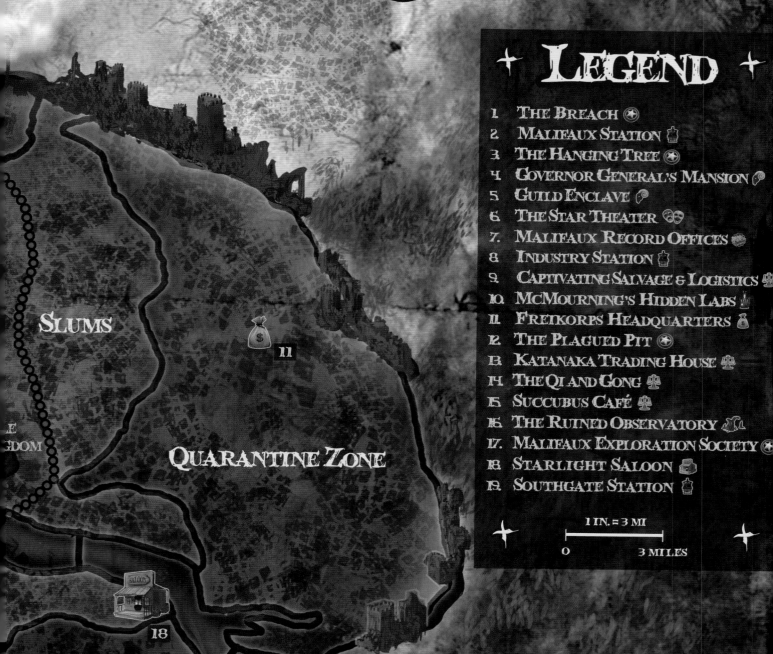

MAP OF MALIFAUX CITY

LANDS

LEGEND

1. THE BREACH
2. MALIFAUX STATION
3. THE HANGING TREE
4. GOVERNOR GENERAL'S MANSION
5. GUILD ENCLAVE
6. THE STAR THEATER
7. MALIFAUX RECORD OFFICES
8. INDUSTRY STATION
9. CAPTIVATING SALVAGE & LOGISTICS
10. MCMOURNING'S HIDDEN LABS
11. FREIKORPS HEADQUARTERS
12. THE PLAGUED PIT
13. KATANAKA TRADING HOUSE
14. THE QI AND GONG
15. SUCCUBUS CAFÉ
16. THE RUINED OBSERVATORY
17. MALIFAUX EXPLORATION SOCIETY
18. STARLIGHT SALOON
19. SOUTHGATE STATION

1 IN. = 3 MI

0   3 MILES

SLUMS

E
EDOM

QUARANTINE ZONE

11

SALOON

18

TO LATIGO AND THE
BAYOU

Like Falling Snow

September 20, 114 PF

The Event

The voices lingered in Hoffman's head, scattering every thought he desperately tried to follow. The energy of the mysterious wave dissipated gradually, but his breathing grew shallow and quick to match the quickening of his heart. Panic replaced the tingling in his fingers as the last of the magic from the Event left him.

The last time he had felt anything that closely matched this powerful bombardment of energy was on the train when he and his brother had come through to Malifaux.

Ryle's smile filled him with hope. It always had. Big and strong, Ryle had everything Hoffman wished he could have for himself. Coupled with an athletic prowess few could match, Ryle had a social ease, which made him friends with every man he met. Hoffman studied his brother with awe as he could shift his mannerisms and colloquialisms with unconscious alacrity. Perhaps not the most naturally handsome man in London, he nevertheless was the envy of most men when he could walk into any pub or society ball and, without intent, soon find himself in the midst of the most sought after women in the city. Everyone envied Ryle's style and embrace of life; Hoffman was no exception. However, so many people thought his jealousy must run deep. It did not. Hoffman revered his older brother and followed him everywhere. He looked upon him with unadulterated respect and love and would never have wished him less. Ryle was almost unaware of his good fortune and stood at the apex of humility. In fact, he was driven most to protect his younger brother, even at the cost of his own position, and Hoffman knew that, in many ways, he owed his life to Ryle.

Hoffman shook off the reverie of his brother as he once was, chastising himself for allowing the thoughts to lull him with happier times, distracting him from his current struggle. He pulled himself over, and his mind reeled. His eyes remained heavy, and even when he managed to force them open, he had trouble focusing his vision. A coughing spasm wracked him as he fought to push himself upright. Smoke and ash from the nearby burning observatory dusted his shoulders like snow.

Once, when they were young, Hoffman watched Ryle and some of the other boys playing rugby in the back of their parents' expansive country estate. It was late fall, and the boys' breath came visibly in clouds about their faces as they ran in the brisk air. All of them ignored the cold as they wore their uniforms cut just above the knees. They'd slap and rub their bare skin to warm it between plays, and even though their skin was pink and sore, they played on. Hoffman watched from the comfort of an upper room, his chin resting on both palms as he sat in his wheelchair parked before the window, wiping the condensation from the window with his handkerchief.

Ryle looked up to see his younger brother watching them, laughing and playfully chiding one another as they debated the imaginary lines forming the field's boundary between each play. They could never agree upon the lines, and playful shoves led to wrestling matches between sides that looked, for all intent, exactly like the rugby plays they debated over. They laughed and clapped one another on the backs.

When Hoffman rubbed his window clean again, he could not see Ryle down amongst the others. Though they shoved and writhed about in manly play, Ryle was always quickly identifiable. Thick flakes of snow began to fall, enveloping the players in a sheet of soft white.

A hand fell upon his shoulder, causing him to jump. "Sorry, chap!" Ryle said with a laugh. Hoffman smiled; he hadn't noticed Ryle come into the house and enter the study. "No need for you to hide in here alone. We could use a referee." He motioned to the boys, knocking into one another again amidst the thickly falling snow. His hand squeezed Hoffman's shoulder.

Hoffman jumped as the desiccated arm of the dead reached out from the debris near his face, grabbing him at the shoulder as sickly gray ash fell. He screamed out and batted the bony fingers clutching at his neck and frantically pulled himself away, dragging his limp legs through dust and rubble. Scrambling back against a block of upturned flagstone, he shielded his face from attack by the undead. He whimpered and shook, finally peering over his forearm after several long moments without the expected assault. He rubbed his eyes quickly, unable to focus, preparing to fight one of the unholy risen. His hands curled into rather ineffectual fists, and his teeth chattered as his fear mounted. The hand reaching for him was, truly, that of a dead man, its face just visible from the edge of the rubble. But it showed no sign of reanimation as its mouth was agape and its dry eyes had shrunken within its deep sockets. Even the position of its body demonstrated no real indication that it was intentionally reaching for him.

The anxiety and adrenaline got the best of him, and his sobbing turned to a weak nervous laugh as, despite himself, he was overcome by fear. He drew himself against a large group of upturned cobblestone protruding from what was part of the street. It had been broken free long ago, though. He pulled himself to it and slapped each side of his face as smartly as he could given his exhausted state. "Pull yourself together, Old Boy," he said aloud, rubbing his eyes once more. His hands tingled, and a thin arc of pale violet electricity crackled faintly down his arm and across his chest.

The blue lightning arced from passenger to passenger as Ryle flailed on the floorboards of the train that ill-fated day they rode through the Breach. Everyone sat frozen in time, unmoving as the thick bands of electricity buzzed and popped, moving from person to person, coursing through their chests and out their skulls as the bolts sought another person.

Hoffman wasn't locked in time like the others, but reaching his hand toward his brother took terrifyingly long moments. Ryle, though, flailed in acceleration as the lightning arced from every passenger to strike him.

When the great tendril of electricity rose up and struck him like a whip crack, he bucked and howled, contorting off the wooden bench and around the floor, much like Ryle had been, though less severely. Still, the pain was intense, and he howled, unable to control his spasming limbs.

Shaking off his stupor, his eyes darted from one nearby object to another, sure that an insurmountable adversary moved amidst the thick ash and settling dust. He soon discovered that there were a substantial number of dead bodies in various stages of decomposition surrounding him, but none seemed to move or attract his attention. He found a small wrench in his back pocket and used it as a weapon to club what might have been the smallest Malifaux rat in the City. It was small even by Earthside standards. He did not hesitate to kill it. The plague still ravaged and the creature could kill him without realizing it, he justified. In reality, he felt so weak and ineffectual and needed a moment of control to right himself.

As the ash from the exploded building created a softening of the early morning light and sound, muffling everything, his sense of isolation and seclusion was heightened. The bodies of the dead lay strewn beneath rubble and debris, and some had merely collapsed in a heap. The bodies represented the full range of decomposition as a testament to their reanimation and control of a Resurrectionist master. In equal number were the fresh remains of youthful gang members and other innocent townspeople that had come to wage battle, fervently following the command of a strange and sinister man Hoffman had only heard of through rumor. None of the bodies seemed to move in that unholy state of reanimation, but Hoffman could not shake the anxious twitching of his blurry eyes as every small movement near him caught his attention, only to be disturbed by some other imagined adversary in his peripheral vision.

He could hear no voices of the machinery around him now. It was the first time since his arrival in Malifaux less than a month earlier. Only having a vague awareness of his full potential over the manipulation of machines, he didn't understand the meaning of this sudden loss of ability. He tried again, attempting to reach into the odd space of a construct's alien psyche, speaking in strange images and whispers.

Movement before him jerked his vision toward the same dark-fleshed corpse that he had imagined reached out to him. Blinking rapidly to clear the fog, he saw it unmoving, its eyes having rolled up into its skull, mouth agape and long fingers pointing. Another crackle of purple electricity arced from the braces he bore on either leg and danced around his torso and up his throat.

The blue lightning in the car subsided as the train ground to a halt, digging through the gray dirt beside the track. Screams of passengers replaced the electrical crackling and popping, and Ryle's screaming died along with the energy that wracked him, but the sound of Ryle's horrified plight echoed within his mind as he slipped into the dark fog. He fought the drowning sensation of sleep, struggling to come to the surface of consciousness to call for someone to help his brother.

"You did this!" he heard a woman shriek. "Arcanist!" His eyes opened briefly and with great effort he sought her, framing her features with the blur of his sinking mind. She cowered, pointing with mouth agape at the two men that had entered the car, standing just beyond him and his brother. She was filled with fear and anger. "Arcanists!" she screamed again in accusation. One of them ended her life with a crack of his pistol, momentarily silencing the others.

He couldn't hold on any longer and succumbed to the weight of sleep that bore down upon him, watching as the villains reached for him as his eyes involuntarily closed.

He jerked when the crashing weight of a Peacekeeper construct cracked the mortar between the cobblestones beside him, the ripples of the tremor rippling through his torso and rattling his teeth. He cried out as he looked upon the face of Ramos above him, lost in the broken vision of his mind and replaced by the image of the Arcanist he blamed for the attack upon him and the train. "Arcanist!" Hoffman howled, still confused about what was real.

Ramos reached down to him with his right arm and grabbed hold of the writhing violet tendril of electricity. He pulled it from Hoffman's throat, and it hissed and crackled as it flailed. It burned, and Ramos' leather glove melted away along with the thick canvas of his overcoat, exposing the thin pistons and spinning gears of a mechanical arm. He unleashed his own electrical fire through that exposed limb, and the pale electricity evaporated in a small thunderous clap.

Hoffman's perception cleared, and his fear eased as the Arcanist terrorist from the train morphed into the familiar face and voice of his friend Dr. Ramos, who answered the accusation of "Arcanist" still hanging in the air.

"Yes," Ramos said. "But we are not what you think us to be. Come."

"What?" Hoffman asked. The purple energy no longer crackled around him, and he could think clearer, but he still doubted his perception, and Ramos' statement made no sense to him.

"Come," Ramos said, reaching out with his mechanical arm to help Hoffman stand. "We will speak, but this is not the place for it." Faint morning light penetrated the ashy haze, and the brass cylinders of Ramos' arm gleamed. Hoffman's hand stretched, but as he saw the oiled hydraulic shaft and silently spinning servos, now exposed from the cloth and leather that had been burned away by the lightning, he withdrew his hand in a snap.

"You're an Arcanist," he said, now fully aware of whom he addressed.

"Yes. But we are not what you think we are."

It made striking sense, and Hoffman reeled from the truth and the ridiculous clarity of his deception. The machines of his laboratory and throughout the mines were so clearly beyond mere mechanical science. The lumbering behemoth Steamborg, Hank, a human and machine abomination followed every small command from Ramos without pause or question. That was no coincidence he worked in the mines. And his own brother, Ryle...turned into a monstrosity. Hoffman had ignored the clear truth, obvious, now, out of desperation for it to not be so. Ramos was not just an Arcanist, but an abomination, himself, of grafting technology and twisted magics. One of the same abominations that Hoffman was charged to find and apprehend. Of course, the Charter was far more specific in addressing the abuses of grafting technology, and articulated prosthetics were common enough and well within the rights of anyone. Hoffman made a leap in blame and hatred.

Still lying on the broken street, his legs limp before him, he said gravely, "Viktor Ramos. You are under arrest for crimes against the natural order."

"Do not be a fool," he interrupted, growing quickly irritated.

"You are charged with illegal grafting according to Guild Charter 425, sub-section Two, and conspiring against Guild order in organizing the terrorist group—"

"I'm warning you, Hoffman," Ramos said with terrifying authority. "We are not what you have been made to believe. But I will not have you undo what I have begun. What I've accomplished." Hoffman had not noticed their presence before, but two great constructs stood ominously behind Ramos. One was a humanoid giant known as a Guardian, its excessively large sword resting upon its massive iron shoulder. It was one of the earliest constructs designed and built, largely under the supervision of Ramos, and it stood beside his most recent construct design, the Giant Arachnid that stood higher than a man's waist and was easily as long as a man was tall. Ramos made no movement nor word of command, but the two stepped forward toward him. "Every construct in Malifaux heard your call when that wave hit," Ramos said. "Even I, enveloped in that same powerful inundation of aether," his mechanical hand clutched into a fist before his face. "Even I could hear your plea above all the screaming voices in my head. So powerful. So much potential. But I cannot bear to lose what we have fought so hard to accomplish."

Hoffman had nowhere to go and wouldn't be able to get there even if he had. The small wrench in his hand might as well have been a feather against the two constructs coming for him.

He could not describe his ability to perceive the metal and machinery around him with his mind. It was very different from holding something in his hands and much more like an emotional response. He felt comforted by the presence of machinery. Reaching out with his mind, he found his Hunter construct behind him, standing a silent watch. He knew it was inoperable, twisted with ancient metal of fences and sewer grates from around him as the purple aether of the Event had infused him with unbridled power. It now stood motionless as a deformed and abstract statue, looking only vaguely like the feline Hunter it had once been, now standing bipedally and more massive than ever. He could sense no sign of its once quick-processing logic engine.

Far above him, however, he felt a Watcher construct, and he latched onto it with his mind, calling it to him. Another Watcher circled the debris of the Observatory, obeying its last command, and he summoned that one to him as well. Neither would help against Ramos, a Guardian, and a Giant Arachnid, but when they were close to him, he could use their processing power to think more clearly, himself.

Ramos' constructs stepped forward, moving toward Hoffman, blocking any possible escape.

Ramos would win. He was an Arcanist operating right in the middle of the Guild. He was responsible for the mines, the most important reason anyone was in the godforsaken place to begin with. And he was responsible for Ryle.

Hoffman's fear was replaced with hate and anger at the betrayal and lies. He yelled, just a single syllable of his mounting rage, and his mind beat against the simple logic engine of the Guardian just in front of Ramos. It took a final step forward, its footfall reverberating through the ground as its vast weight struck. Ramos realized too late that he had underestimated Hoffman, and he jumped back as the great sword clattered to the ground and its armored hand snatched at its former master, no longer in control of it. He realized his loss and made no effort to reclaim it from Hoffman, instead focusing upon the large arachnid scampering forward a step and then back, confused as Hoffman pressed his will against it, too. Where Hoffman's power manifested more subconsciously, Ramos had to weave his commands on the current of aether that coursed around all things. Hoffman did possess great power, he had no doubt, but his manipulation of those invisible forces of magic were certainly substantial as well.

Ramos struggled to control the arachnid, but the Guardian's hand wrapped around his torso and squeezed, disrupting his focus. The circular saw blade mounted flat against its abdomen came free from its safety locks and spun, cutting through the air. The Guardian lifted him, pulling him closer. Ramos commanded the arachnid to remain stationary, and it obeyed him, but Hoffman fought for control over its weapon and it pivoted on its hinged accordion arm, spinning now vertically as the arm extended toward Ramos.

Ramos rarely felt fear and never succumbed to panic. But he was accustomed to control and authority in all of his dealings. Coming here to rescue Hoffman, he did not expect to so quickly lose control to the seemingly helpless man. The arachnid's blade drew closer, and he felt fear. He stilled his emotions and focused, drawing the aether into a controllable weapon. Blue electricity formed around his neck, and he channeled it into a blast that would ignite the construct's internal mechanism, frying it in a great electrical fire. But at Hoffman's mental command, the metal plates in the circular port hole in its chest popped open, exposing a facetted amber crystal. It burst into a rapidly flashing strobe of brilliant yellow light, blinding Ramos just as he released the electricity. The tendrils of energy snaked down his arm, but he lost control of it, and it popped out of existence with little more than the spark of static electricity.

The blade drew closer. Ramos grabbed the Guardian's wrist with his own mechanical hand and pressurized the pistons of his arm to squeeze, crushing the armature of the Guardian's arm, attempting to break free of it. The metal of its wrist buckled and bent, and he crushed it so that gears clanged against one another and the pneumatic seals ruptured, releasing a blast of steam shooting from the side. Still, it did not release him. He twisted desperately but ineffectually to block the circular saw and could barely reach his mechanical right arm around to block the blade, and it bounced aside in a shower of sparks as the tempered blade cut through the softer brass casing of his fist.

He would have died at the hands of his own constructs if not for Ryle. The towering hulk lumbered out of the shadows and fell upon the large spidery construct, his own hydraulic fist several times more powerful and formidable than Ramos'. It left the rounded head of the construct dented with a deep depression. The great hand grabbed hold of the twirling blade, and the teeth dug through his armored palm, but he twisted sharply and the blade snapped, half of it flying into the leg of the Guardian with a clang.

Hoffman, having finally managed to struggle to an awkward stand, recoiled at the vaguely recognizable features that were once so enviable. Now, hulking and more monstrous than human, the damaged flesh stretched over bone and muscle wouldn't heal against the wires, metal bolts, and tubes of copper and brass. Where Dr. Ramos had integrated the mechanical components "to save" Ryle, the flesh adjoining it withered into a sickly pallid gray. Around his upper chest, the skin appeared like drying leather stretched taut, exposing ribs and his collar bone as it shriveled and died. Metal plates were screwed into his flesh at different places, and the surrounding flesh was a beaten purple that darkened into gray. Ryle lifted his massive bulk from the large arachnid, sparks and steam issuing from beneath the damaged plate above its cracked logic engine. If Hoffman could have somehow overlooked the decay of Ryle's body, the severity of the grotesque visage before him made him recoil in horror. Much of the initial trauma through the Breach had been to Ryle's brain, and large portions of his skull had been cut away, now replaced by iron and brass. A large gauge where his right ear had been now marked the steam pressure within that drove the pistons and mechanical organs throughout his body. Numerous tubes protruded from the back of his head to attach at various points to organs and appendages, allowing him to function now in a parody of humanity. What revolted Hoffman most was, oddly, the *remaining* flesh of his lower jaw. With his

throat torn away and replaced with flexible tubing, his jaw rested agape and thick foam drained from each side of his mouth. The surrounding flesh was connected at every side by metal, and it was drawn tight in desiccation, fully exposing Ryle's yellowing teeth and ashen gums.

Hoffman staggered away from his brother. Unable to look upon him, he held up his palm toward Ryle to block the sight. Pressing his mind against machines was an ability growing more and more familiar to him, and he commanded the shambling construct to disengage. He thought of the lab where he had spied Ryle spending most of his time, standing motionless in place for days on end, and he silently commanded his brother to return there. Ryle did not comply.

The Gatling gun, heavy enough to require two men to carry but held by Ryle in just one hand, clattered on the rubble, and he lumbered toward Hoffman who struggled to step away. The brothers were a sad mirror of stiff scuffling, each walking with effort.

"Stop!" Hoffman commanded aloud, pressing his will once more against the artificial logic engine integrated into the brain of his brother. Ryle walked on, his arms outstretched toward Hoffman, the gears and servos clicking as his great fist uncurled, the metal talons reaching for him.

Hoffman took one final awkward step back, pulling the strap of his leg brace desperately with his thin hand, and screamed as Ryle's hands fell upon him. He turned away from his brother, eyes clenched shut, awaiting his attack.

"Brother," he felt the push of a machine against his mind. He saw snowflakes, thick and heavy, falling in the dim light of the moon, struggling to penetrate the cold precipitation.

"Ryle?" he called desperately into the depths of that dark night. The silhouette of a man walked just beyond the edge of his perception. "Ryle!" In the snowfall of his waking dream, Hoffman needed no braces to help him stand, and no paralysis kept him from running toward the dim shape of his brother. Yet as he ran, the snow fell thicker, and the light of the moon waned until the ghostly outline of his brother was enveloped by the snow and darkness. "Ryle!" he screamed again, and his voice echoed into the night of his dream. He fell to his knees, feeling the cold against his ankles and shins. His eyes were clenched tightly as tears rolled down each cheek.

The wind blew wet against his face, and he heard the whisper, "You can help me, brother."

He opened his eyes and the dream was gone. He was on his knees as ash continued to fall from the burning observatory beyond Ramos, still held aloft by the Guardian. Ryle had released his grip on him, allowing him to fall to his knees on the broken paving stones in the Quarantine Zone, and walked away.

Hoffman regarded Ramos and the two understood the conflict was abruptly over. "Where's he going?"

Ramos said, "Back to my lab, I'd guess."

"Why – why doesn't he stay here – with me?"

"He's ashamed."

The realization struck Hoffman. "He feels? He still feels?"

"Yes. Though vaguely." Ramos finally freed himself from the grip of the Guardian and straightened his overcoat, dusting himself as he stepped toward Hoffman. "And less every day. He cannot bear for you to see him."

"I think I saw him. In my mind."

"I can keep him alive, of course. But his humanity, his spirit, I fear those are beyond me. You, though, you may be the one able to help him."

"Yes. That is what he said to me. How can I do that?"

Ramos pulled him to his feet and helped him stabilize his balance. "I'm unsure. But I can assist you in figuring it out. You may be strong, but I'm not without my uses, also." No one had ever used "strong" to describe Hoffman, and he was filled with determination. "Come," Ramos said. "Let's return to the lab."

"No," Hoffman said. "Justice and the Judge are in there." He hitched a thumb to the burning remains of the once massive observatory.

"They're dead," Ramos said flatly.

Hoffman nearly protested but caught himself. "Likely," he agreed. "I concur. But that section there," he said with a point, "is mostly brick, little timber. It's near the front foyer where she attacked the risen throng. She may be there. If only her body. We must try."

Ramos considered the area, smoking timbers and debris piled high. He held his mechanical hand before his face, the heat of the fire and the breeze of the wind dead upon the metal as the fringe of his coat smoldered near his shoulder. He was exposed, and if more Guild operatives came for the rescue operation, there would be little excuse he could offer. Cold, calculating, circumstances rarely worked beyond his planned control.

"You are right, Hoffman," he said. "We must try. Send in the Watchers. Help me salvage some of the remains of your statue here," he said, pointing to the twisted remains of the Hunter, "and the large arachnid."

"What are you doing?"

"Making some helpers. More eyes. A lot of legs to help navigate the rough terrain." Within minutes of tearing apart the larger constructs, Ramos had a small oblong ball of wires, thin gears, and joined rods. With a twist of its torso he brought the small arachnid to life, its single eye glowing blue as the makeshift logic engine lit within its hastily crafted body. Ramos gave it a simple edict and basic set of command parameters, and it scurried away across the debris, unhindered by the wreckage.

Working together, the two quickly made a small army of arachnids released upon the smoking observatory.

It took little time for Hoffman to understand that Justice would not be found no matter how many mechanical arachnids they made. They were efficient in their task, scurrying about the building's wreckage, unimpeded as if it were open ground. When they detected any sign of a body, they could scuttle down through the narrowest gap between brick and timber. The Guardian, though a first generation construct with a crushed forearm, still proved equally invaluable as it excavated the debris with speed and ease. The futility was not in their inability to find the bodies – it was in the vast number of bodies they continued to find in the rubble. They found hundreds of corpses nearly everywhere they dug, all in various stages of decomposition. The darker, more dry and leathery flesh were clear to the two scientists as the broken remains of undead, risen to obey a Resurrectionist powerful enough to reanimate a great throng of the unholy creatures. They called it "resurrection" which infuriated Hoffman and most other settlers. It was a horrible mockery against them. The reanimated corpses were once friends, relatives, comrades. They were made to do the unnatural bidding of someone that defied not just the law of the Guild, but of a much higher natural law. The remains of the walking dead were expected, and seeing them now, finally at rest, brought a strange comfort to Hoffman. But among the remains were a disturbing number of young bodies and some quite old — both oddly out of place in the battle that had ensued early in the morning. Hoffman thought they might have all been members of a unified gang that had descended upon the observatory to lay claim to it. Looking at the bodies, now, he saw that the gang members represented only a portion of the most recently dead. They must have been unnaturally compelled to attack, he concluded. The realization that they were victims, innocents made to act at the will of another, made him swoon. His eyes fell upon the remains of a mere child, just a boy, and he retched.

Clearing his throat, spitting into the rubble, he called to Ramos, nearby. "You were right," he said. "We cannot find them here." He knew Ramos was anxious to depart, could see the mounting agitation on his features and scowling expression. "I am ready to leave this damnable place."

Ramos met his eyes and certainly heard his surrender. Rather than agree, the notion that they could not succeed irritated him even more. His thick brows furrowed, and his lips pursed. "I'm not done, yet," he said in a low voice, more to himself than to Hoffman.

Always calculating, always determined to overcome every obstacle, Ramos could not stop until he won. Demonstrating the value of his sharp mind, he called all the spiders back to him. He called to Hoffman, "Too many bodies to find a specific two. We're looking for the wrong thing!" Hoffman was puzzled until Ramos said, "Their prime edict is always to seek out soulstones in the mines. Why defy their programming?"

He released them, and they all scampered quickly to the same large mound not fifteen yards away. They poked and scratched at the debris. Hoffman smiled at Ramos who winked at him. Of course Lady Justice would have excess soulstones on her, he agreed appreciatively.

Ramos was a man that stayed one step ahead of others, Hoffman realized. He was also a man that could not give up once he put his mind to something. He had to

succeed, could not accept defeat. It was a great strength, and probably his Achilles' Heel as well.

As the Guardian labored at the excavation, Ramos said, "They're likely dead. Like the others around us."

"Likely," Hoffman agreed.

It was with that expectation that both men jumped when the Guardian pulled one massive slab of concrete aside and the blast of a pistol rang out from the hole, the bullet striking the Guardian square in its head. It, too, seemed to jump, but as it dropped the slab a sword flew from the hole like an arrow, sinking into its chest. The chain attached to the sword's hilt went taut, and with a jerk, the sword came free and flew back into the hole. The Guardian sputtered and jerked, and two blasts of steam whistled from the deep laceration in its chest, and bright sparks popped from the hole in its head. It fell backward, sliding down the mound.

"Not so dead, after all," Ramos said. Thin bands of electricity arced across the metal rods of his mechanical arm, but Hoffman motioned for him to wait.

"Judge!" he called. "It is Officer Hoffman! Are you hurt?" There was no reply. If he were too injured, the Judge might not remember him, even with the identifiable accent, given how new he was to the Guild. "I'm here with Dr. Ramos!" he said. There was no answer. Hoffman struggled up the side of the rubble, his leg harness catching against some protruding debris, and he cursed. Scared half to death that the Judge would kill him, he peered cautiously over the edge of the hole.

Sure enough, the sword pointed at him and at its base was mounted his pistol. The Judge's head was tilted back and his facial bandana had been torn away exposing skin that looked more like the undead they had unearthed. It oozed around thick scabs, and his right jaw and teeth were visible through gaping holes. Two thin strands of flesh remained from his cheek to just above his jaw. Blood from a recent blow to his head caked in his eyes, making him nearly as blind as Lady Justice whom he cradled in the crook of his free arm. Scratches and long lacerations marked her flesh, but she was beautiful, still. Like the bandana of the Judge that protected her blindly, her blindfold had been torn aside and her vacant eyes stared unblinking and milky white. She remained motionless, and both looked dead. Her right arm was twisted too far around and back, clearly broken, probably crushed beyond healing. The fabric of her bodice was dark, but it gleamed on her side, saturated in blood.

"We'll get you out!" Hoffman shouted.

With lips nearly fully decayed from years of exposure to the vile and acidic necrotic fluids he had encountered

under his assignment, and too weak now to carefully articulate his words, Hoffman still understood him to say, "Justice. Take Justice." The Judge struggled to look up at them and his eyes fell upon Ramos and his exposed arm, scrutinizing him. The Judge's sword fell as he succumbed, finally, to unconsciousness.

At Death's Door

September 20

The Event. At the point of impact.

Francisco drew a foot forward, bracing himself on the ground, cradling Perdita's head in the crook of his left arm. "We're in trouble," she had said moments earlier and then stiffened as solid as a knotwood plank. She stared beyond him with eyes still covered in a shroud of black and purple with occasional swirls of silver, like a brief glimpse of a comet in a night sky. Her breathing was so short and shallow he could scarcely tell whether she was alive. His pistol drawn, he held it gingerly as he pulled a strand of hair from her face, stuck to her cheek by a thin film of sweat.

Several paces away, between them and the gaping hole that stretched for miles eastward, stood Santiago, his feet firmly planted apart. Screeching and bellowing howls echoed from the pit as if the very gates of Hell had been opened. "Don't worry, 'Cisco!" he bellowed. "Whatever comes out of that hole will have to kill me twice before I let it by!" He sounded almost convincing as the far surface near the edge of the great chasm continued to break apart and fall, creating an ever growing jagged pit that stretched on and on, swallowing rock and tree like the insatiable jaws of an unholy god. Hundreds, perhaps thousands, of creatures clamored up the side of the sheer rock wall, exposed to the rising sun for the first time in centuries. The Ortegas could hear them drawing nearer as the shrieking grew louder, more distinct. They heard the falling rocks clatter, dislodged by the climbing creatures. Clacking claws and low rumbling moans soon joined the wild shrieking.

"What's comin', 'Cisco?" Niño asked beside him, fidgeting nervously with his rifle.

"Don't know," Francisco said as calmly as he could. "Move off a ways, boy. You're more valuable behind cover anyways." He just hoped they might buy some time for Niño to high tail it out of there. Francisco considered running, too, but knew they'd not get far having to carry Perdita. Niño hesitated but Francisco said, "Go on, now. Get a good shot back there a ways," and the young man reluctantly withdrew.

"Come on, you sons-a-bitches!" Santiago bellowed at the hole. "Let's see what'cha got!"

Francisco hugged his sister close to him and said to her, "I'm sorry, Perdita. You shouldn't even be out here. Maybe none of us should. Sounds like we're in for a helluva time, though. Could use your guns a long as you're here, too." He sighed and then cocked his Peacebringer, loaded with the 'witched bullets created by Criid and the witch-hunter division. "You always managed to get by on your own," he said to her. "Let's see if we can get you through this."

He leveled the gun on the lip of the chasm before Santiago. He wondered what Abuela would say about them. Probably a string of profanity about their reckless irresponsibility. He smiled weakly.

He could not have prepared himself for what came out of the pit. He half expected some Nephilim monstrosity, but a thickly muscled forearm rose up and drove taloned fingers deep into the moist dirt beside the edge and pulled a creature above the side that looked at first human as its head and vacant eyes rose. But its lower jaw was missing, clearly torn from its head as the dried flesh had hardened into a jagged edge around its neck and below its cheek. Even the throat and a great portion of its upper chest were gone, leaving an open cavity exposed to the spine at its back. It could not be living, and as it pulled itself further beyond the edge, Francisco saw the machinery connected to it, driving the physical remains like a grotesque abomination. But he had seen Guild sketches on grafting abominations that turned the stomach and led to the creation of Hoffman's charter and division. What he saw before him was somehow more vile, and, most disturbing of all, it looked old, perhaps over a hundred years, near the time of the first breach opening. The large barrel drum imbedded into its back looked more like raw iron beaten into shape from a forge. No furnace was visible, and no steam issued from exhaust pipes or vents, but its every move was accentuated by an audible whisper of air released or sucked into its mechanical system.

It righted itself on the soft ground, still moist, though most of the standing water in the area had quickly drained over the side of the pit and down into its dark depths. As it stood upright, its entire torso bent backward so that its "face" aimed straight up. Whether it carried too much weight on the machinery integrated into its back or it had become broken and deformed, Francisco could not tell.

Santiago neither cared nor hesitated as he fired his Peacebringer, striking it in its shoulder. It, too, did not hesitate as it shuffled toward him, seemingly unfazed and unconcerned about the wound. He fired once more, and it toppled silently to the ground and made no further movement. The two brothers waited expectantly for it to rise again, but it did not.

Santiago glanced over his shoulder and Francisco, still cradling his sister. "That was easy," he said.

"Si." But neither took comfort in it. The strange shrieking and howling rose from the chasm. Countless more were climbing the sheer wall of the hole, desperate, like moths, to reach the light in their otherwise dark existence.

Three more erupted from the pit at once, charging Santiago. Their bodies were each distinctly different and bore strikingly different mechanical apparatus and various removed body parts. One was man-sized and missing not only its left arm but its entire head as well. It loped directly toward Santiago with its one good arm outstretched. Another was a remarkably fast creature that had its head, torso, and both arms intact, but was severed at the waist, dragging part of its ancient apparatus connected just below the end of its desiccated flesh as it also bound toward Santiago with its arms propelling it like a jackrabbit. The brothers made quick work of them and Niño, hidden a ways behind them, took the third. He fired again at another strange creature just coming over the edge.

More came quickly. "Come on!" Santiago bellowed. "Come on you hijos de putas!"

They fired almost without aiming and reloaded as quickly, but the inhuman creatures kept coming. They were easily dispatched, but within moments of the appearance of the first ones, the edge of the pit was thick with twisted horrors climbing over themselves to get to the Ortegas. Soon, there was a low mound of their corpses that even more clambered over.

It took little time for the Ortegas to determine the single spot each odd abomination had where the mechanika

drove and powered it. Their guns rang out, echoing through the forested region behind them and down into the dark pit before them. They fired as rapidly as possible, but reloading was slower than they could afford. It was while reloading that these partial remains of forgotten corpses overwhelmed Santiago. They leapt upon him, raking dirt encrusted nails across his cheek. One without arms bit into his thigh, and he brought his knee up sharply, striking it violently, and its spine snapped. He slashed at them with the blades mounted to the handles of his pistols while Francisco and Niño fired upon them. The creatures swarmed Santiago who struggled desperately beneath their terrible assault, and Francisco no longer aimed at all, firing randomly into the mass.

Santiago could not withstand them, but he fought valiantly even as they brought him to a knee. Francisco drew himself up, setting Perdita's head gently upon a bed of moss. "I'm sorry, 'Dita," he said. He pulled his dueling sword from its sheath, firing his remaining bullets into the creatures nearest to Santiago. "Niño!" he called. "Time for you to go!" but Niño's rifle continued to bark behind them, and each of his shots were true, taking out one abomination after another. "Go!" he commanded once more, releasing the last of his bullets into the decayed remains of the first to reach him. But he knew Niño would not leave. Probably not even after he and his brother had fallen. No, Francisco knew that Niño was a true Ortega, and he'd stubbornly stand against any adversary. Francisco's sword slashed upwards into one of the creatures, ending it with the same ease with which they had taken out the dozens before. The blade came down in an arc, and he spun, cutting another in half as he slashed around to take another.

Niño's rifle went silent. *Perhaps he fled after all,* Francisco thought. However, Niño had exhausted his bullets. To his credit, every shot he fired had killed its target.

Francisco toppled backward as they wrapped around his legs, biting and scratching and pulling at him. The horrible abomination that finally toppled him had no arms, and the top half of its head was removed in a clean line through the bridge of its nose. Its lower jaw hung slack, and it could not bite. Francisco couldn't tell how it could have even found him with no eyes, ears cut through, and open skull completely empty. It struck him with the stump of its head, whipping its torso at him faster than he thought possible. As he fell, the creature struck at him over and over like a hammer at his ribs. He struggled to push the thing aside and get his feet under him once more, but they pounced upon him, now tearing at his face and neck.

He didn't give up though he knew it was over. He could not see her through the abomination covering his face, but knew they were on Perdita, too.

A great whinnying bleat issued from beyond the pit's edge like the screeching nails of a hateful school marm on the blackboard, but amplified and horrible. It chilled him. The abominations upon him went rigid, frozen and inanimate like statues. Only a moment passed, and they slowly shifted, ready to resume the assault, but the screeching came reverberating out of the great chasm, now louder, closer than before.

The abominations upon him reluctantly crawled or dragged themselves away, leaving him panting for breath on his back in the mud. He rolled to an elbow, grabbing his sword that had been pulled from him. Santiago, too, was left, beaten with bloody lacerations across every exposed part of his body. Pushing himself up, weak and wounded, he said, "I'm not having a good day, 'Cisco." Despite their dire circumstances, he tried to laugh but coughed up blood and spat it on the ground before him.

The sound of hooves striking the rock rose from the chasm. A curved sickle blade lifted above the rim and sank deep into the soil and pulled taut. The gray foreleg of a horse appeared, and its hoof struck into the mud, sinking deeply as it pulled its great weight. The skin was loose and dry in death, like the other abominations. Its other foreleg struck the ground. Large patches of its flesh were removed altogether, showing flexing striations of muscle with thin black tubes protruding and running up its leg. A massive horse skull rose above the edge. Most of it was exposed bone, but tattered remains of leathery flesh dangled from around its jaws and shoulders. Instead of a mane, metal plates overlapped down its neck, each rising to a sharp point along its back. Its eyes were empty sockets, but it leveled its head at Santiago, and twin pinpoints of bright green light flashed from the depths. It snorted loudly and two shots of steam blasted from the open holes of its nostrils on either side of a black iron spike screwed into the bone.

It heaved, and the great bulk of it surfaced. The Rider's arm was merely animated bone pulling at the great scythe. It towered before Santiago. The massive horse, dead, powered by some grotesque magic that merged the corpse and the machinery, regarded him in a steady, detached stare. The Rider's bare skull swiveled on a neck of dry muscle and articulated bands of metal, surveying the Ortegas and the landscape it might not have beheld for many years. It had no lower jaw, and its throat was sunken and unusable, yet it growled a command that was a shrill hiss like a steam valve releasing a bit of excess pressure from deep within. The abominations near them scampered away.

The Dead Rider spoke in that whistling wind to Francisco and Santiago. No doubt it tried to say something, but its words were unintelligible to them. They had interrogated many Neverborn and whatever language the strange being spoke sounded distinctly different from anything they had ever heard before. It lurched forward in the saddle and bellowed in rage, the words shaking them as it howled like a gale.

It raised the scythe above its head, still bellowing incomprehensibly, and that's when Niño came charging from the side, bursting from the underbrush. He screamed as he leapt high into the air. His rifle was his club, and he held it back as far as he could. At the last second, he jerked it forward to strike the rider in its skull with all the might of his lithe body and incredible momentum.

The rifle butt hit its head with the sound of a pebble thrown against a barn door and with about the same effect. The Rider didn't flinch or seem to notice. Niño even knocked the wind out of himself as his body struck the side of the towering creature.

Santiago, however, hit the monstrous figure from the other side, and he carried far more mass and momentum than his cousin. His shoulder struck the Rider, and he pushed mightily against the saddle to dismount the creature, assuming it would be more assailable on its back, unable to wield that sinister scythe. The horse, imbalanced from Santiago's charge, took a step, and the Rider did get knocked back. But it was much more resilient than the small abominations they could dispatch so easily. It was considerably stronger, too, not only remaining mounted, but it snatched Santiago by the neck and held him aloft by that single skeletal arm, crushing his throat while Santiago struggled and kicked, hoping to break free. It growled and spoke again, deep and hateful.

Francisco charged it with his dueling sword, and the Rider did nothing more than continue to berate or threaten Santiago while the horse reared, kicking Francisco as it rose and knocking him back.

In the midst of the Rider's speech it said, "Gran Kythera," which resonated within each of them. It lifted Santiago higher and shook him as he said it. Then it threw him bodily against Francisco.

It spoke one last thunderous statement, still beyond their comprehension, pointing at Perdita as if in accusation, and charged into the dense foliage of the bayou's edge, away from the dark chasm from whence it had come. The dead hooves clattered into the distance in a straight line as though it rode with purpose.

"What in hell was that?" Santiago said around a wheezing cough. The dark bruise marks of the Rider's skeletal fingers already formed along his throat.

Francisco wasted no time and, despite his aching muscles and mounting exhaustion, he snatched the rigid body of his sister from the damp vegetation. He said, "I don't know what it was, but it let us live and it bought us some time. Vamos before those things come back." Santiago and Niño nodded in quick agreement, and they walked hurriedly away from the gaping maw of the chasm. Truly, not one of them knew where they were in the expansive bogs, and they had no sense of direction to lead them out, but they needed no vote to agree that the best direction to go was straight away from that huge pit, and as quickly as possible. So, when Francisco stopped, the others looked gravely concerned. "Wait," he said. "You're not going to like this. We need to take one of those things back with us."

Santiago snorted. "Like hell."

Niño was too small to carry one, they all knew, and Francisco stared his brother down. "Go get one," he said. "Be sure it's dead."

"They were already dead when they came up to say, 'hi'!" and he scowled at Francisco, holding his ground.

"Santiago," he said sternly.

"Dammit, 'Cisco. If one of those things so much as tickles me, I'm going to throw you over the edge of that hole." Not that they felt any safer by it, but when he reached the mound of abominations, he took just a moment to cherry pick one of the carcasses, kicking them quickly aside to find one missing its arms. He even grunted quickly over the corpse, tearing its lower jaw off and discarding it onto the pile. "Don't want it to bite me," he said, jogging up with it, dragging it with fingers hooked under its upper teeth. "We waiting around for the dinner bell? Let's go!" He was all but running through the thick growth, the others just a step behind him.

SEPTEMBER 29
Guild Enclave

Perdita had not stirred since falling at the epicenter of the great wave, though the doctor studying her remained hopeful that it was only a matter of time before she would shake off the stupor and awaken.

Doctor Carl Morrow, head of the Psychosis and Paranormal Department at the Guild Sanitarium stood beside her, wringing his hands as he stared at her intently. He smiled, thankful to have another prominent Ortega back in the ward. And the beautiful daughter of one of his favorite and most intricate, albeit difficult, patients was a welcome addition to the typical menagerie he had to feed and water.

Her brothers had insisted on returning her to Latigo instead of admitting her into the Sanitarium, but when Abuela was brought to the City to assess her and had to admit that even she could not help the young Perdita, they had to acquiesce and admit her.

Doctor Morrow watched her eyes, open since the Event more than a week earlier. They were still swirling with purple and silver, and they never so much as twitched, staring resolutely forward. He still liked staring at them. They remained fully dilated despite differing light around her.

"What are you thinking about, my little Ortega?" he asked her, wringing his hands more fervently, leaning closer, looking into her eyes. Within just inches of her ear, he lowered his voice to just a whisper. "What's happening in that little head of yours?"

Within the dark fog of her mind, Perdita floated, usually unaware of herself and her surroundings.

The whispering voices in her mind started to fade as she had been carried from the site of the Serpent and the Fallen Red Cage. The voices that consumed her mind when the purple wave hit were banished when the echoing voice of the Dead Rider had spoken, sending them fleeing from her mind.

She fought to reclaim herself and might have if not for her brothers bringing her here. New whispers joined the droning multitude hiding in the darkness surrounding her. Of course, she had only the briefest glimpse of those thoughts that might be wholly hers before they were again suppressed by the dark fog of whispering voices. So she did not know she was in the Guild Sanitarium. She only vaguely knew who she was.

Kel Darrow Kar, she heard the whispering voice above her, quiet and unintelligible. *Til Gran*, it said. *Thar gran*. It made no sense, and she sought escape in the dark depths. *Perdita*. Her mind came into focus. "Perdita," it whispered, so faintly she could scarcely hear it at all. "Til Gran Kythera Dow, Perdita. They told you we were dead."

Who are you?

"The students." She could say nothing, yet conveyed her bewilderment. "The students of the Kythera ruins."

You went mad, they said.

"They would. Perhaps we did."

You're here?

"We cannot leave. We discovered it, Perdita."

What?

"The Kythera truth. The Grave Spirit. It seeks to live. It cannot live where there is life. We found the truth." Its whispering drew faint and tenuous as the other whispers in the shadows pulled this one voice away. "They are freed," it said, screaming in the darkness, but its voice was so far away now; it was like a gentle gust on a calm day. "All will be lost." There was a pause, and she thought it had left her as the other voices sought dominion of her once more, crowding her small circle of light in the midst of the darkness. Soon she would be enveloped by it entirely. *Tombers*, it said. *He knows.*

She blinked, and Doctor Morrow jumped, squealing. Perdita's eyes fluttered and she was gone again, her eyes closing slowly.

Santiago rubbed his tired eyes as Francisco yawned.

Doctor McMourning ignored them, continuing to examine a bit of the flesh pinned to the soft wood of his examining table, worn smooth by the hundreds of bodies that had lain upon it.

The brothers were tired because of their days and nights at the Guild Sanitarium. They were not technically allowed to be with their sister, but their rank made it difficult to herd them out. Santiago, in particular, seemed to welcome the challenge of anyone trying to get him to go anywhere. Francisco simply outranked anyone that might have asked him to leave. So one of the two was always getting access to the ward that housed her. They had a bad feeling about her being in that place.

"So what's going on with Jonathan, Doc?" Santiago asked abruptly, losing his patience even though they had been there only a few minutes. McMourning gave him the creeps just like that mousy Doctor Morrow did.

McMourning regarded him coolly, and then slowly pulled a dark glove down upon his hand, stretching it tight upon each finger. "There's something I don't understand," he said.

"That's why we brought Jon to you," Santiago said gruffly. McMourning gnashed his teeth. Behind him, Sebastian, his assistant, smacked his lips, smiling vacantly, holding a power saw, the exposed blade well blackened from numerous cuttings through flesh and bone. Thankfully, it was not currently in use.

"Yesss..." McMourning said. "I understand. But you said it crawled out of that pit, that it's one of hundreds like it."

"Many hundreds," Francisco added.

He drew their attention to the apparatus attached to the base of its torso. "This power equipment, here," McMourning pointed to the steam apparatus. "You said they all have this? It runs on a small steam chamber.

Build enough steam and the pressure drives small pistons in this chamber here. Then it—"

"Right!" Santiago interjected with a scowl. "Steam powered. Like a Peacekeeper. We know."

McMourning hated him. "Where's the fire chamber? Where's the water reservoir? Well, here," he pointed, "but the lower half is gone, leaving the chamber empty. What makes these things work?"

That silenced Santiago. McMourning's mind raced as he struggled to understand the thing. Francisco said, "Resurrectionist creation?"

"Certainly not," McMourning said, too sure, too quickly. He shook himself and then tried to cover, saying, "Well, I wouldn't think so." He pressed the flesh, cut away from the cadaver's side and pinned to the table. It was dry leather. "This is too old. Many centuries. Many. Studying other discarded remains that were animated and brought here from other conflict with Resurrectionists, it seems that the Resurrectionists need a much more recently dead cadaver." That part was true. The best illusion was one built on a foundation of truth, and he was good at maintaining an illusion.

"Maybe they've learned to raise ancient Neverborn carcasses," Francisco offered.

"That's exactly what has me puzzled." McMourning examined the flesh beneath a large and thick magnifying lens mounted to a band around his head. "It's not the age of this centuries old cadaver that has me puzzled. This creature . . . was human."

Malifaux Exploration Society

Many occupied areas of the Slums are decidedly poor. Even the colorful neighborhood of Little Kingdom, despite its Eastern charm, still exists in the shadow of poverty. One notable exception to this is a large villa tucked away in a long-abandoned neighborhood, secluded from the less affluent of the central Slums. Unlike the vacant heaps of rubble around it, the grounds of the villa are well-maintained. The high walls surrounding the property have been refurbished; its iron-shod gates restored. If not for the surroundings, a visitor might think they were standing in front of a lord's home in London. Any would-be trespassers are deterred by the great hunting mastiffs that wander the lawn.

The villa is home to a collection of adventurous souls who call themselves the Malifaux Exploration Society. The Society's founder, Sir Justin Cooper, spent most of his youth and middle age on safari in Africa, enjoying the pleasures and privileges his minor lordship afforded him. Thoroughly jaded by these experiences, Lord Cooper turned his eye to the Breach, to another world.

On a whim, he organized a safari to Malifaux, killing a Razorspine Rattler in his first hunt. The thrill reinvigorated Lord Cooper's long-dulled sense of adventure. Smitten with what he called "a land of eternal adventure" in dispatches to his wealthy colleagues Earthside, he invited them to join him in Malifaux. Like Cooper, they relished the dangerous thrill of the hunt and together spent a fortune restoring the villa and forming the Society. Since then, the group has had its ranks swelled by minor lords, jaded merchants, and spoiled heirs. Every member is a long-time hunter who has found new purpose in the opportunity to hunt creatures far more dangerous than those at home.

The explorers venture into the Quarantine Zone nightly on Midnight Safaris, scouring for quarries worthy of their considerable skills. The Guild is all too happy to accommodate the Society and its eccentricities as the Society has supplied reconnaissance, detailed maps, artifacts, and hefty bribes to the Governor General's office in return for freedom to explore, an arrangement both parties find mutually agreeable. Rumors circulate that the Society is something more than it appears. If it is so, the Guild has not cared enough to investigate. Perhaps there is truth to the rumors; perhaps they are nothing more than stories told to entertain the poor residents of the Slums. After all, the Society does not make much effort to ease the plight of its poor neighbors.

The Coming Storm

October 6

The bayou was strangely quiet and still. Lilith brushed aside a branch, heavy with frost, and walked across the thin film of ice covering the murky water. The ice could not have supported the weight of any normal person or beast, but it gave her little concern. Even the long blades of grass, covered in a sheath of white, hardly swayed at her passing. No footprint on the soft, still unfrozen, soil marked her movement through the marsh.

The bayou gave her, Zoraida, and many of the Neverborn natives shelter because the humans found it so difficult to navigate and remember their way. Only the damnable Ortegas seemed willing to hunt through the wetlands, and they were increasingly proficient at navigating the difficult region. Of course, that was before the Event. Since the Red Star fell, the Ortegas were strangely absent from the bayou and the somewhat dryer forests north of it near their own compound.

Lilith's breath froze in a fog before her as she paused to survey the surroundings. She chastised herself for allowing her mind to wander, brief though it was. Thinking of the Ortegas distracted her, and this close to Zoraida's hut, she knew that even she could not afford to lose focus. The three thorn elms were to her left as they should be, but the bayou's single towering Jasmine, supposed to be to the right of them, was nowhere to be seen. She cursed silently. Where was the Jasmine tree? Rare and fragile in normal conditions, its thriving in the bayou was an impossibility that fortunately marked the last stage of the journey to Zoraida's hidden home.

She scanned the foliage in each direction from the three thorn elms and even stepped side to side to see if they were hidden by other trees. Especially with their branches weighted by the frost, she thought the landmarks might be further obscured than normal. She couldn't see it. But then, the scent of the jasmine flowers caught her, sweet and soft. She looked up. Looming directly above her stood the jasmine tree, its tiny flowers white and gleaming in the frost that would surely wither them. She cursed again, blaming only herself for falling into Zoraida's trap. She spun, rethinking her position in the swamp and saw with her mind rather than her eyes, for they were never to be trusted this close to Zoraida's shack. She thought of a position more than fifty yards behind her where both the three elms would stand to her left and the jasmine to her right and in between would be the hut. Sure enough, past the thin trunk of the flowering tree, there before her were the thick stilts that raised the hut above the water of the swamp that rose and fell so severely by the passing of Malifaux's moons.

Sighing as she stepped past the tree, she had to acknowledge Zoraida's power once more. To other Neverborn, Lilith was known as "The Master of Malifaux", able to bend and reshape nature to fit her needs. But Zoraida's power confounded her, and not for the first time. Humans had been in Malifaux only four short years, but they told tales of Zoraida that made her somehow more feared than either Lilith or even Pandora, even though Zoraida had tormented the humans far less than either of the two seemingly younger Neverborn women. Odd, too, that only a few of the settlers had even come into contact with her in the swamp, and she had left them each alive. Lilith found it remarkable that she held such power of fear over them. They told tales of the hut of the witch that walked the marsh on giant chicken legs and how the hag was so evil that she wanted to steal all the children away and eat them up. Of course, that was a tale of warning the more cruel of the adults told their children to keep them from going into the forest or swamp. It was sinister, and she was sure Pandora exploited that fear when she could. The hut did not walk about on its own. That would be ridiculous, but for anyone that found the hut once, it could certainly seem that it must be able to walk away if you tried to find it again and never could. That was her power. She turned a person's thoughts against them, turning them away from the hut in confusion. Lilith thought she only had a brief thought of the Ortegas but realized now that Zoraida's formidable hex probably had her repeat the same thought over and over as she walked past the three elms and nearly past the Jasmine. She smiled. She would have walked right past those stilts without ever looking up to see the hut, thinking them trees as they had thick vines and grasses growing over them.

She didn't take her eyes from the stilts suspending the hut above the dark soil of a mound just below it. She thought only of Zoraida and the subject of their meeting. It should have taken only a few moments to traverse the final distance between her and the hut, but it seemed to take much longer.

Zoraida's voice called out from a rocking chair near the edge of the rickety porch. "Ah, right on time!" she called. "Didn't get turned around in the swamp, did you?" She cackled, high and grating. Lilith knew the old woman had watched her approach with glee. Probably focused even more of her mystical twisting of the obfuscation against her. Zoraida, no doubt, reveled in the confusion she could impose on a powerful being such as herself.

Lilith wrapped the fabric of spiritual energy around herself, thicker here in the swamp where life and death occurred in far greater magnitude than in the City where man denounced, even suppressed the natural ebb and flow of those energies. There was a reason they said she was the Master of Malifaux. She extended her will and found one of the dark crows perched on the rail just beyond the old woman. In a snap, she and the crow were transposed, shifting in space. The crow fluttered in surprise where Lilith had been, and Lilith, now on the rail beside Zoraida, leaning against a support post with one leg outstretched said, "Not at all," in answer to Zoraida's question which made the old woman jump and shriek. Wide-eyed, she turned to Lilith and, regaining her wits and realizing what Lilith had done, cackled again, her laughter loud and echoing throughout the swamp around them.

For one such as Lilith, Zoraida seemed to age before her eyes, wrinkling, withering, and dying with every breath. It had been only several months since she had last sat with the crone, yet Zoraida seemed so different to her – tired and weak. It was such a shame that so much power could be contained in something so brief and fragile. Not for the first time did she marvel at how a human could rise up so quickly to amass a power rivaling her own.

"Winter has come early to the Bayou," Lilith said as the hag's laughter subsided.

"Yes. And it's quieted the croaking frogs."

"Will they survive the cold?"

"This?" Zoraida said, waving her gnarled hand, coarse and calloused on the fingertips and across the thick pad of her open palm.

"No, the coming storm."

Zoraida grew grave, thinking on it and looking out into the darkness of the swamp. "Oh," she said, "They'll suffer. They're not ready. This cold should be a month off at least. Silurids, frogs, the 'gators. The gremlins, too. They follow the seasons and prepare for the next. Always on the future, the instincts are. I'd predict they'd suffer too greatly in the storm that comes. But they adapt. If they trust those instincts." She drew the worn pelt around her torso, already wrapped in several layers of old canvas she used to construct her many dolls from.

"It's a shame," Lilith said. "It's not their fault, and they'll suffer the most. The humans, holed up and cozy in Malifaux, will hardly notice that the cold came earlier than normal. That it's more severe than in previous years. Will they know of December at all?" Zoraida rocked quietly, thinking on it, looking out into the swamp that protected her. She might be safe from an accidental visit from humans stumbling upon her, but December was different. Each of the Tyrant Entities posed a very real threat for they would consume everything. Lilith continued, saying, "A Rider has come. A Dead Rider, from out of the Necropolis."

"Yes. And it wasn't the first." Lilith was surprised. "One came to me. Before the Event. Its sword glowed like the sun but could not penetrate the depth of the shadow beneath its cowl even when it held the sword beneath its face. It spoke, but I could not understand it and thought, at first, it had come to slay me. It stood before me for only a minute, maybe two. The sword changed as it spoke, reflecting a sun on its surface that passed in seconds rather than hours. Even starlight and the twin moons reflected on its surface as it spoke, though it was mid-morning and the sky was obscured by the trees and a thick fog that surrounded us."

"I was not aware that the Hooded Rider had come," Lilith admitted. "I always assumed it would come to me. It was foretold that it would come to the Neverborn, so it might as well have come to you."

"I am not Neverborn," Zoraida said.

"Semantics. You are in spirit."

"Not in blood."

"Yet the Hooded Rider came to you. Why does it stir, now?" she asked.

Zoraida shared her bewilderment, clicking her tongue as she thought. "I've spent many hours since our encounter scrying on that. It came with Plague, awakened when It consumed that vile human that found it in the Necropolis. I told you we should have walled It up better." Zoraida looked at her accusationally.

"You did. You also agreed that we had taken enough precautions to secure the Necropolis. You protected it just as you did your hut, here."

"True. No human could have found it by walking toward it, even by accident. The hex would have turned them."

"Yet man found a way. The riot, the burning building that fell. It carried the human straight to Plague in the water, filled with man's own waste and filth. You believed we would stop the coming of the end."

Zoraida nodded. "We have twisted the threads of Fate until they are knotted. First, the Tyrants, of course, then us. Now the humans. With each that I unravel it seems I create four more. Man did not find a way to bring the end – Fate did. We cannot control it. Cannot stop it. How could any man even have survived that deluge in the sewer? Battered for miles beneath the water like that. Could you have, Lilith? No, Fate is active and alive. It has brought the end despite our meager attempts to sway it."

"Man meddles with the power haphazardly. Almost reveling in the ability to twist Fate. They knot it. Did you make a mistake in opening the Breach again?"

"Hard to say," Zoraida said, thinking on it. "Their world crumbles in decay, the spirit sucked dry. But man is as resilient and full of life as the creatures in this swamp." She smiled, making the connection. "And if they can trust their instincts, perhaps change all of this."

"Or they bring the end."

"Yes. Perhaps. December stirred, and when the Breach opened, He rose, finding a vessel in that girl. Plague, too, rose through man."

Lilith added, "And that lunatic, Seamus, actually tried to raise the Grave Spirit. Now the fabric surrounding this world has been torn. Spirits are no longer trapped on the other side. The Plagued nearly succeeded in ascending."

Zoraida dismissed the notion with a wave. "He's simple-minded. He didn't know what he was doing. Didn't consider the power of the other Tyrants to keep him from succeeding. Especially the Grave Spirit. It's a wily one, that's for sure. I sense Its hand in thwarting the Plagued. The Resurrectionists are so dangerous because they don't even understand the power right at their fingertips. Haven't even thought about the spiritual power because they're so trapped by their own perception of self in the physical."

"That may change now."

"Yes. The Three Kingdoms girl. They may figure it out. They're just so used to thinking that the men are the stronger of the genders. Imagine if Fate had given the Plague you or that damned Ortega girl?" Zoraida rolled her eyes.

"Plague was stopped. But the others continue to rise and meddle in the affairs of man. The Red Star has fallen, releasing the imprisoned."

Zoraida rocked gently, stroking the head of one of her makeshift dolls. Lilith found it amusing that it seemed to hug her hand as she pet it. "It has already chosen a vessel, too, I fear."

Lilith nodded in agreement. "Volcanic activity in the Badlands to the west."

"The Badlands? I wasn't expecting that. What's left in the Badlands for Him?"

Lilith laughed. "You? Taken by surprise? So this cloud has a silver lining, after all!"

Zoraida smiled, too. "Everything is clouded. Hard to read."

"So, will she stop the Red Prisoner or help him ascend? We thought that Daw's sacrifice would strengthen the dam and hold them all at bay. Daw is perpetual. Always teetering between this world and that. But it was not enough. I fear your gamble has only made the end come sooner."

"I've been trying to tell you, Lilith. Fate is alive. Our presence may have awakened the slumbering Tyrants earlier than you expected, but your attempts to keep them asleep, imprisoned, was nearing an end as the Neverborn numbers began to swell again. They exist where there is life. And they wish to ascend as they always have. To fulfill their desire for immortality, godhood. If not for the humans, we would have brought them and fought them alone. Consider the changes to the Silurid and Gremlin over the last several hundred years. The vegetation, too. I think the gamble was necessary."

"The humans are strong. They embrace change so quickly. But their power is being used by the Tyrants."

"We will find those strong enough to oppose them."

"Pandora's part. Speaking of which...why is she not here?"

"More twisting of Fate's threads. She must deal with Candy. Another surprise. Another obstacle. Who could have seen this coming? Candy was not ready to grow. Not for many decades. She could have been such a powerful tool and resource. That damned Event. It wasn't supposed to come so soon."

"She is still powerful. Still useful."

"But not in control. Not of herself and certainly not by us. She's like *your* sister." Lilith winced, ashamed at the mention of Nekima. Zoraida continued, "She revels in the pain she inflicts. She loses sight of her purpose. We need the humans alive. We need them strong, not broken."

"The Breach is another abomination," Lilith said. "Twisting the natural law. Every time we've sought to fix it, to repair the damage to the natural law, we've only fueled the coming end. Should we not close the gate now? More and more of those despicable creatures continue to pour through every day; children stomping through the flowers, unaware of their own destruction."

"Maybe it is time for that," Zoraida agreed. "Everything is happening so fast. Faster than I imagined."

"It always does." Lilith suggested, "What about that man that leads them? Could he not be used as we had intended for Daw? To block the tear in the fabric between this world and the aether?"

"He has his own desire for great power, that is true. But he is a man that does not believe in sacrifice of himself to get it. We need another."

"What about Nytmare? He has aligned himself with the boy from across the Breach. They twist reality like you twist Fate."

Zoraida turned to regard her and the suggestion. It had merit. She nodded, and the smile upon her face accentuated the great many wrinkles. "Yes. He plans his own ascension. We should confront that one."

"Not you. He won't respond to you. He doesn't acknowledge your right to the Neverborn. He would certainly respect *my* right to appeal to him, but I probably should not, either," she said. "For all his power to reshape the physical world, he only understands the psychological."

"Everything points back to Pandora." The hag cackled. "The girl is being tested. The Event nearly did her in."

"She's gotten too familiar with the humans. They're getting in her head as she gets into theirs." Lilith stood and walked to the edge of the wooden porch and turned to Zoraida before jumping down. "I'll find her. I'll get her to confront the Nytmare, see if we can catch up to Fate's machinations before it's too late." She regretted leaving, a sensation she felt more and more. "Will I see you again?" she asked.

"You've asked me that the last several times we've parted," Zoraida said dismissively. "I have years left."

"Years. Years might as well be seconds. I just met you and you were a capricious girl."

"Pshaw. That was well over a hundred years ago."

"Seems like yesterday. You were beautiful."

"More beautiful than you."

"Don't get carried away." Lilith winked at her and was gone, heading to the City to find Pandora. Time and Fate had moved faster than them, and they would pay for their every moment of doubt and hesitation.

Brian Tuttle rounded the corner of Gorges Street into the alley between Mrs. Dillard's Orphanage and Richard's Apothecary, taking the familiar shortcut back to his bakery. He had tarried too long at the orphanage, surprising the little ones with some fresh tarts. In his haste, a loaf of bread rolled out of his basket, and he quickly picked it up, discreetly brushing it off, sure no one had seen him drop it.

He was wrong.

Candy was just ahead, and she said to him, "Mistakes happen, huh?"

He yelped and stopped short, clutching the rest of the loaves from the morning's delivery against his chest. He hadn't seen her there, of course, but his surprise came not so much from her presence in the typically unused alley as much as by how she looked. Leaning against the wall with her back slightly arched, she was every bit as tall as him but long and thin. Pretending she wasn't aware of her bare leg, she lifted a foot slowly along the brick wall, her stocking pulled tight to her knee while the other had drooped to her ankle. Her skirt was many times too small for her and covered only the upper half of her thigh. Tuttle hardly noticed the sheen of her skin was more smooth and white, like cold porcelain, than the creamy tan of a normal girl. Her exposed legs and the tight shirt that lifted above her navel with each breath were positively scandalous. Even a woman of ill-repute would not be so outlandishly attired, and he took a reluctant step toward her, intent upon chastising her for her lewd presentation. Slack-jawed and bulging eyes, he was too dumbstruck to speak.

Candy twirled a lock of her flaxen hair, smiling at him, innocently. Her stance and mannerisms were that of a girl many years younger and, if not for the subtle curves of her body, he might have sworn she was a child. With wide eyes and gentle smile she said, "I'm so jealous of those orphans."

He did sincerely intend to reprimand her for her deplorable state of dress. He'd get to it. To start, however, he said simply, "Oh? I'm sure they've not heard that before." He laughed nervously. "Why should *you* be jealous of them?"

"Oh, to have someone like you. You know," she said slowly, around a slight smile, "to bring them tasty treats. I have a bit of a sweet tooth, myself." She raised one of her sweets to her mouth.

Sweat thickened upon his chest and beneath his arms, yet his mouth went dry. He could not look the girl in the eyes, but everywhere he looked made him more and more uncomfortable as his roving eyes could only fall upon some part of her that should be forbidden for him to see. "Oh," his voice trembled, "I just do what I can." His collar was suddenly very tight, he realized, choking him.

"Is that so? Well, you are a giving person aren't you?" He said nothing but gulped hard. He was having difficulty thinking. Every thought he had was of the girl, far too young to deserve the thoughts of a lecherous man like him. "I'm kind of an orphan, too," she went on. "Do you have anything left to give me, mister?" He shook, and his eyes fluttered. She was there, in his mind, and he was reaching out for her. The girl was not wrong for how she dressed, how she looked. It was his fault, he thought. He was to blame. A person should be responsible for himself. Her narrow hand fell upon his shoulder, and its gentle weight was enough to push him to his knees. The loaves he carried tumbled before him and his eyes fluttered, too heavy now to open.

In his mind's eye, he looked down upon himself from above. He saw a man brought to his knees before the presence of a young woman, too innocent and harmless to understand that her developing body could affect a grown man so profoundly. It was his affair to manage, and he failed. It was his responsibility to control the lustful urges that compelled him more like an animal than a productive member of society. He struck himself with an open palm, hard enough to wrack his whole body, and then struck again, splitting his lip.

Candy smiled. She reached out and took his hand in both of hers and leaned toward him. Close she said in a deep voice, "Now, now. No need to be so angry." She held his hand in both of hers and pulled it to her cheek, to have it caress her jaw with his knuckles. He shook visibly, his eyes rolling up into his head.

She had not been a real woman for long, and she reveled in the amplification of her power. She had no desire for the pathetic creature before her, of course, but she pulled his face to hers, kissing him passionately. She could feel his pulse beating frantically in his neck. She released him, and he gibbered incoherently, eyes rolled back and foam dribbling from the corner of his mouth.

In his mind, he was desperately whipping and beating himself for his own despicable thoughts. He could not punish the stain of sin away and had such deep self-loathing that he could only desperately continue to berate and punish himself, ashamed for what he could think and ashamed he had hidden it so deeply for so long. She removed his baking cap and ran her fingers though his thin hair. "There, there," she said. "It'll be okay, now." He continued to strike his own face, bruising and bloodying himself.

Pandora found her like that, hovering over him, smiling as she watched him suffer, trapped in the nightmare of hate and self-judgment. "Candy!" she commanded angrily. "What are you doing?"

Candy barely looked up. She shrugged absently. "Practicing?" she offered in explanation.

"You don't need any practice," Pandora said in chastisement. "Now end this. Its damned bleating is going to draw attention."

Candy rose, standing considerably taller than Pandora, now. She seemed to have no urgency to obey Pandora, her elder now only in technicality. "I can't stop it," she said with a smile. "I'm not actually doing anything."

Pandora stomped toward her. "End it," she growled.

Candy pouted, looking very much like the petulant child she so recently was. Arms folded defiantly, she turned from Pandora, nose high and lower lip jutting forward.

Pandora stepped toward her, and Candy braced herself for Pandora's punishment, but the older girl bent, reaching into Candy's basket on the ground beside her and withdrew the long scissors she kept there, glaring at the young girl. Pandora jerked quickly and drove the end of the sheers through Tuttle's neck and out the other side, covered in blood and flesh. He fell back with a gurgle, his blood pooling around his head and slowly drained down the slight decline in the alley to a sewer grate nearby. His body continued to twitch as the psychological torture Candy brought upon him lingered until his very end.

Turning abruptly to Candy, Pandora said, "I told you to put the creature down!"

Candy wanted to ignore her, to demonstrate her newfound independence and courage, but could not help but defend herself. "What does it matter?" she retorted. "They do not matter to us. They are worthless."

"You know better than that. There's a plan."

"What plan?" Candy snapped. "To find a savior for Malifaux? In one of these...animals?"

Pandora, too, grew impatient. "Control yourself! Not out loud. Not here!"

"Why?" She rolled her eyes as she said, "Are we in danger?" She pointed at Pandora angrily. "Like you've never done what I just did? Have you, 'Dora?"

Pandora's features softened. "You're right," she said more gently. "I know. It is frustrating to think we need them. We have dominion over each of the humans we confront. And I hate them here as much as you do."

"Then why go through this? Why pretend? I hate them. Hate them!" she screamed, purposefully loud enough to carry beyond the alley and into the ears of the pedestrians nearby.

Pandora did not care, and she looked away, down at the box she held absently at her side. "We did this. We let them loose. We must fix it. The others believe we need a human. One strong enough to do what we may not be able to do alone."

"The 'others'? Zoraida? Lilith? Then why aren't they here in Malifaux looking? We're endangering ourselves every day!" She stomped and her stocking fell further down her calf. Her hands were balled fists at her side. Pandora smiled, reminded that despite her new physical maturity she was still every bit a young girl.

Neither realized it, but Lilith looked down upon them, hidden behind the thick stones of a chimney on the building beside them. She remained perfectly still, making no noise to alert the girls of her presence. She waited for Pandora to gain control of the young girl, to assert her authority lest Candy realize her growth brought her even greater potential than she realized. Instead, Pandora drew Candy to her in an embrace. She spoke quietly but Lilith heard her distinctly. Pandora said, "We do our part. Until we can determine our own path." Candy hugged her back. Pandora said, "You are what you are, a Woe of lost innocence. Of course you must do what you are meant to do. This simple creature," she said with a motion to the corpse of Brian Tuttle, "surely wasn't strong enough for our uses. Just follow the plan until we can be free to do what we are both meant to do. And don't call too much attention to ourselves."

Lilith's teeth ground quietly from her hiding place. Candy was not the only problem to fix, apparently.

Revelations

October 12

The large wrench slipped from the bolt as it suddenly gave way. Rose Crowshaw gasped as her knuckles struck the metal plating of the copper turbine. "Dammit!" she cursed in a rather unladylike fashion. She winced and jerked away from the Breach portal support arms that loomed above her. She spat one profanity after the other as she squeezed the gaping wound. Blood flowed through her fingers and dripped upon her overalls.

The bright blue disc of light that spanned nearly thirty feet popped, and the droning hum momentarily ceased. The light emanating from the Breach winked out of existence, too, showing the rising hills to the north of Malifaux through the thick metal arms that typically held the strange portal in place. Then it came right back, humming and buzzing in that otherwise endless drone, opaque and swirling with eddies of blue and white. If, like Rose Crowshaw, a person were to look upon the portal with welding goggles on, they'd not only preserve their eyesight, but they might be able to see the strangely swirling and faint movement of ghostly silver figures, smoke-like and gossamer. Wearing such dark lenses obscured the images of the Breach, too, making it difficult to describe what it looked like with any surety. As descriptions of the strange gateway rarely agreed, most people merely left it as "Blue, and so damned bright it'd make the sun blink."

The pain in her knuckle subsided slowly as her own special, and secret, ability quickly pulled the flesh together again. New skin formed over the wound, pink and soft, and the throbbing pain still coursed through her, sending strange and uncomfortable waves down her spine. She shivered with each heartbeat.

Anasalea Kaeris, a special contractor for the Miners and Steamfitter's Union, approached. She asked, "Everything okay?"

Crowshaw wrapped a greasy rag around the wound, now well on its way to being fully healed. "Oh, yes," she said. "No problem, really. Didn't know anyone was near." They both looked at the other steamfitters working well within earshot. It was enough to puzzle Kaeris, and she made no effort to mask her curiosity.

She said, "Must have been a good crack of the knuckle. It's bleeding out pretty good," but Crowshaw knew the bleeding had miraculously ceased. "Let me see it. You probably need to see the medic."

"No, no," Rose said as unemotionally as possible. "It's really nothing. I just got excited." The wound would be fully healed in minutes and the very last person she wanted to know about her was Kaeris. That woman was a bloodhound, and she had been "meeting" with just about everyone of prominence in Malifaux, though "interrogation" was probably a more appropriate term.

She needed to shift attention. "This damned Breach just won't stabilize," she said, gently tapping the metal frame with her great wrench.

"Was it the derailment this past summer?"

Crowshaw shrugged, though both women knew it had nothing to do with the derailment. "They tell me it was the Event. I'm just a steamfitter. They don't tell me nuthin'. Just 'It's broke. Fix it'."

Kaeris was shrewd and not easily led down the wrong path. She knew at once that there was more to the young M&SU girl than she wanted known. Kaeris pushed, saying, "Odd to assign a Steamfitter to the Breach, though. It's a pretty unique construct to sustain aether, from no living source, to hold open a portal between worlds. Mostly electricity, isn't it?"

Rose Crowshaw grew more anxious and wiped her brow with her filthy rag, putting more grease and oil upon her already dirty face than the perspiration it removed. "Yeah. But these boilers over here drive the small turbines that create the electricity." Her voice was quiet. "Actually, not many of us know about electricity and how it works. I just spend too much time puzzling it out, I suppose."

Kaeris understood its operation, of course. If rumors were to be believed, the intimidating woman could likely stabilize the construct holding open the Breach herself. Maybe that's why she had come out to the portal. "But that apparatus you were working on when the wrench slipped – it has nothing to do with the steamfitting or conversion to electricity. In fact," and Crowshaw gulped, "It's part of the converter that sustains the aether modulation. Isn't it?"

Crowshaw wiped her forehead again. "I just...I just had a hunch. I should have sent for an engineer," she admitted.

"You should have sent for Viktor Ramos. Or me."

"Sorry. It won't happen again."

The white wall of light flickered again and, for a moment, blinked out of existence with a pop. Crackling electricity suddenly flared around the sustaining arms, arcing bolts between them until the Breach re-opened with a gentle rumble of thunder.

If they could not stabilize the Breach, whole fortunes might be lost in shipping delays. More importantly, although no one ever made any mention of it, the fear of the Breach closing as it had a hundred years prior was as great a fear to each settler in Malifaux as encountering a Razorspine rattler. Small tendrils of electricity crawled over the armature as Kaeris took the wrench from Rose Crowshaw. She didn't take her eyes from the Breach although it was blinding, and she said, "Looks like you didn't get cut that badly after all."

Rose realized she had removed the rag from her hand to wipe her brow and returned it to a pocket in her overalls, forgetting about the wound. Her blood had spilled on the ground before her and even stained her pant leg. Yet, in the span of their discourse, the wound had fully healed.

"Get back to work," Kaeris said, and Rose thankfully withdrew and would spend the rest of the morning avoiding the intimidating M&SU contractor. Both women knew they'd be speaking again.

Kaeris took the wrench and worked on the same apparatus that Rose Crowshaw had been. After all, the frequency modulation was clearly out of sync. She was a patient woman but was anxious to find out how the young steamfitter could know about such advanced mechanisms without any training or, at the least, without having seen any of the engineering drawings of the full device, so intricate that only a handful of people might comprehend its basic operation.

Most important, however, was stabilizing the Breach. No one wanted to be trapped in Malifaux. They sought dominion over this world, to conquer it. But an inability to rely upon resources from Earth would lead to their inevitable downfall.

Molly Squidpiddge bent her face against the wind that tore into her pallid flesh, biting with frozen sleet. She could not be hurt by it and barely felt what was likely a bitter cold. Her arms and face were bare to the elements, but she pushed through it as she might have when she still lived. Seamus had chastised her for such behavior, even recently. She assured him that she wanted only to blend in with the humans – to not draw attention unnecessarily. Seamus said she was clever. She drew enough attention. Although her level of decomposition was markedly different than the dry, desiccated, and deteriorating flesh of Seamus' other Belles, her flesh was still deathly pallid, and her eyes were too flat, conveying her deathly state as well.

"Is it cold?" the head of Philip Tombers asked from the crook of her arm where she carried it, cradled like a child. She held it against her breast, so he was reluctant to say anything. It wasn't that he necessarily enjoyed her breast pressed against his cheek as he couldn't exactly feel that, either. He just didn't want to be thrust back into the damnable sack that was his typical abode and transportation. At least they had upgraded it to soft velvet instead of that infernal burlap.

"No," Molly said as the sleet pelted them. "It's not too cold."

The burlap itched, he had complained.

You can't feel it, they argued.

It smells like old potatoes, he retorted.

You cannot smell, either, they quipped.

It still has bugs crawling around, he offered.

They came with you, not the sack.

Still, Seamus bought him a nice velvet bag to shut him up. Tombers didn't know why Molly had pulled him out, but it was nice to look around, even if he sometimes rolled toward her and the fabric of her dress was all he could see.

They moved easily through the dark alleys, taking a twisted path around a dilapidated and abandoned building adjacent to the Quarantine Zone. Few people walked openly in this dangerous section of the City on a normal night, but with the stinging cold, the two were alone. "Almost there," she said to the head. She conveyed little emotion in her speech or mannerisms, but her voice remained strangely lyrical and soothing even in its monotone.

"Where?" he asked.

"Quarantine Zone."

He knew that. He should have asked why they were going to the Quarantine Zone, and he nearly did, but he bit his tongue. She might stick him back in his bag if he got too chatty.

The Guild had secured the Zone well and had few illegal trespasses into the sector. Molly, however, was soon standing upon a mound of debris of broken stone and wood, several city blocks in. If the Guild were patrolling the area, Molly demonstrated no anxiety about standing out in the open. She turned him so that he could see, but the wind and freezing rain limited his sight. "The Guardpost," she said. His eyes adjusted to the darkness, and he slowly focused upon the burnt remains of a wall and the lower stonework that remained, dark from the fire that had consumed the upper wooden structure.

The rain began to turn to thick flakes of snow.

He could see the stain of fire around the ruins. The cobblestones near the Guardpost remains were blackened as well. They faced the City, her back against the heart of the Quarantine Zone. He could see the line around the perimeter where the fence had been, just several months earlier. The Guild had moved that line several blocks further in, expanding the Quarantine Zone as it encroached upon the City.

"Molly?"

"Plague. It lived here."

Tombers looked around, shifting his eyes best he could to see whatever it was he was meant to see. For once, he was silent.

She said, "They burned it. To stop it. Guards and innocents with the disease lured to the Plagued. A Guild officer burned the Guardpost and all of the victims he found here. He meant to burn the plague so that it would not spread. He was clever. But he failed."

Tombers added, "I overheard Nicodem's conversation with Seamus afterward. The plagued mob attacked his observatory. Why?"

She did not respond. Instead, Molly turned, facing the heart of the Quarantine Zone. Rising before them was a great mound of bodies, piled high and haphazardly. Hundreds of bodies were dumped without compassion in a pile that spread before them and loomed significantly above Molly. It was wide and she had to turn slowly so that he could take it all in.

"Damnation," Tombers said, aghast.

"This is not where the plague was stopped. It is where it began. Where the Plagued Tyrant lost control of it. In the slums bordering the Guardpost, Plague lingered." Molly went silent and the two surveyed the mound whose circumference spanned at least fifty feet. "The Plagued Pit," she said, meaning the pile.

"It's more like a hill than a pit," Tombers offered.

"It is a pit. Deep." She was silent again, which was her custom. None of Seamus' Belles spoke, save Molly, and she only did so reluctantly. Speech typically reduced her to a coughing and spasming fit in which she spat up blood, bile, or mucus. Sometimes all at once. When she spoke again, Tombers could not believe that she sustained a long discourse, uninterrupted by her violent expulsion of bodily fluids that simply would not dry out like the other girls. She said, "One citizen avoided another; hardly any neighbor troubled about others, relatives never visit. Such terror has been struck into the hearts of men and women that brother has abandoned brother, and the uncle his nephew, and the sister her brother, and even the wife her husband. What is even worse and nearly incredible is that fathers and mothers may refuse to see and tend their children.

Molly didn't know how she knew all this. Like many things, she just knew.

Tombers saw their faces, calm in death. In fact, as he looked from one face to another in that vast mound of bodies, they each looked too calm, too accepting of the death that was visited upon them. No faces frozen in terror, or anguish, or remorse. It was like they expected death and could not resist it and did not try.

"Such was the multitude of corpses brought to the churches every day and almost every hour that there was not enough consecrated ground to give them burial, especially since they wanted to bury each person in the family grave, according to the old custom. The cemeteries were unable to accommodate them. They found it fitting to dig the Plague Pit here, at the Guardpost remains, and dump the bodies where they believe it began. They dug this pit where they buried the bodies by hundreds. Here they stowed them away like bales in the hold of a ship and covered them with a little earth, until the whole trench was full."

Her voice was beautiful even when she spoke of these horrific conditions. It had a strange echo that reminded him of dreaming.

"Why are we here?" Tombers asked her.

"They may come for these bodies. Nicodem or the others. To raise them. Make an army of the Plagued dead to wage their war. Can it be stopped?"

Thomas Colburn had been in Malifaux for four years. He had come across the Breach in the very first wave as a prominent young Guild Guardsman. With no family ties to hold him back, he enthusiastically volunteered for extra duty and special assignments. With such passion and drive he quickly rose through officer ranks and set his sights on the elite divisions within the Guild.

He had a personal fascination with the walking dead. His focus upon the Death Marshals was interestingly circumvented by Samael Hopkins, himself, who requested Officer Colburn specifically for a mission into the western Badlands, despite the dozens of volunteers that had stepped forward for the assignment.

He scratched the thick stubble on his neck, limping into Malifaux and spat beside the checkpoint gate, a superstition none of the earliest pioneers forgot, and dragged his bum leg back into the City. He adjusted his wide-brimmed hat, his thick oiled duster, and the black patch across his eye. He was nervous, he had to admit. Since that incident in the Badlands three years earlier,

he had not been back in the Guild enclave. He felt that the Guardsmen at the checkpoint followed his every move, but he no longer recognized a man among them and knew he was all but forgotten among those that might still be in the ranks. Malifaux chewed up and spat out too many young people eager to prove their mettle, and everyone understood that it was foolish to get close to anyone in the Guild. There was little compassion. Little friendship.

He tipped his hat to the sentry at the gateway fences that separated the Guild's official buildings from the general populace. As he predicted, they stopped him from limping past. "Just a minute there, mister," one said, stepping around the wooden post beside the small checkpoint building, holding up his hand while the other rested on his holstered Peacebringer.

"I'm retired Second Lieutenant Thomas Colburn," he said sternly to the Guardsmen.

The two guards looked skeptical and studied the broken man before them, dragging a leg, eye patched with a jagged scar that ran the length of his entire face. Reaching for his credentials held on the inside of his dark duster, the lower two digits were missing from his hand, and a purple scar ran the length of his palm where half the hand had been torn away.

They examined his paperwork, confirming his sincerity. One said, "Sorry, sir. Didn't recognize you."

"No. 'Spose not. Been out of the City for some time."

"Out'a the City?" They thought he must be pulling their leg. "What do you do with yourself out there, Mister Colburn?"

The "mister" stung him a bit. No officer's title. "Rancher. Raise cattle. Just north'a here a ways. Not too far into the wilds, of course," he said, supporting their supposition that a broken man like him should not be off on his own outside of Guild protection.

"Okay, cowboy. What brings you back in?"

"I need to see Officer Hopkins as soon as possible."

They laughed. "Hopkins? You want to see Hopkins?"

Colburn straightened himself the best he could but the old wound to his lower back made it difficult to stand straight without wincing. "Stand aside now, Private," he said and moved to enter the conclave. The Guardsman stopped him. "Private?"

"New regulations. Can't just saunter in off the streets and have a meeting with the likes of Samael Hopkins."

"I'm an officer in good standing," he said sternly. "I'll find someone that can address me properly."

"Inactive duty. Like I said, different regulations than when you were around last, I 'spect." Colburn ground his teeth. He hadn't come back to Malifaux to be turned away so easily. "We'll send your request up the pike. They'll let you know when they can see you."

Another guard, hidden from his view behind the checkpoint station said quietly to another, "Haven't even seen Hopkins in months. Don't we need to report requests to see 'im?"

They had Colburn wait. Soon they were escorting him through the Courthouse building adjacent to the Witch Hunter holding facility where he intended to go all along. Leaving him sitting in a stiff wooden chair for too long, his good leg tingled as the circulation was cut off, and he began to fidget uncomfortably. They had taken his pistol, of course, and his typical habits of adjusting his hat, his eyepatch, and holster were so ingrained in his movements that he jumped in brief panic every several minutes when his hand fell on dead space at his hip. He lived on his own out there, and his gun was at his side every minute, including sleep. Having it removed was as painful as losing half his hand.

"I understand you've come to speak with Officer Samael Hopkins," a smooth voice emanated from the darkness surrounding the outer edges of the room. Colburn could not discern the speaker, remaining there in the shadows just beyond the dim light of the kerosene lamp suspended above the table he sat behind. Colburn had not even noticed the man enter the room, and he jumped at the voice.

"Think I made that clear enough," Colburn said. "Don't need to talk to no lawyer. Need to talk to a Stalker, and one high enough so a job'll get done and not get mixed up in some paper shuffling."

The man in the shadows stepped forward so that his lower legs were within the yellow light of the lamp, yet his face remained hidden in the shadows. He wore the fine leggings and stark white stockings of a lord from back across the Breach. "You'll find that I'm no mere lawyer," the man said in that low voice. "But I understand your sentiment." Colburn fidgeted uncomfortably though the man before him was little more than a dandy by his dress and mannerisms and a bit too fragile looking. Something in his demeanor struck Colburn with fear that rippled down his back though. It perplexed him. "I'm Lucius Matheson, Mister Colburn. You might have heard that I, too, appreciate getting a job done." He had heard of the mysterious Secretary. Few had ever seen him. Colburn had to wonder if his various encounters with prominent figures in Malifaux were a blessing or a curse. "I understand you're here to speak with Officer Hopkins." He could not see the Secretary's face shrouded in the shadows around him, yet he still looked away. "I see in your file, Mister Colburn, that Hopkins spoke highly of you. Quite."

"Thank you," he said reluctantly.

"What brings you here, looking for Hopkins?"

Something beyond his understanding was afoot, and he realized he was only accidentally caught up in it. Some conflict between this imposing figure and Hopkins. "There's a problem – out on the range."

"I do not see how this concerns Hopkins."

"Maybe it doesn't," he had to agree. He raised his head to muster the courage to stare into the dark silhouette before him. "But it's odd. Supernatural. Even in Malifaux. Something's changed."

"I do not see in your file how you became an expert on such matters."

"That's why I wanted to see Hopkins. He'd believe me. He'd get the job done."

Lucius Matheson remained still and silent before him, and his discomfort grew. He fought to convince the Governor's Secretary to take his plea seriously and at least send a contingent of inspectors out to his ranch. By the end of his tale of his own animals growing belligerent beyond reason, Matheson ordered Colburn to lead him back, to show *him* the behavioral anomaly. There was a hint in Matheson's tone that if Colburn had not accurately conveyed the true nature of the state of affairs there, he would bear a terrible price at misleading him. Lucius listened intently to Colburn's tale. He couldn't have known that conditions on his ranch would have grown so dire in the time it had taken to journey to the City and meet with the Secretary.

At that moment, back on Colburn's ranch, one of the three ranch hands he had hired remained alive, though he cowered in the corner of the stable, pinned against the barn wall and unable to reach the fence where he might have crawled under, nor could he reach the open barn door. There would be no escape through the barn anyway. All of the cattle were in there in greater numbers, clearly more comfortable in the dark than out in the light.

One of the steers came closer, and he shrank further against the wall, trembling and whimpering. Its eyes were wide and the dark pupils constricted, showing more whites than they should. Although physically impossible for a cow to growl, when the beast lowed, it was a guttural and throaty reverberation that sounded more like a growl than any lowing the hand had ever heard before. It made a deep and throaty moo, and its lips were pulled away from the two rows of flat teeth. Blood dripped from around them, and it chomped, more like a wolf than a bovine would chew from side to side. Thin strands of flesh dangled wet and glistening from between its back teeth. Its lips pulled away from the teeth, crimson and slick with blood. The bovine stalked him, assessing him as prey. Another big steer, more confident than the first, lowered its head, eyes just as fierce and insane with the thirst for blood, and charged the cowering ranch hand. He screamed and covered his face with his forearms against the impending doom. The first steer knocked it aside as it charged, and it crashed into the wall beside the addled rancher. It lowed strangely at the other, regaining its footing, and they squared off, each growling a deep-throated warning to the other.

Before the ranch hand's eyes, the first steer, mouth still dripping blood and frothing saliva, shook and quivered. It stomped the ground hard with its forelegs, like a tantrum. Abruptly, bony spines, long and flat, like great arrowheads, burst from its back along each vertebra. It howled, the noise echoing throughout the valley. An additional bony spike burst from each of its shoulder blades. The other cattle around the corral went through a similar transformation. The two stalking him were enraged.

In a flash, they charged at one another, howling as their heads knocked violently against each other's, their long horns slashing madly at the neck and shoulders in possessive rage. More cattle circled the fray and charged the rancher, desperate for his flesh. They slammed against one another, beating their heads in explosive cracks of bone on bone. As their blood flowed they began to turn on one another, not just to exhibit dominance over their human prey, but to devour themselves. Soon, several saw the weakness and exhaustion of another and quickly had it toppled. They made short work of it, tearing its throat open with their long horns. Their faces were covered in blood from injuries and gorging.

The rancher hoped to slink away from the carnage, to find refuge beyond the sturdy gates of the corral. As he fled, eyes on the insane massacre, he stopped short when the heavy puff of breath just above him fell upon his neck. He looked up into the face of one of his favorite animals on the ranch. An old boy, gentle as a kitten, always the first to comply with the rancher's herding. It huffed again. Then it raised its great head to the sky, crying in madness in the odd lowing that sounded much more like a wolf's howl. It was the last thing the ranch hand heard.

The cattle consumed the flesh of each of the ranchers but turned on one another before they could finish, enraged by their desperate thirsts for blood.

Nearby carrion birds descended upon the bloodbath, eager to take advantage of the cattle's distraction for one another to pick at the visceral remains in the open. As they ate, one vulture, gorging upon the flesh dangling from a ranch hand's ribs, snapped at another, suddenly desperate to have the meat for itself. They quarreled and tore at one another and soon, more birds that had descended to the irresistible feast found themselves striking at birds or cattle, desperate to have any flesh, any blood.

By the time Colburn and Lucius Matheson, his face hidden behind a full face mask, could return to the ranch to examine the "strange and territorial behavior of the livestock", the sound of the screeching and howling had subsided. The barn and corral was awash with blood and partially devoured carcasses. The dirt could not absorb the blood that pooled among the remains.

Lucius was not a man taken easily by surprise. Witnessing the horrific carnage before him, he pulled his horse to a halt and surveyed the horrible scene. "What the hell?" he whispered.

His horse fidgeted. Lucius pulled it away from the ranch, and it huffed with a guttural reverberation in its throat that sounded strangely like a growl. The horses of the guardsmen accompanying them snapped at one another.

The great Hanging Tree loomed above Leveticus, and he stood, bent at his midsection, looking not too dissimilar from the gnarled and ancient tree that rose in mockery of life, itself. It bore no leaves and the bark peeled, but its roots ran deep and sap still flowed when the tree was tapped, proving it still lived on, no doubt feeding upon the bones of those that had been buried around it.

Leveticus stood in the depths of the great tree's early morning shadow, peering down the long sloping valley to Malifaux below.

The young girl, Alyce, sat upon a square tombstone behind him, staring not at the City, but the Governor General's mansion that loomed beyond the graveyard, across the road. She was contemplating how difficult it would be to take out the guards assigned there and make off with the fortune she was sure it housed.

"Do you feel it, girl?" he asked, his voice dry and taut.

Alyce said, "What, the cold? Yeah, it's making my skin crawl."

"No, not the cold. The feeling of inevitability?"

"Does it feel like boredom? If so, then yes. I feel it."

He chuckled, and the long white brows above his narrow eyes lifted. "Not that, either. Can you sense that something's not right?"

"Oh, you mean how you've kept me out all night looking down at the City and at a bunch of houses out beyond the City, too, and now I'm tired? I agree. It's not right."

He thought she'd be able to sense it like he did. Her arm was not the only part of her that had been replaced; wires and mechanika ran deep into her and attached at various points to her spine and up into her brain. He thought that by now she'd be closer to death, to sense it more like he did. He could not teach her about it as he had expected. She was far too willful, too attached to life to feel the barrier of death pressing upon her. He could feel the buzz in his prosthetic leg and arm of brass, copper, and iron. But deep within his chest, where his heart had once been, he felt it most. "Death," he said flatly. "It's all around."

"Good observation. We're in the cemetery. Under the Tree. There's death all around, all right."

"Why must you be so willfully disobedient?" he asked, but he loved her combative nature. Her passion was so starkly contrasted against his stoic and disinterested demeanor.

"Why's your doohickey glowing?" she asked.

He lifted his staff so that the green stone attached to the end of it was directly before his face. It glowed faintly. He nodded and sighed. "It usually does this when I'm about to die," he said casually.

Bearing the Burden

October 12

"Have you figured out how they are animated?" Nicodem asked, leaning close to the abomination on the table.

"I haven't a clue," Doctor McMourning admitted, his gloved hands held loosely behind his back. They twisted and fidgeted anxiously.

Nicodem poked the flesh of the cadaver, cut in a square from the muscle beneath, one side still connected to the body. It was pinned to the wooden slab at the two corners of the skin. It was thin and dry like paper. Nicodem felt the firm flesh, hard and brittle, with his forefinger. McMourning didn't approve. The undertaker traced the tube protruding from its wrist that traveled within his forearm, to exit at its armpit and into its open chest cavity. The tubing connected to a metal tank approximately four inches in diameter and, although imbedded within the thing's chest, there were numerous dials, gauges, and adjustable knobs to the adjoining apparatus. With the inner organs removed and the front of its chest fully absent, perhaps the original reanimator, clearly a prodigy of resurrection and grafting, could continue to make modification on the design and operation. "How did our anonymous friend reanimate a corpse so old, so disconnected from its spirit and forgotten in the depths of time?" He asked softly, more to himself than McMourning.

Still, McMourning responded. "That's exactly why I called you here. The grafting technology makes no sense. Like it's superfluous, an afterthought. Half of the internal apparatus aren't even connected."

Nicodem was skeptical. "This chamber," he said, pointing to the internal cylinder, "it's the necrotic pump, no?"

McMourning grinned a broad and toothy smile. It made Nicodem scowl in contrast. "Yes. They keep thinking it's a steam boiler."

Nicodem opened the small hatch at the top of the rusted cylinder, and the stale and acrid odor of necrotic residue struck him at once. It was long dry, of course,

but the smell would linger forever. "Steam? Why would they think so?"

"Narrow-minded, of course. They get fixated on one idea and cannot accept any other."

"Then what do you make of the pump and necrotic assemblies if they're 'superfluous'?"

"My theory is that this corpse has been reanimated several times." Nicodem lifted his head from examining the disconnected apparatus within the remains. "I cannot tell which might have come first: a reanimation using more conventional Resurrectionist arts such as you employ, or the grafted mechanika that may have first driven it."

"And now they've been awakened again. By the Event?"

He shrugged. "Possibly. But many modifications to this corpse have been made over the numerous years since its original demise. Although dead flesh does not scar, of course, lacerations into it decompose differently than surrounding tissue. Some of these inner components have been added to the original design and older material is discarded but left mounted where it was. What's most fascinating is not how it has been reanimated--"

"Of course it is," Nicodem interrupted. "Raising a single corpse, over and over, despite injuries to the flesh – this could be the missing piece to our puzzle."

"Yes, yes. We will study this thing, of course. But, listen. This corpse is ancient."

"Neverborn. Some ancient practitioner ahead of his time."

"Much of the technology is too modern. And the corpse isn't exactly Neverborn."

"Then human. From the first Breach exploration a hundred years ago."

McMourning smiled that broad, ridiculous smile that made him look like a carved Jack-o'-lantern. He cracked his knuckles and looked practically overjoyed. "It's not human, either. It's far older than the other Breach, as well. This has anatomy similar to both humanoid species. Like it's descended from both. Many generations removed from the originals."

Nicodem's scowl drew deeper. "We know that small breaches open from here to there all the time. They must have brought some humans over and conducted some experiments?" Nicodem offered. Even he was not convinced.

McMourning's expressive face conveyed his distaste of the theory. "Not like the Neverborn we know. They would cross-breed with a human? That seems the kind of thing only a human would do." His grin returned to the discomfort of Nicodem. "Seems the kind of thing *I* would do." He began wringing his hands, excited at the prospect. His mind was already busy thinking of the difficulties in the endeavor, the delicious impossibility, and the joy of overcoming it. He detached further and further from Nicodem, into his own realm of science and the twisting of the natural law that was his dominion.

His pondering was interrupted as the bulbous head of McMourning's assistant, Sebastian, popped from around the heavy wood door to the dissection lab. "Pardon and 'scuse me, suh," he said, his thick tongue smacking within his mouth and his fleshy jowls quivering. "But there be a inspectuh or two waitin' to ask a few questions of ya, suh." One of Sebastian's eyes pointed to the ceiling above the two Resurrectionists while his primary eye may have fallen in the general direction of either McMourning or Nicodem. "And I may be so bold, Doctor," and his voice dropped to a hoarse whisper, "but I b'lieve they got a Death Marshal along." Sebastian sounded like a buffoon; just a simpleton off of Old London's impoverished streets. He was far from any of those things, Nicodem knew. It was all an act, obfuscating the truth of a man who knew and understood far more than any might suspect.

McMourning didn't seem to notice Sebastian or acknowledge his statement. So it was Nicodem who said, "Stall them, Mister Sebastian. Give them a tour of the good Doctor's examining room. That should give them something to be excited about." Both men smiled at one another. Sebastian because it added to the illusion of his simplicity. Nicodem merely to add to the illusion of his genteel politeness. Both knew the Guild Inspectors would find nothing incriminating in this mortuary. Not that McMourning was overly cautious. On the contrary, he was addled and absently forgot he even stood upon Guild facilities. Sebastian, however, hid everything for his master.

"Of course, suh. I b'lieve 't'will." He waddled off to keep the Guild inquisitors running in circles.

"Doctor," Nicodem ordered, his voice more commanding than his thin frame would suggest. McMourning's eyes fell upon him. "Guild Inspectors? Death Marshals?"

"Yes, and it's their third visit, so I imagine it'll be an uncomfortable afternoon."

Nicodem sighed but managed to refrain from rolling his eyes. "What have you done to garner their attention?"

"Work *you* requested, actually. Trying to make a better warrior. And I stole a page from your book. Like you use those crazy sword wielding Nipponese monstrosities, I've been working with some deceased Guild Guardsmen. That's why the Inspectors are here. A couple of Guild autopsies 'seem to be missing'," he said in a mocking lilt.

"So did you succeed? Can they shoot?"

"They can, but not worth a damn. I'm still fiddling with their brains to see if I can access that part of their training and get them to remember. So far, if you give them the typical weapons they were trained to use in life, they seem to try to shoot the sword and slice with the gun. Doesn't even matter if you switch the weapons to the other hand." He drifted off in thought, again forgetting the gravity of the Inspectors waiting to question him. He was thinking of the brain and the layout of the organ, already contemplating how he might revise his last attempts.

Neither felt any urgency to either finish their discussion or evade the Guild Inspectors.

Nicodem gave no thought to the Guild officers within the building when he said, "We cannot afford to wait much longer. What of the reclusive scientist you once spoke of? Could he give you any insight into this problem? Identify something you're overlooking? It's been long enough and neither of us have made any significant progress."

McMourning winced. It clearly offended him to suggest he could not solve this problem. "He's no longer a teacher. No longer my professor, that's for sure."

"No. You said he came to Malifaux to escape the law that condemned his experimenting on the deceased. Is he still here conducting those experiments?"

"I don't have a bloody clue. It's been over a year since we spoke. I hear he's not been in the City in nearly as long. Maybe he's gotten himself killed out there in the wild, poking his nose in a Nephilim nest." McMourning hated to admit that anyone was a better scientist, but his old teacher was something of a prodigy and pioneered an entirely new way of looking at the function of the anatomical form. In fact, he might have inadvertently invented the Resurrectionist art, though that was not exactly his intention. He would say that he wanted to improve upon what nature had begun. It was, however, enough to have him driven out of the University at Ingolstadt (where McMourning had enthusiastically studied beneath him), his research compound in the Orkney Islands, and finally from his lab in North Africa where he was rumored to have conducted horrifying experiments that were intolerable to civilized man. In fact, his experiments were deemed as "crimes against humanity" though McMourning considered them nothing short of revolutionary and inspirational. Doctor McMourning, in fact, pursued the work of his old professor so doggedly that a report from Scotland Yard, though vague and clearly misrepresentative of the facts, so inspired McMourning that he, too, fled the Old World to take up residence in Malifaux. Now, like the professor that gave birth to a science of longevity and staving off death, itself, the law had come knocking upon *his* door. The narrow minds of the simple man sought to judge what it could not possibly comprehend, he thought.

"Doctor!" Nicodem barked, shaking McMourning from his reverie. Those times were long gone and the old professor surely devoured alone in Malifaux's wilds. "Stay focused," Nicodem said, clearly annoyed. McMourning understood. He had little use for the living. They were all a mere irritation to him. Ironic since his own research was focused on bringing an eternal life from the ashes of death, to give back what must be taken from all living things.

The thought reminded him of the key piece to the unsolvable puzzle. "What of your new prodigy? What's her name?"

"Kirai."

"Hmm. Whatever. Have you implanted a spirit into one of our empty vessels?"

"No." Nicodem cursed beneath his breath, irritated at the string of setbacks that kept them from initiating plans that should have already ensured their freedom from the vigilant probing of the Guild and any other eyes that sought to keep them from their destiny. "Keep working on the Guild autopsies, then. We need something that can properly challenge those who oppose us. Give me that and you will have the place to conduct the research you wish, unimpeded. Now, what of this problem with the Inspectors?"

McMourning waved his hand as if brushing aside a fly. "I'll kill them. Dress them up like the autopsies that went missing. Two birds, one stone, that sort of thing."

Nicodem couldn't help but roll his eyes that time. "There will be a paper trail. More inquiries about why *these* Guild officials went missing."

"Ugh! Yes, you're right. What a nuisance they are."

"You will, no doubt, use them to conduct the next wave of experiments. Will you not stop until Lady Justice, herself, comes to ask you some questions?"

McMourning looked surprised, assessing whether Nicodem were serious or joking. Then he remembered who he was addressing. "Justice? Have you not heard?"

"What?"

"The Lady is in the infirmary across the street."

Nicodem nearly staggered. Eyes wide he asked, "Here? She's wounded?"

McMourning rolled his eyes, then, mocking Nicodem. "I'd say. She's only regained consciousness once since your Observatory fell on her. You nearly killed her."

"Really? That was months ago. She's still comatose? I assumed she escaped unscathed. I thought she was indestructible. And I nearly killed her."

"Nearly. Don't get too proud of yourself. You blew her up and your whole complex fell on her and she still breathes. But, yes, she suffers. One side of her body is crushed and she struggles even to breathe."

"Which side?"

"It matters?"

"She swings the sword with the right."

McMourning nodded. "That's the crushed side."

Nicodem nodded, pleased by the discussion with McMourning after all. "Well, then. I'll depart, out the back way, of course. You have visitors, and I wouldn't like to keep them waiting any longer." In fact, he heard the clack of their boots upon the wood beyond the chamber door and Sebastian's voice echoing down the hall, ensuring McMourning wouldn't be taken by surprise.

Nicodem tipped his hat to McMourning as he slipped through the narrow secret door hidden behind a shelf of books, beakers, and other lab equipment. As he pulled the shelf closed behind him, the main door to the chamber opened, and McMourning stood stoically beside the partially dissected remains of the abomination hauled back to his lab from the open pit within the bayou. The two Inspectors brushed past Sebastian in a huff, but he merely smiled and nodded at each as they passed. The Death Marshal, wide-brimmed hat pulled low over his brow, leaned a shoulder against the opposite door frame, too close to Sebastian for comfort. The assistant seemed not to care and smiled absently at him, too, licking his lips audibly, nodding happily at the officer. The Death Marshal turned to regard him, the upper portion of his face obscured in shadow. The lower part, however, caught the light briefly as he slowly returned the nod to Sebastian, and it was oddly discolored and gray, with thin tendrils of flesh pulled taut from cheekbone to jaw and exposed musculature beneath, as if part of the skin had rotted away. At first, the assistant suspected leprosy, but realized this Death Marshal was not fresh off the Guardsman line, rather, a seasoned veteran of the position that had come into contact with too much necrotic fluid, charged with the acidic chemicals and magics that allowed a Resurrectionist to infuse a corpse with more than mere mindless shambling, but with the brief inclination of emotion that Nicodem demanded.

Bringing a Death Marshal was warning enough, but this one might be one of the highest of their ranks. Perhaps had been elevated to the command of the department while Justice and the Judge recovered.

"Doctor McMourning," one Inspector began. "The leads you had given us turned out to be dead ends, I'm afraid." McMourning stood emotionlessly beside the corpse on the gurney, eyes fixed upon him. "Questions keep us coming back to you, it seems. Oh, yes, you've been very helpful in leading us to new suspects, but they have a tendency to give us one dead end after another. Any idea why that might be?"

McMourning raised his eyebrows and cocked his head to the side. The beginning of that mischievous grin tugged at the corner of his lips. "Dead end, you say? Dead end. I find that interesting." He reached out and lifted the scalpel from beside the partial head of the corpse. Casually, without hurry, he stepped forward toward the Inspector. It was likely because of the casual manner in which he moved that none of the men reacted at all. He showed no sign of aggression or of fear. He simply held the instrument of his office and even the Death Marshal, eyes upon McMourning throughout and trained to suppress any danger before it might get out of control, failed to react, leaning, still, against the doorframe opposite Sebastian. As McMourning reached the Inspector, his arm slashed from its position at his side up to the Inspector's neck, the long but narrow blade slicing easily through his throat so deeply that the blade struck the spine at the back. A thick stream of blood sprayed to his left from the severed jugular, but the motion of the blade up and through the left sent a trail into the face of the second Inspector, causing him to jump and shriek. At the sight of the blood, McMourning became a blur, dropping his arm quickly. The scalpel flew through the room, striking the Death Marshal in the shoulder as he, too, came alive. He had begun pulling the gun from his holster but McMourning's scalpel severed enough of the nerves that his entire arm fell limply at his side.

He was no coward, but no fool, either, and with the experience of the office behind him, he knew exactly what he faced in that dissection lab. He jerked back, to flee and gather the reinforcements necessary to bring this villain to proper justice, but as he moved through the entry, Sebastian reached out and grabbed the scalpel still protruding from the officer's shoulder and pulled him to a halt as if it were a leash. The Marshal howled in unexpected pain as the narrow blade twisted deep within his flesh. His other arm came up to bat the fleshy man away, but, much faster than he could have predicted, Sebastian had the scalpel out of his shoulder and sliced cleanly through the officer's throat. Like the Inspector, his head lolled back, away from the deep cut, and he fell lifelessly, his hat at the feet of Sebastian, still smiling vacantly as if nothing were at all amiss.

The second Inspector trembled between the two corpses, bleeding out on the floor, the dark pool enveloping his feet from either side. He bore a firearm, but was too shocked to remember it, instead, standing in place, eyes wide and lower lip trembling.

McMourning stepped over the body at his feet, his boot slurping at the sticky blood around it. He put his open palm against the man's face, above the nose and fingers stretched out across the breadth of his head. He pressed the man back against the wall and down into a crouch. The Inspector gibbered incoherently and tears came to his eyes. Not exactly the image of the pinnacle of manly bravado the Guild liked to project of its law enforcement. McMourning's grin was broad and his eyes sinister as he spoke down to the man below him, now powerless and stammering for mercy, knowing he would soon be dead.

"Let me see," McMourning said. "Those missing autopsies that's caused all this fuss…you remember them, Inspector?"

"Y-Yes," he stammered.

"One was killed by a sword, through the jugular. Say, just like your friend here. I remember that. But the other Guardsman – how did he die, again?"

The man's eyes darted back and forth in confusion and mounting panic. "B-Bludgeoning. To the h-head. P-Please don't do this. I—We can work out a deal."

"Yes. That's right." He did not take his eyes from the Inspector but held his hand back toward Sebastian, palm open. Sebastian was already approaching him with a large wooden mallet. It didn't seem possible, but McMourning's smile widened, now bright and toothy, as he took the mallet from his assistant. The smile spanned his entire face. "Bludgeoning to the head." He grunted and the mallet came down heavily upon the Inspector's head.

Geissel Metalworks

The Guild maintains its authority in Malifaux through political might and martial strength. Constructs, great automated beasts like the Peacekeeper, are a pillar of that strength. Machines of steel and brass, automations of cogs and gears, from armored plate to drive axel, almost all of their components are produced by Geissel Metalworks. Since their humble beginnings in the Old World, the Geissels rose from peasant beginnings to become one of the wealthiest and well-regarded manufacturers Earthside. Most ships and trains have Geissel fittings, gears, and rods, all stamped with the familiar cracked anvil logo that has represented the finest in metalwork for well over three centuries.

When the Breach reopened, the Geissel board saw an opportunity. The company lost a branch office when the Breach closed a century ago, but logs and accounts still sat in the musty corporate vaults of Glasgow. The company knew well the profits to be made in Malifaux. They immediately approached Guild representatives for contracts to establish a factory in the City. The Guild conceded to the request, reasoning that should the Breach close for any reason, an established metal crafting factory would be beneficial. The Guild, also heavily dependent on Geissel components for Constructs, knew it would be less expensive and easier to maintain the machines with materials on hand rather than waiting for them to arrive from Earthside.

Geissel invested a fortune on the endeavor. Scouting teams under the direction of the Governor General – a close friend of Angus Geissel, the company's patriarch – located a suitable site for a metal working plant in the Industrial Zone. Renovation teams and lifters under Guild guard built the factory to full working condition in less than a year. Further expanded by a second smelting plant and foundry, the complex is the largest in Malifaux.

Today, Geissel Metalworks supplies nearly all of the materials needed for Guild Constructs operating in Malifaux. In addition, they supply a myriad of other products. From clock gears to bullet casings, the company has made huge profits supplying the needs of the settlers. Jack Geissel, Angus' nephew, looks out into the City nightly from his offices. In the black smoke and screeching metal of the foundries, he can sees the profits roll in and the Geissel coffers fill.

AVATARS

MANIFEST

Twisting Fates introduces a new model type to the Malifaux skirmish game: Avatars. Avatars represent a Master's ability to channel increased aetheric energy into itself, manifesting on the table during the Encounter as a new model with different stats and abilities.

Avatars are not hired before an Encounter begins. Instead, players have the option of using some of their Soulstones to attach a potential Avatar to each Master during hiring. Once the Encounter begins, the Master must complete Manifest Requirements to unlock the Manifest Action which calls the Avatar into play. The full rules on how to attach and Manifest Avatars are included in this chapter.

NEW MODEL TYPE: AVATAR

The following rules apply specifically to Avatars:
- All Avatars are Unique.
- An Avatar must be attached to a Master during Crew Hiring (see Attaching Avatars below).
- Avatars can only enter the game through the **(*) Manifest** Action (see Manifesting Avatars below).
- An Avatar's Talents and Spells cannot be used or copied by another non-Totem model.
- Avatars can be affected by Talents and Spells that reference the model they replaced by name.
  *Example: Kirai, Avatar of Vengeance remains a "friendly Kirai" for the Seishin's **Spirit Sheath** Ability.*
- An Avatar counts as both an Avatar and Master for game effects, Talents, and Spells, unless they specifically state they affect or cannot affect Avatars.
  *Example: An Avatar has the **Use Soulstone** Ability just like a Master does.*
- An Avatar still counts as the Master it replaces for all Encounter purposes, included, but not limited to, calculating VP. *Example: Marcus, Avatar of Instinct can complete Marcus' Master-specific Primal Source Scheme.*

ATTACHING AVATARS

Avatars do not have a printed Soulstone Cost. Instead, when hiring his or her Crew, a player has the option of attaching one Avatar to each of his or her Masters **by spending two Soulstones per Master from his or her available Soulstones.**

Each Avatar indicates which Master it can be attached to as *Avatar (Master Name)* in its Characteristics. That Avatar may be attached to any one Master in the player's Crew with that name.

Example: The Avatar of Dread lists Avatar (Seamus) in its Characteristics. This means that the Avatar of Dread can only be attached to Seamus, the Mad Hatter.

The attached Avatar is not deployed at the start of the Encounter, but instead remains out of the game and cannot be interacted with by any game effects other than the **(*) Manifest** Action (see Manifesting Avatars below). Players must announce what Masters in their Crews have attached Avatars, but not specifically which Avatars, when announcing their Crew compositions.

MANIFESTING AVATARS

There are two components to Manifesting an Avatar during an Encounter: the Avatar's Manifest Requirements, and the **(*) Manifest** Action.

Manifest Requirements

The first component in Manifesting an Avatar is the pair of Manifest Requirements. Each Avatar possesses two unique Manifest Requirements (sometimes referenced as Requirement), which can be completed in any order the player chooses.

A Requirement indicates what the Master must do in order to check it off as completed. Once the Master satisfies the listed Requirement, the player checks off that Requirement as completed. Players can track their Master's progress toward completing these Requirements on the the Avatar's Stat Card.

Some Requirements can take multiple Actions or activations to complete. In these cases a Requirement has multiple bullet holes to check off. Check off the bullet holes as they are met, but the Requirement is not completed until they are all checked off. Some Requirements state they must take place over multiple activations or Turns; this is considered part of the Requirement.

Some game events may contribute toward completing **both** of a Master's Requirements. When that can occur, the Master's player must choose which of the two Requirements the event will contribute toward. It cannot benefit both Requirements.

MANIFEST REQUIREMENTS

1- Sonnia Criid inflicts 10 **Wd** on enemy models with Spells.

2 - Sonnia successfully casts **Inferno** twice.

MANIFEST CLOCK

Turn	0 Requirements Met	1 Requirement Met	2 Requirements Met
1	Cannot Manifest	Cannot Manifest	Cannot Manifest
2	Cannot Manifest	(All)	(2)
3	Cannot Manifest	(2)	(1)
4	Cannot Manifest	(1)	Choose (1) or (0)
5	Cannot Manifest	Choose (1) or (0)	(Automatic)
6	Cannot Manifest	(Automatic)	(Automatic)

MANIFEST ST

When Sonnia Criid perform
Action, follow the Manifest

- Remove from the game
  Sonnia Criid.
- Discard all Tokens and en
  Sonnia Criid.
- Replace Sonnia Criid with
  Conflagration.
- Sonnia, Avatar of Conflag
  immediately discard one
  perform a Healing Flip.
- Replace the Sonnia Criid s
  card with the Sonnia, Ava
  stat card for the remaind
  Then continue Sonnia, Aw
  Conflagration's activation
  Replaced model.

Manifest Requirement Example:

*Kill one enemy model with the **Magician's Duel** Spell.*

*Colette du Bois must successfully kill one enemy model with her **Magician's Duel** Spell as one of her Manifest Requirements. Once she has done so, her player checks off the bullet hole indicating that Requirement has been completed.*

Multi-Requirements Example:

*Successfully cast **Illusionary Forest** during two different Turns.*

For Lilith to complete this Requirement, she must successfully cast the Spell twice AND these castings must be on two different Turns.

Multi-Event Requiremen

*Inflict 10 **Wd** on enemy m*

*Successfully cast **Inferno** t*

Both of Sonnia's Requirem she casts Inferno she mu helps meet her Inferno Re Requirement. It cannot m

0 Requirements Met	1 Requirement Met	2 Requirements Met
Cannot Manifest	Cannot Manifest	Cannot Manifest
Cannot Manifest	(All)	(2)
Cannot Manifest	(2)	(1)
Cannot Manifest	(1)	Choose (1) or (0)
Cannot Manifest	Choose (1) or (0)	(Automatic)
Cannot Manifest	(Automatic)	(Automatic)

Manifesting is the **(*)**
of the Action depends on
ny Manifest Requirements
indicated on the Manifest

**Master cannot Manifest
an Encounter.**

es one of its Manifest
Manifest Action. Meeting
nent reduces the **Manifest**
on the Manifest Clock. The
each Avatar's Stat Card for

nifest Action is "**Choose (1)
r can choose which AP cost

f the Master has met both
anifest Action's AP cost is
Master **must** perform the

Manifest Action at no AP cost at the beginning of its activation, before it can perform any other Actions. The Master can sacrifice (remove from its Soulstone Pool, not discard) one Soulstone each time it activates to avoid taking this Action.

If the Master completes its second Manifest Requirement during Turn 5, once the event which completed the Requirement is resolved, the Master immediately takes the **Manifest** Action at no AP cost before it can take any other Actions, even those generated by a Trigger. The Master can sacrifice one Soulstone each time it activates to avoid taking this Action.

Automatic Manifest Example:
*Colette Du Bois has one Manifest Requirement completed. At the start of Turn 6 she **must** take the **Manifest** Action. Colette's player decides she would rather leave Colette's Master form in play, and therefore sacrifices one of her Crew's Soulstones to prevent it. Note, in Colette's case she must **sacrifice** the Soulstone, her **Artificial Soulstone** Ability would not apply. Colette continues her activation as normal. Later in the Turn, Colette **Reactivates**. She must again sacrifice a Soulstone or automatically take the **Manifest** Action.*

Manifest Steps

When a Master takes the **(*) Manifest** Action, its Controller takes the following standard Manifest Steps in order (these Steps are repeated on the Stat Card). Some Avatars require additional special Manifest Steps, such as placing Markers or Summoning/Placing additional models into play. These Steps are stated where appropriate in that Avatar's specific Manifest Steps.

- Remove from the game all Totems attached to the Master.
- Replace the Master model with the Master's associated Avatar.
- The Avatar may immediately discard one Soulstone to make a Healing Flip.
- Replace the Master's stat card with the Avatar's stat card for the remainder of the Encounter.
- Continue the model's activation as normal for a Replaced model. Additional models Summoned or Placed activate as per the Summoning or Placing rules.

Manifesting Example:

Jim is building a Colette Crew. He removes two Soulstones from his available amount and attaches the Avatar of Deception to Colette during Crew building. When it comes time to announce Crews, Jim states he has attached an Avatar to Colette, but does not specify the Avatar of Deception.

*Colette performs the **Illusionist** Action three times. These Actions must take place over at least two separate activations.*

*Colette kills one enemy model with the **Magician's Duel** Spell.*

*During the Encounter, Colette completes the **Magician's Duel** Requirement, filling in the bullet holes on her Avatar Stat card. On Turn Four, Jim decides to Manifest Colette's Avatar, and she takes the **Manifest** Action, checking the Turn 4 line of the Manifest Clock and paying the **(1)** AP cost for having met one Requirement.*

Jim then follows the Manifest Steps in order.

- *Remove from the game all Totems attached to Colette Du Bois.*
- *Discard all Tokens and end all effects on Colette.*
- *Replace Colette with Colette, Avatar of Deception.*
- *Colette, Avatar of Deception may immediately discard a Soulstone to perform a Healing Flip.*
- *Place two additional Colette, Avatar of Deception models into play within 3" of the first.*
- *Using the **Shell Game** Ability, secretly nominate which model is Colette, Avatar of Deception and which models are the Decoys.*
- *Replace the Colette Du Bois stat card and this card with the Colette, Avatar of Deception stat card and the Decoy stat cards for the remainder of the Encounter. Then continue Colette, Avatar of Deception's activation as normal for a Replaced model.*

MANIFEST REQUIREMENTS

1 - Colette performs the **Illusionist** Action three times. These Actions must take place over at least two separate activations.

2 - Colette kills one enemy model with the **Magician's Duel** Spell.

MANIFEST CLOCK

Turn	0 Requirements Met	1 Requirement Met	2 Requirements Met
1	Cannot Manifest	Cannot Manifest	Cannot Manifest
2	Cannot Manifest	(All)	(2)
3	Cannot Manifest	(2)	(1)
4	Cannot Manifest	(1)	Choose (1) or (0)
5	Cannot Manifest	Choose (1) or (0)	(Automatic)
6	Cannot Manifest	(Automatic)	(Automatic)

MANIFEST STEPS

When Colette performs the **Manifest** Action, follow the Manifest Steps in order.

- Remove from the game all Totems attached to Colette Du Bois.
- Discard all Tokens and end all effects on Colette.
- Replace Colette with Colette, Avatar of Deception.
- Colette, Avatar of Deception may immediately discard a Soulstone to perform a Healing Flip.
- Place two additional Colette, Avatar of Deception models into play within 3" of the first.
- Using the **Shell Game** Ability, secretly nominate which model is Colette, Avatar of Deception and which models are the Decoys.
- Replace the Colette Du Bois stat card and this card with the Colette, Avatar of Deception stat card and the Decoy stat cards for the remainder of the Encounter. Then continue Colette, Avatar of Deception's activation as normal for a Replaced model.

HOFFMAN, AVATAR OF AMALGAMATION

Malifaux Station, four months after the Event.

The *Pellucidar* burst from the ground like a nail punching through rotten wood. Boulders the size of wagons flew through the air, ripped from beneath the earth by the mighty drilling machine as it surged clear. Its huge, serpentine body reared up, then collapsed onto the railroad tracks leading into Malifaux Station. The impact was so fierce the tracks rippled like water.

On Platform Two, men and women were standing in open-mouthed shock. None of them noticed Hoffman's arrival, or the uniformed men at his heels.

"You've forced it to the surface, Mr. Hoffman, sir!" wheezed the out of breath Guild Guard Sergeant. "I take it we just, er, turn it off now? Yes? Let the Union sort it out?"

"Ah, no," remarked Hoffman. "I may have lied to you very slightly about that bit. Sorry, sergeant, but this one's gone rogue. It won't let us just turn it off. More importantly, it is coming this way!"

The drilling machine's side propellers had dug into the ground, ripping huge sections of rail apart and driving it forward. The drilling cone on the front spun with a deafening shriek. The crowds on the platform screamed and ran as the *Pellucidar* roared past, chunks of masonry and slabs of paving scattered in its wake.

Hoffman dived for cover, debris raining all around, and once again he felt it. The metal, the machinery all around him, embedded underground, wrought within the buildings, the iron supports for the roof, the station boiler, the great rail engines and their cars. He was not just aware of them. They were aware of him. Not just aware. They wanted something. They wanted to...

...his harness was buckled from the impact of the *Pellucidar,* barely halted by the mass of metal in front of him. He felt the harness move, gathering splinters of iron from the railings and brass from the carriage lamps. It knitted together and he rose, and the mass of metal rose with him.

With an ear-splitting shriek, cold steel burst loose from the brickwork it encased and lead ripped free from the roof of the station. Hoffman focused the energies of the Event, feeling the metalwork and the machinery responding to him eagerly. The raw metal formed itself around him, cradling him, snapping together into titanic legs and bending into a torso, integrating with his harness as he rose higher and higher. He let the metal call to him, pulling his awareness... *his soul*, he surmised...out of his body and into the metallic behemoth forming around him. His body collapsed as the last bit of his essence spilled into it, caught by one enormous arm and cradled like an infant to its body.

...they wanted to *protect* him...

The *Pellucidar* coiled back on itself for another pass. Hoffman strode toward it, every step bringing more metal ripping from the buildings and structures around him. As he approached the stationary engines in the classification yard, they broke apart to join him, wheels and couplers bulking out his shoulders, valve gear and pistons strengthening constructed arms. Sheet steel layered together around an iron track handle, and suddenly he held a sword ten feet long and a burning desire to wield it in anger.

The *Pellucidar* recoiled, its soulstone-powered mind wary of this new threat. Hoffman flung his iron arms wide, and all the steel in the station issued a roar of challenge. Then the drilling machine lowered its head, racing towards him on another attack run. Whatever might happen next, he knew, the metal would do what it could to protect him, like a brother. He raised his sword and ran to meet the *Pellucidar* head on.

HOFFMAN, AVATAR OF AMALGAMATION

50MM BASE

AVATAR (C. HOFFMAN), CONSTRUCT, M&SU MEMBER, SCAVENGER

WK/CG	HT	WP	CA	DF	WD
6/-	3	7	5🧠	3	10

MASSIVE BLADE	
RG	⚡ 2
CB	6🧠
DG	3/4/5

ROOMSWEEPER	
RG	⌐10
CB	5
DG	2/3/4💥

TALENTS:

Abilities

Amalgamated Form: At the start of this model's activation, its Controller nominates one of the following effects. That effect lasts until the start of this model's next activation:

- **Speed:** Flight, Cg 6
- **Survival:** Armor +2, Regeneration 1
- **Suppression:** (+1) Ranged Expert

Assimilate Edict: After this model kills a Construct, it may nominate a specific Action possessed by that Construct. This model gains that Action until the end of the Encounter.

Empowered: This model receives +1 **Ca,** up to a maximum of +5, for each other friendly Construct within 4".

Immune to Influence

Mark of Amalgamation: Other friendly Constructs gain **Armor +1** while in base contact with one or more friendly Constructs.

Precious Cargo: This model suffers +1 **Dg** from 🟊, (𝖷), and 💥 effects that inflict damage.

Weapons

Massive Blade: Paired.

Roomsweeper: This Weapon's Attack Flips receive 💥.

Actions

(0) Consume Construct: This model may use this Action immediately after it kills an enemy Construct with a melee attack. This model performs a Healing Flip.

(0) Suppress Edict: Target enemy Construct within 8" of this model performs a **Wp → Ca** Duel with this model. If target loses the Duel, this model's Controller nominates one specific Action or Trigger possessed by the target. The target may not use the nominated Action or Trigger until the end of the turn.

(2) Flurry

Triggers

Cb (🧠⚔) Scorpion Strike [Massive Blade]: After this Weapon inflicts damage on defender, defender must win a **Df → 12** Duel or receive **Paralyzed**.

SPELLS:

(all) Do Not Go Softly
(CC: 16🧠 / Rst: - / Rg: C)
This spell may be cast only when this model has 3 or fewer **Wd** remaining. *AR: This model suffers 1 **Wd**. If this reduces the model to 0 **Wd,** completely resolve the Spell before removing it from the game. This model performs a Weapon **Strike** against each model in LoS. For the duration of this Spell, this model may make ranged **Strikes** while engaged.*

(0) "Resistance is Futile!"
(CC: 12📖 / Rst: Ca / Rg: 8) Target model gains the Construct Characteristic until the Start Closing Phase.

(1) Insinuate Will
(CC: 14⚔ / Rst: Ca / Rg: 10) During target enemy non-Master Construct's next activation, if the target Cheats Fate, this model's Controller may discard a Card. The target's Cheated Card is considered to have the same value and suit as the discarded Card instead of its own value and suit.

MANIFEST REQUIREMENTS

1 - C. Hoffman kills two enemy models with **Strikes** performed with the **Machine Puppet** Action.
2 - C. Hoffman successfully affects a target enemy non-Master Construct with the **Override Edict** Spell.
OR if no enemy non-Master Constructs are in the game:
C. Hoffman successfully affects two target non-Master Constructs with the **Override Edict** Spell.

When C. Hoffman performs the **Manifest** Action, follow the Manifest Steps in order.

MANIFEST STEPS

- Remove from the game all Totems attached to C. Hoffman.
- Discard all Tokens and end all effects on C. Hoffman.
- Replace C. Hoffman with Hoffman, Avatar of Amalgamation.
- Hoffman, Avatar of Amalgamation may immediately discard one Soulstone to perform a Healing Flip.
- Nominate one **Amalgamated Form** Ability choice to be in effect until Hoffman, Avatar of Amalgamation's next activation.
- Replace the C. Hoffman stat card and this card with the Hoffman, Avatar of Amalgamation stat card for the remainder of the Encounter. Then continue Hoffman, Avatar of Amalgamation's activation as normal for a Replaced model.

JUSTICE, AVATAR OF BALANCE

Buck's Tail Cemetery, seven weeks after the Event.

She moved with a sure-footed grace through the tombstones despite the thick blanket of darkness covering the cemetery. All but silent, she approached the soft glow ahead, her greatsword held easily in her hands.

The two men worked, oblivious to her approach, the rough sound of shovels and the rougher language they used helped to mask her movements until she was no louder than a ghost among the dead. She froze when the shovels stopped, wondering for a fleeting moment if they had felt her presence. Then one spoke.

"This here's the one, Bob," he crowed.

The other voice, Bob's she assumed, shushed the first. "Hisst, Pinkle. You wanna wake the dead? Of course this is the one, it's the name that old codger wrote down for us."

"You know I don't have the letters, Bob," Pinkle mumbled.

"Sorry, lad, you're right. Look, this is the right one." She heard the thunk of a shovel hitting wood. "Give me a hand."

She could hear a bit more scraping and the sound of the two men muscling something heavy out of the ground. She used the noise as cover to get close to them. She ducked down as she heard them climb out of the grave, putting her back against the cool slab of a tombstone. More grunting and noise, she was sure they were employing pry bars to open up the coffin.

"Here it is, told you!"

She could hear more scuffling as the two men helped themselves to the jewelry she knew was on the body. She decided it was time and stepped out into their feeble lantern light. "Enough!"

The voices she had suppressed after the events at the observatory came to her in a whispering rush. They spoke in absolute truths, how every action fostered a mirrored action, how the universe craved a balance, seeking to compensate action with reaction. They shared with her how to unlock that balance, how to become its agent. She could see, briefly, two winged creatures, one with the head of a raven, the other a ram's head. They appeared to be locked in a cosmic struggle, each gaining an advantage over the other only briefly.

"Hands where I can see them," she ordered as the image faded from her mind.

Pinkle's arms thrust up from within the coffin, hands filled with gold. Bob's remained behind the lid. She leveled the greatsword's blade at Bob. "Now."

He raised his arms, swinging the shovel he had held onto at her head. After all, she was blind, the stories went. She ducked his swing, the magic filling her as she moved. She repositioned herself, using her blade to guide Bob to the edge of the grave and held him there, the sword's tip poking him in the chest.

"H...how did you find us?" Pinkle asked, paralyzed with fear. Lady Justice turned her bandaged eyes on him, summoning crackling bands of aether to bind his arms and feet. He yelped and dropped the jewelry at their touch.

"The 'codger' told me before he died. You sicken me; he was a defenseless old man."

Bob shrugged. "He buried it with her, better in our pockets than stuck in the ground."

She leaned in close to him, her gaze pinning him through the blindfold. "You take, you never give, Bob. I can see it in your heart. There is no peace within you...no balance. But you can help me, you can give me something. You can give me your life."

Bob glanced back, feet slipping over the edge of the grave. He snapped his arm forward, and the derringer he kept hidden slid into his hand, propelled by a mechanism strapped to his forearm. The pistol fired as he felt pain explode in his chest. He tumbled back into the grave, the final darkness reaching out for him.

Lady Justice touched the line of blood where the bullet had grazed her cheek. "Now you and the codger are even," she said to the dark hole as she dragged Pinkle to his feet and led him off into the night.

JUSTICE, AVATAR OF BALANCE

50MM BASE

AVATAR (LADY JUSTICE), DEATH MARSHAL

WK/CG	HT	WP	CA	DF	WD
3/-	3	6	6🜚	5🜚	12

GREATSWORD

RG	⚔ 2
CB	6🜚
DG	3/4/6

TALENTS:

Abilities

Fear Not Death: This model receives +2 **Wp** in Duels with the Undead when it is the defender.

Hard to Kill

Mark of Balance: At the start of the Activate Models Step, this model gains one of the following effects. This model cannot gain the same effect two turns in a row. The effect lasts until the end of the End Closing Phase.

Ram: ⚙10. Friendly models receive 🂠 to their Attack Flips when their attacking stat is lower than the target's defense stat.

Crow: ⚙10. Enemy models receive 🂡 to their Attack Flips when their attacking stat is higher than the target's defense stat.

Weapon

Greatsword: This Weapon's Damage Flips receive 🂠.

Actions

(+1) Melee Expert

(0) Adjust the Balance: ⚙6. Friendly models win Duels on a tie instead of losing them.

(0) In Pursuit: Nominate an enemy model. Push this model up to 6" toward nominated model. This model receives 🂠 🂠 in Duels with the nominated model when using its **Cb**, **Df**, **Ca**, and **Wp** until the end of the turn.

(1) Last Rites: ⚙6. Sacrifice all Corpse and Scrap Counters not carried by models.

Triggers

Cb (🜚) Critical Strike [Greatsword]

Df (🝳) Reposition Foe: After attacker misses this model with a melee **Strike**, Place attacker up to 4" directly away from this model.

SPELLS:

(0) Fate, the Great Leveler
(CC: 16🜚📖 / Rst: - / Rg: C) Each player with more Cards in Hand than the maximum Hand size discards down to his or her Crew's maximum Hand size. Each player with less Cards in Hand than the maximum Hand size draws up to his or her Crew's maximum Hand size.

(1) Aetheric Shackles
(CC: 12🜚✗ /Rst: Wp /Rg: 12) Bury target model. At the start of each Closing Phase, target must win a **Wp → Wp** Duel with this model or remain buried. Unbury target within 3" of this model when the target wins the Duel or if this model is removed from play.

(1) Blind Justice
(CC: 12 / Rst: - / Rg: ⚙6) Friendly models ignore increases in **Rg** and **Df**, and any Duels required from Spells or Talents to target models.

(1) Even the Odds
(CC: 13🝳 / Rst: Ca / Rg: 6) Target enemy model engaged with a friendly model suffers **Dg** equal to the number of **Wd** already suffered by that friendly model. If the target model is engaged with multiple friendly models, this model's Controller chooses the friendly model.

(2) Restore Equilibrium
(CC: 14🜚📖 / Rst: Wp / Rg: ⚙10) Effects on models losing their Resist Duels immediately end. All Tokens on models losing their Resist Duels are immediately discarded.

MANIFEST REQUIREMENTS

1 - Three other friendly models must receive the **Cb** bonus from Lady Justice's **Inspiring Swordplay** Ability.

2 - Lady Justice kills two enemy models that are in this model's melee range while it is affected by the **Sword Style** Spell.

When Lady Justice performs the **Manifest** Action, follow the Manifest Steps in order.

MANIFEST STEPS

- Remove from the game all Totems attached to Lady Justice.
- Discard all Tokens and end all effects on Lady Justice.
- Replace Lady Justice with Justice, Avatar of Balance.
- Justice, Avatar of Balance may immediately discard one Soulstone to perform a Healing Flip.
- Nominate either the **Mark of Balance's** Ram or Crow effect to affect Justice, Avatar of Balance.
- Replace the Lady Justice stat card and this card with the Justice, Avatar of Balance stat card for the remainder of the Encounter. Then continue Justice, Avatar of Balance's activation as normal for a Replaced model.

PERDITA, AVATAR OF REVELATION

High above the Badlands, five months after the Event.

There, she thought to the creature beneath her, *near the dry wash.*

The creature's bat-like wings adjusted. They turned toward the tan ribbon of the dry wash, two pairs of eyes watching events unfold, both hoping they would reach the site in time. Perdita could make out the shape of the overturned wagon. Two wheels aimed at the sky while several large dark shapes flew above the wreckage, occasionally diving toward the smaller dark shapes clustered near the wagon.

That's quite a few of them, and we are alone. A wave of reassuring emotion was the creature's only response.

Alone. She was often alone now. Ever since the Event she had kept mainly to herself. She disliked what she saw all too often in others, things she would never have registered before the purple wave changed her. She found it difficult to sense Santiago's beastlike aggression, Francisco's jealousy, and even young Niño's uncertainty. And then there was Papa...it broke her heart to see the sane man trapped behind insanity's walls. Whenever her familia put their hands out in support and concern, she turned her back on them, preferring the solitude of the Badlands and rides on the strange creature with whom she shared this unexplainable bond.

She could not bring herself to name it, as if giving it a name would somehow complete whatever transformation she was going through. Instead, she would call to it and they would fly across the Badlands, never straying near the chasm that had caused all of this.

When they had first seen the wagon, she wondered what a pioneer family was doing so far from the trails. But she had put the thought aside. Pioneers were always a bit loco, striking off into the wilds like they did. Only now that she had decided to check on the little wagon's progress did she realize what danger its owners had stirred up.

The creature roared a challenge as they dived toward the cluster of Nephilim. Her Peacebringers were already in her hands, and the two shots she fired took the closest of the monsters in the head, sending a corpse tumbling to the ground. The second was torn in half by a single bite from the creature's distended jaws as they landed.

She took stock of the situation quickly, surveying the options she had of surviving this. Six massive Nephilim stood between her and the pioneers. Two of the monsters ignored the small cuts and wounds dotting their bodies, while a third's arm dangled loosely at its side. Three of the five pioneers in the wagon's shadow lay either dead or dying; the coppery tang of their blood fouling the otherwise dry Badlands air. The remaining two brandished their weapons – a small knife and old pistol – as if they were a relic blade and Peacebringer, pleading for her help. She almost laughed at the absurdity of it all.

One of the Nephilim charged her, furiously beating wings lending it momentum. She did not have to direct the creature. It leaped from the ground and the Nephilim passed beneath them, its claws closing on empty space. She leaned over the creature's side and her guns barked, driving the Nephilim to the ground, bullets tearing through its shoulders and wings.

Then it happened. The whispers filled her thoughts once again, urging her to look harder. She looked again at the Nephilim. They were filled with rage, yes, but something more. A feeling of loss and longing, a parental emptiness, directed at the wagon. The pioneers, too, were filled with something. It was ugly and stained their features with remorseless cruelty. The whispering ceased, replaced with a very real mewling coming from the overturned wagon.

Sickened, she kept her pistols trained on the Nephilim. They held off their attack, sensing her confusion. The pioneers no longer plead for her aid, now they begged her to not look in the wagon. As her hand reached for the rough canvas she saw a flicker of movement and fired, shooting the old pistol out of the pioneer's hand before he shot her. She tore the canvas flap back and gasped.

The tumbled stack of cages each contained a Nephilim youth, a "Tot" the family called them. They bore evidence of malnourishment and abuse, pitiful creatures. She saw them clearly, something vaguely human in their suffering and fear.

She hissed at the pioneers. Sharing a wordless exchange with the Nephilim, she urged the creature to take flight, ignoring the sounds of carnage behind her. *We truly are all monsters,* she mused. The creature did not reply.

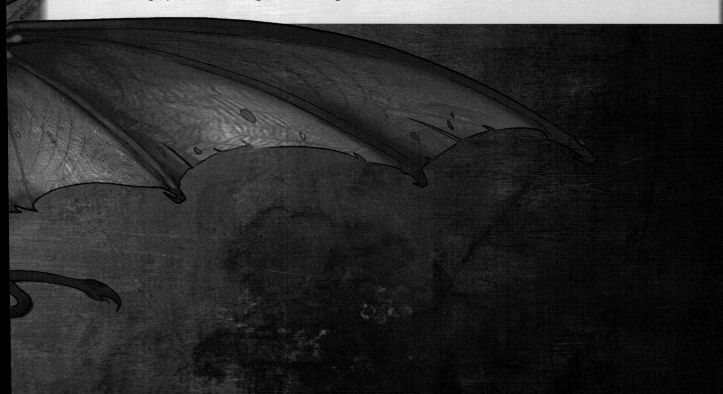

PERDITA, AVATAR OF REVELATION

AVATAR (PERDITA), BEAST, FAMILY

WK/CG	HT	WP	CA	DF	WD
6/10	3	8	6🌀	5	11

PEACEBRINGER		LACERATING JAWS	
RG	⌐12	RG	2
CB	7🌀	CB	6
DG	2/3/5	DG	2/3/5

TALENTS:

Abilities

Companion (Family)

Flight

Immune to Influence

Mark of Revelation: At the start of the End Draw Step, this model's Controller can reveal any number of Cards from his or her Hand and discard them. This model's Controller draws one Card for each Card discarded in this way. These drawn Cards must be revealed and remain revealed until used. These revealed Cards are still considered part of the player's Hand.

See the Unseen: This model ignores increases in **Rg** and **Df**, and any Duels required from Spells or Talents to target models.

Terrifying → 12

"We're All Monsters": This model counts as having the **Neverborn** characteristic for Talent and Spell effects.

Weapon

Peacebringer: Paired.

Actions

(+1) Fast

(0) Grounded: 🌑8. Enemy models lose the **Flight** Ability while within or entering the 🌑. If the enemy model was moving over terrain it could not enter without the **Flight** Ability when it entered the 🌑, it must end its movement in a legal position on the table as close as possible to, but not on, that terrain.

(0) The Light of Truth: 🌑8. Friendly models, including this model, receive ➕ to any **Wp** flips they perform.

(2) Diving Attack: This model **Charges** an enemy model ignoring LoS, terrain, and intervening models. If the **Charge** move ends without the target in melee range, end this model's activation.

Triggers

Ca (🌀💀) Catharsis [Lies Uncovered]: This model's Controller draws one Card.

Cb (🌀💀) Honest Kill [Peacebringer]: This model gains one Soulstone after it kills a model that has one or more printed Spells requiring a **Wp** Resist Duel.

Cb (🌀) Bites and Bullets [Lacerating Jaws]: After this model resolves a successful attack generated by its **Diving Attack** Action, it immediately performs a **Strike** with its Peacebringer which targets the same model. This model gains **Gunfighter** while resolving the **Strike**.

SPELLS:

(0) Spellbreaker
(CC: 16🌀 / Rst: - / Rg: 18) Discard all Tokens and end all effects on the target model +1 additional model within 3" of the target per 🌀 in the casting total. Wounds on the model cannot be discarded.

(1) Lies Uncovered
(CC: 15🌀 / Rst: Df / Rg: 8) Target model's Casting Flips receive ➖ when casting a Spell requiring a **Wp** Resist.

(1) No Secrets
(CC: 16🌀 / Rst: - / Rg: C) This model's Controller discards any number of Cards from his or her Hand and then draws an equal number of Cards from his or her Deck. The drawn Cards must be revealed to all players before being put into the Controller's Hand. This Spell may be cast once per turn per Crew.

MANIFEST REQUIREMENTS

1 - Perdita successfully Triggers **Anticipation** twice while targeting enemy models.
2 - Perdita must kill two enemy models using the **Execute** Spell during the Encounter.

When Perdita performs the **Manifest** Action, follow the Manifest Steps in order.

MANIFEST STEPS

- Remove from the game all Totems attached to Perdita.
- Discard all Tokens and end all effects on Perdita.
- Replace Perdita with Perdita, Avatar of Revelation.
- Perdita, Avatar of Revelation may immediately discard one Soulstone to perform a Healing Flip.
- Replace the Perdita stat card and this card with the Perdita, Avatar of Revelation stat card for the remainder of the Encounter. Then continue Perdita, Avatar of Revelation's activation as normal for a Replaced model.

SONNIA, AVATAR OF CONFLAGRATION

Redemption City, moments before the Event.

The creature was certainly not a leader among those transcendent beings, she surmised, translating quickly, instinctively. *It did not lead. Did not desire dominion. But it conquered. All fell to its consuming wrath.* Frantically, she skimmed ahead. *… They rose against the serpent seeking to quench the flames of destruction and damnation. The Tyrants and lowly throng they sought dominion over put aside their conflict to confront the one burning beast, Cherufe.* Then, reading almost peripherally, her heart stopped when she read, *…Its return will mark the end. It will burn below the Last City. It will consume those that come after us, to live in the city above the Necropolis from beyond. Cherufe will choose one of them to deliver it from final bondage; the final key to its bonds.* She quickly flipped the page and the symbols came together as the prophesied image of the one that would again free the demonic Tyrant Cherufe. The blurry, smudged and abstract image caused her heart to stop and a gasp choked in her throat. It was her.

…Cherufe will feed endlessly from her burning spirit…

Sonnia's eyes widened. Samael Hopkins, sipping his steaming coffee from the entrance of the small library, drew her attention, saying, "Uh, Sonnia. Any idea what the hell that is?" He nodded against the biting cold toward the sky that grew red, illuminating his features strangely in the dim, early morning light.

He thought it was nothing more than a large shooting star, but when he turned to her, she seemed crestfallen, saddened at seeing the object blazing across the sky. "What is it, Darlin'?" he asked, unaccustomed to seeing her shaken.

Moments later he was consumed by pain and nausea and his body crashed against the doorframe. But it was Sonnia's transformation that dispelled the otherwise consuming anguish he experienced. A thick column of fire burst through the floorboards, sending long daggers of splintered wood flying and burning. The raging pillar engulfed her and blasted through the roof above. Within the quickly churning fire he could see her, risen from the ground and held aloft by tendrils of fire that ate through the building and caused him to shrink away as it singed his flesh but brought her no harm within the growing conflagration.

He scuttled away on his backside, out of the building with fire licking after him. It consumed the structure, devouring it in a raging inferno that grew far more quickly than seemed possible.

Arms outstretched, Sonnia rose through the growing hole in the roof, the fire dripping from her arms in sheets. She leaned forward and flew toward the buildings of the Neverborn ruins. A thick cone of fire leapt from her mouth, engulfing building after building in raging flames. The pillar behind her stretched up, and Samael thought he saw a massive head form in the conflagration, watching her do Its bidding, laughing on the crackling fire that hissed and devoured the buildings in a heat that dispelled the biting wind.

SONNIA, AVATAR OF CONFLAGRATION

50MM BASE

SOULSTONE COST: MANIFEST

AVATAR (SONNIA CRIID)

WK/CG	HT	WP	CA	DF	WD
4/6	3	7	8 /	5	10

SALAMANDER

RG	3
CB	5
DG	2/3/5

TALENTS:

Abilities

Ablaze: This model is immune to Burning Tokens.

Adaptive Mind [Ca]: When this model uses this stat, it can add either of the stat's suits to the total, but not both.

Blazing Counterspell: When this model or any model within 3" of it is targeted by a Spell, this model's Controller may discard two Cards or one ▦ suit Card to cancel the Spell before the starting casting total is generated. The casting model then suffers 2 **Dg**.

Flight

Magic Resistant 2

Mark of the Conflagration: While this model is in play, all other friendly models receive +1 to the resisting Statistic when resisting Spells.

Oppressive Heat: Living models must win a **Wp → 13 Duel** when making melee **Strikes** against this model. A model losing the **Wp** Duel receives ⊟ to the Attack Flip.

Weapon

Salamander: This Weapon ignores **Armor**. Models damaged by this Weapon receive one Burning Token.

Actions

(+2) Casting Master

(0) Feast on Fire: (⋊)6. Discard Burning Tokens affecting models. This model heals 1 **Wd** per Burning Token discarded.

(1) Pyre Command: Place one Pyre Marker placed by this model up to 2" in any direction.

Triggers

Ca (⬡▦) Incessant Inferno [Searing Wave]: Models suffering damage from this Spell gain one Burning Token.

Cb (⬡▶) Horrific Burns [Salamander]: If this Weapon inflicts damage on defender, this model's Controller Pushes the defender up to 3". After this Push, enemy models within 5" of defender must perform a **Wp → 12** Morale Duel.

SPELLS:

(0) Searing Wave
(CC: 18▦ / Rst: Df / Rg: (⋊)8) This Spell only affects enemy models. If at least one model lost its Resist Duel, this model performs a 2/3/4 Damage Flip which cannot be Cheated. Any model losing its Resist Duel suffers the flipped damage +1 **Dg** per Burning Token it has.

(1) Light 'Em Up
(CC: 14⬡▦ / Rst: Df / Rg: 8) Target model + 1 additional model within 3" of the target per ▦ in this Spell's casting total gains one Burning Token.

(1) Pyre
(CC: 14▦ / Rst: - / Rg: 12) Place two 50mm Pyre Markers at least 1" from any model. These Markers are **Ht** 5 and obscuring. A model suffers 3 **Dg** when it moves into base contact with a Pyre Marker, begins its activation in base contact with a Pyre Marker, or ends one of its Actions in base contact with a Pyre Marker. Models damaged by the Marker receive one Burning Token. These Pyre Markers remain in play until this Spell is cast again.

(1) Violation of Magic
(CC: 17⬡▦ / Rst: Wp / Rg: 10) Target model suffers 1 **Wd** + 1 **Wd** for each point its **Ca** is over 5. If the target is killed by this Spell, Summon a Witchling Stalker to the target before it is removed from play.

MANIFEST REQUIREMENTS

1- Sonnia Criid inflicts 10 **Wd** on enemy models with Spells.
2 - Sonnia successfully casts **Inferno** twice.

When Sonnia Criid performs the **Manifest** Action, follow the Manifest Steps in order.

MANIFEST STEPS

- Remove from the game all Totems attached to Sonnia Criid.
- Discard all Tokens and end all effects on Sonnia Criid.
- Replace Sonnia Criid with Sonnia, Avatar of Conflagration.
- Sonnia, Avatar of Conflagration may immediately discard one Soulstone to perform a Healing Flip.
- Replace the Sonnia Criid stat card and this card with the Sonnia, Avatar of Conflagration stat card for the remainder of the Encounter. Then continue Sonnia, Avatar of Conflagration's activation as normal for a Replaced model.

Kirai, Avatar of Vengeance

On the riverboat, *Royal Flush*, six weeks after the Event.

Ikiryo shredded the Death Marshal from the inside out. Kirai watched impassively as its fingers burst through his belly and ripped him open from sternum to groin.

They will never leave you alone, Ikiryo said, sweeping from the ruin of the man's body and advancing on his companion.

The remaining Death Marshal backed up, but his escape was blocked by the massive paddle of the riverboat, thundering behind him in a cloud of spray. Shots whipped through Ikiryo's body, narrowly missing Kirai herself.

They will hunt you. They will never stop. But we can make them fear. Ikiryo reared like a serpent and lashed forward, disappearing into the Death Marshal's chest. He staggered, clutching at his chest, then his throat, and then his head. He opened his mouth to scream...

We can make them fear us! came the voice of Ikiryo from the man's throat. Wide-eyed, the man turned awkwardly to face the huge, wooden blades of the paddle roaring past, inches from his face. His hat, caught by a blade, spun away as if shot. The man brought his arms up in front, out of Kirai's sight. His body shook violently. Then he raised his arms to either side. Blood jetted from the ragged stumps where the paddlewheel had sheared off much just below his elbows.

We can make them feel such terror.

Then the man thrust his head forward and the spray turned red. His body was pulled from the riverboat deck by the wheel, then smashed into the machinery below. Ikiryo flew up to whirl around Kirai.

All around her, the riverboat was in uproar as her spirits battled the Death Marshals. Again and again, Kirai had sent out Ikiryo to rend and tear, to carve bloody vengeance in the flesh of the living who persecuted her so. It hurt to unleash Ikiryo and savor her vengeance, but...

It is not enough.

"No," whispered Kirai. The Gaki howled in unending hunger as screaming throngs of passengers disrupted the efforts of the remaining Death Marshals. "I swore I would not let this happen again."

It is the only way! Many will escape our judgment if you do not!

"You killed the innocent!" Ever since the purple wave had struck, Kirai had found new ways to loose the bonds on Ikiryo, and more and more, Ikiryo demanded they be loosed. The blood spilled could never fill the void in Kirai, but... "I cannot let you do it!"

You want this!

"No," whispered Kirai, but she knew it was a lie the moment it left her lips. "Very well, just this once, and *just* the Guild. Not the innocents like last time."

Ikiryo smiled and Kirai reached out to her, reached within herself. Ikiryo swirled around her and Kirai's form tore into ribbons of smoke, joining with her spirit-self. In moments, a monstrous spirit with claws like swords reared above the blood-soaked planks of the doomed passenger ship.

Well, not as many as last time! said Kirai, and loosed a blood-chilling scream.

KIRAI, AVATAR OF VENGEANCE

50MM BASE

AVATAR (KIRAI ANKOKU), SPIRIT

Wk/Cg	Ht	Wp	CA	Df	Wd
4/-	3	6	6✗	4	9

RAZOR SHARP FINGERNAILS	
Rg	///2
Cb	7✗
Dg	2/3/5

PITIFUL WAIL	
Rg	⌐6
Cb	6
Dg	1/1♟/2♟

TALENTS:

Abilities

"Avenge Me!": When this model is removed from the game, each other friendly Spirit in play immediately performs one melee **Strike** targeting an enemy model in its melee range.

Immediate Revenge 2: Models inflicting damage on this model with ranged attacks suffer 2 **Wd** after resolving the damage.

Mark of Vengeance: After a friendly model within 10" has been killed by an enemy melee **Strike**, before that model is removed from play, this model may be Placed in base contact with the killed friendly model. Remove that model from play. After Placing this model, it may perform one melee **Strike** targeting the enemy model.

Spirit Anchor: When a living, Spirit, or Undead model is killed within 8", Place one Seishin in base contact with this model.

Spirit Touch: Melee attacks made by this model ignore **Armor**.

Spiritual Alacrity: This model gains **Fast** if it is in base contact with two or more friendly Spirits at the start of its activation.

Spiteful Aura: ⚫8. After an enemy model inflicts Moderate or Severe damage to a friendly Spirit within the ⚫, including this model, that enemy model suffers 1 **Dg**.

Terrifying → 13

Weapons

Razor Sharp Fingernails: This Weapon's Attack Duels use either the target's **Df** or **Wp**. Declare the statistic used when declaring the attack.

Pitiful Wail: Models damaged by this Weapon receive ⊟ to their Defense, Resist, and **Wp** Flips when defending against Spirits.

Actions

(+1) Instinctual

(0) Direct Spirits: (✗)12. This model's Controller may Push friendly Spirits in the (✗) up to 4".

(0) Spirit Surge: Target a friendly model within 8" that is engaged in melee. Push this model up to 8" toward that model. If this model ends the Push in melee range of one of the enemy models engaging the targeted Spirit, this model may discard one Card to perform a melee **Strike** targeting one of those models.

Triggers

Cb (✗ ✗) Maul [Razor Sharp Fingernails]: This Weapon's Damage Flips receive ⊞ ⊞.

Df (✑) Eye for an Eye: After resolving a melee attack in which this model suffered damage, this model performs a melee **Strike** targeting the attacker.

SPELLS:

(0) Despairing Sigh
(CC: 13✗🦇 / Rst: Wp / Rg: C) (✗)6. This model's Controller Pushes non-Spirit models 4" directly away from this model. Models with the **Ruthless** and **Terrifying** Abilities lose those Abilities.

(0) Vengeful Smite
(CC: 14✑✗ / Rst: - / Rg: C) This model's next Attack Flip this activation receives ⊞ ⊞.

(1) Spiritual Messengers
(CC: 14✗ / Rst: Df / Rg: 12) Target two models in range. Each target must be in base contact with a different Seishin. If both targets lose their Resist Duels, Switch them.

(1) Vicious Jubaku
(CC: 13✗ / Rst: Wp / Rg: 12) Target model loses all suits associated with its **Cb** stat until the end of its next activation.

MANIFEST REQUIREMENTS

1 - Ikiryo Summoned by Kirai Ankoku must kill two enemy models.
2 - Kirai Ankoku has the Spirit Characteristic during two different turns.

When Kirai Ankoku performs the **Manifest** Action, follow the Manifest Steps in order.

MANIFEST STEPS

- Remove from the game all Totems attached to Kirai Ankoku.
- Discard all Tokens and end all effects on Kirai Ankoku.
- Replace Kirai Ankoku with Kirai, Avatar of Vengeance.
- Remove from the game Ikiryo Summoned by Kirai Ankoku. Kirai, Avatar of Vengeance may perform one Healing Flip if Ikiryo was removed.
- Kirai, Avatar of Vengeance may immediately discard one Soulstone to perform a Healing Flip.
- Replace the Kirai Ankoku stat card and this card with the Kirai, Avatar of Vengeance stat card for the remainder of the Encounter. Then continue Kirai, Avatar of Vengeance's activation as normal for a Replaced model.

McMourning, Avatar of Athanasia

McMourning's Secret Laboratory, moments after the Event.

The Event changed everything for Douglas McMourning. The cacophony of strange voices, speaking in a multitude of languages at once, formed strange dream-like images in his mind. McMourning was more accustomed to hearing voices in his mind than others, and he knew better than to resist the urges they encouraged in him. He was used to it.

Others found the Event wrought with an agonizing and blinding headache. For him, however, it was a moment of revelation.

Spending his life in an endless quest to defy the natural processes of death, to stave off the inevitable demise of life, his experimentations had gone beyond anything anyone had ever imagined possible. But he could never overcome the essential missing ingredient that gave his experiments purpose. Not until he gave himself to the voices. When the purple wave had passed and the crackling energy ceased its static snapping, he slowly shook off the stupor that enveloped him and faced the large behemoth of a man he had created. He realized, sadly, it was just a construct of flesh like the many others he had created before.

McMourning stepped close to the monster. "Step forward," he commanded. It did not move. He scowled. Did the Event burn it out, he wondered? It was shambling and groaning stupidly just moments before. A disappointing development, given the hopes he had for *this* Construct. He and Sebastian had gone to great lengths and expense, even hiring that dullard Mortimer, to assist in exhuming the late Captain Gideon to procure his brain. He scratched the side of his pointed nose and ran the gloved fingers of his blood-soaked hands through his long and disheveled hair.

"Well, damn," he cursed. "Of all the luck. The minute you have an epiphany is the minute some *setback* occurs. Fate hates me," he surmised, already considering an alternative brain. Perhaps that ass Francisco Ortega would be a better donor? If not Francisco's, he would love to get his hands on the Judge's cerebrum.

But his true revelation was that his entire plan was flawed. Where he and the other Resurrectionists tried so hard to re*create* life, he realized suddenly that the answer lay in a different path altogether. He had a plan to create a vessel of great proportion that could contain his will. Rather than recreate life, the voices told him a way to eternally extend life. A truly independent Construct would not be necessary; instead, one that McMourning could inhabit once his current body failed him, perpetuating his life indefinitely – well, that would be a creature to be reckoned with!

The problem, he realized, concentrating on the failure of the experiment, was not the *brain*. The problem was the body. The voices whispered to him once again, and he cocked his head to one side, listening. This one was simply not...well, *grand* enough to chamber the aetheric energy, they explained. He would need more body parts. *Many* more body parts...

"Thank you," he said to the empty room. "Something that will quake the ground with each step is needed, you're right of course; something that will withstand all manner of abuses. Right, then. Simulacrum 28 is a failure. On with Simulacrum 29!" His smile broadened and his eyes darted back and forth in eager anticipation to begin.

McMourning, Avatar of Athanasia

30MM BASE   **SOULSTONE COST: MANIFEST**

AVATAR (McMOURNING), GRAVEROBBER

WK/CG	HT	WP	CA	DF	WD
5/7	2	7	7✘	5	12

PROBES AND SCALPELS

RG	⚔ 2
CB	5✘
DG	2/3/4

TALENTS:

Abilities

Crawling Doom: This model's **Df** flips against melee attacks receive ⚀. **Wp** and **Df** flips made by enemy models within 3" of this model receive ⊟.

Companion (Simulacrum 29)

Mark of Athanasia: During the Start Closing Phase, if a friendly Simulacrum 29 is not in the game, McMourning, Avatar of Athanasia may discard six Body Part Counters to Place a friendly Simulacrum 29 in play within 6". Immediately inflict 5 **Wd** on that model.

Organ Recycling: When this model gains a Corpse Counter, it gains two Body Part Counters instead.

Regeneration 1

Walking Wall: This model gains **Armor +1** while it is within 3" of a friendly Simulacrum 29.

Wicked

Weapon

Probes and Scalpels: Paired.

Actions

(+1) Passion for his Work: Discard one Body Part Counter. This model receives **Fast**.

(0) Scalpel Slingin': Perform a **Rg** 6 Probes and Scalpels **Strike**. If the target is wounded by this attack, Push this model into base contact with target. This is considered a melee attack.

Triggers

Ca (⚑✘) The Horror! [Castoffs]: A model losing the **Cb** Duel falls back.

Cb (⚑✘) "CutCutCUT!!" [Probes and Scalpels]: If this model was Pushed into base contact as a result of **Scalpel Slingin'**, this model immediately performs another Probes and Scalpels **Strike** targeting the defender.

Cb (✘) A Piece for Me: After damaging defender with a Probes and Scalpels **Strike**, this model gains one Body Part Counter.

SPELLS:

(0) Castoffs

(CC: 14✘ / Rst: - / Rg: (ᚢ)10) This model's Controller Pushes each Corpse Counter not carried by a model up to 5" toward a single target enemy model in the (ᚢ) range. If one or more Corpse Counters end this Push within 1" of the target or were already within 1" of the target, the target must win a melee Weapon **Cb → 12** Duel. Increase the Duel's TN by +1 per each Corpse Counter within 1" of the target after the first. If the target loses the Duel, it suffers a Damage Flip of 1/2/4 which cannot be Cheated.

(1) "Perfect!"

(CC: 11✘ / Rst: - / Rg: 6) This model or target Undead model performs a Healing Flip. If the target is Simulacrum 29, the Healing Flip receives ⚀.

(1) Rancid Transplant

(CC: 14✘ / Rst: Df / Rg: ⚔ 2) Discard one Body Part Counter. Target receives "**Easy to Wound 2**: Damage Flips against target receive ⚀⚀." until the end of the Encounter.

MANIFEST REQUIREMENTS

1 - McMourning gains five Body Part Counters from enemy models.
2 - McMourning kills an enemy model under the effects of the **Rancid Transplant** Spell.

When McMourning performs the **Manifest** Action, follow the Manifest Steps in order.

MANIFEST STEPS

- Remove from the game all Totems attached to McMourning.
- Discard all Tokens and end all effects on McMourning.
- Replace McMourning with McMourning, Avatar of Athanasia.
- McMourning, Avatar of Athanasia may immediately discard one Soulstone to perform a Healing Flip.
- Replace a friendly Flesh Construct in play with Simulacrum 29.
  OR
- If there is no friendly Flesh Construct in play, McMourning, Avatar of Athanasia must discard four Body Parts Counters or suffer 3 **Wd**. Then Place Simulacrum 29 within 3" of McMourning, Avatar of Athanasia.
- Simulacrum 29 is worth 8 Soulstones when determining an Encounter's victory conditions.
- Replace the McMourning stat card and this card with the McMourning, Avatar of Athanasia stat card for the remainder of the Encounter. Then continue McMourning, Avatar of Athanasia's activation as normal for a Replaced model.

Simulacrum 29 – Minion

50mm Base

Soulstone Cost: Placed

Construct, Undead, Unique

Wk/Cg	Ht	Wp	Ca	Df	Wd
4/6	3	5	3	4✗	11

Enormous Fists

Rg	2
Cb	7✗
Dg	2/4/7

Talents:

Abilities

Bulletproof 1

Companion (McMourning, Avatar of Athanasia)

Fine Tuning: This model may nominate one of the following effects if it is within 3" of a friendly McMourning, Avatar of Athanasia at the start of its activation. The effect lasts until the end of the End Closing Phase.

- This model's Attack Flips receive ⊞. This increases to ⊞⊞ if McMourning discards two Body Part Counters.
- This model's Defense Flips receive ⊞. This increases to ⊞⊞ if McMourning discards two Body Part Counters.

"Fire Bad": This model suffers +2 **Dg** when suffering **Dg** inflicted by 🔥 effects.

Hard to Wound 2

Hard to Kill

Protect Progenitor: After an enemy model targets a friendly McMourning, Avatar of Athanasia within 3" of this model with an attack, the Avatar of Athanasia gains one of the following Abilities for the duration of the attack: **Bulletproof 1**, **Hard to Wound 2**, or **Hard to Kill.**

Strength-Born Will: This model may use its Enormous Fists **Cb** instead of its **Wp** when resisting a Spell.

Undead Construct: When killed, this model generates three Corpse Counters and no Scrap Counters.

Walking Morgue: A friendly McMourning, Avatar of Athanasia may **(0) Interact** when within 2" of Simulacrum 29 to discard up to three Body Parts Counters. This model then performs one Healing Flip for each Body Part Counter discarded.

Weapon

Enormous Fists: This Weapon ignores the **Armor** and **Hard to Wound** Abilities.

Actions

(2) Flurry

Triggers

Cb (🔮✗) Massive Trauma [Enormous Fists]: If this Weapon's Damage Flip inflicts Severe damage, the defender suffers another Damage Flip with the same fate modifiers plus an additional ⊟. The additional Damage Flip cannot be Cheated.

Cb (✗🦅) Rip in Half [Enormous Fists]: After killing an enemy model with a **Strike** with this Weapon, all enemy models within 6" immediately perform a **WP → 11** Morale Duel.

Df (🔮✗) Grab!: After the attacker misses with a melee **Strike**, Push it into base contact with any part of this model's base.

Spells:

(0) "Destroy!"
(CC: 8 / Rst: - / Rg: C) This model's Damage Flips receive ⊞⊞ when inflicting damage on breakable terrain.

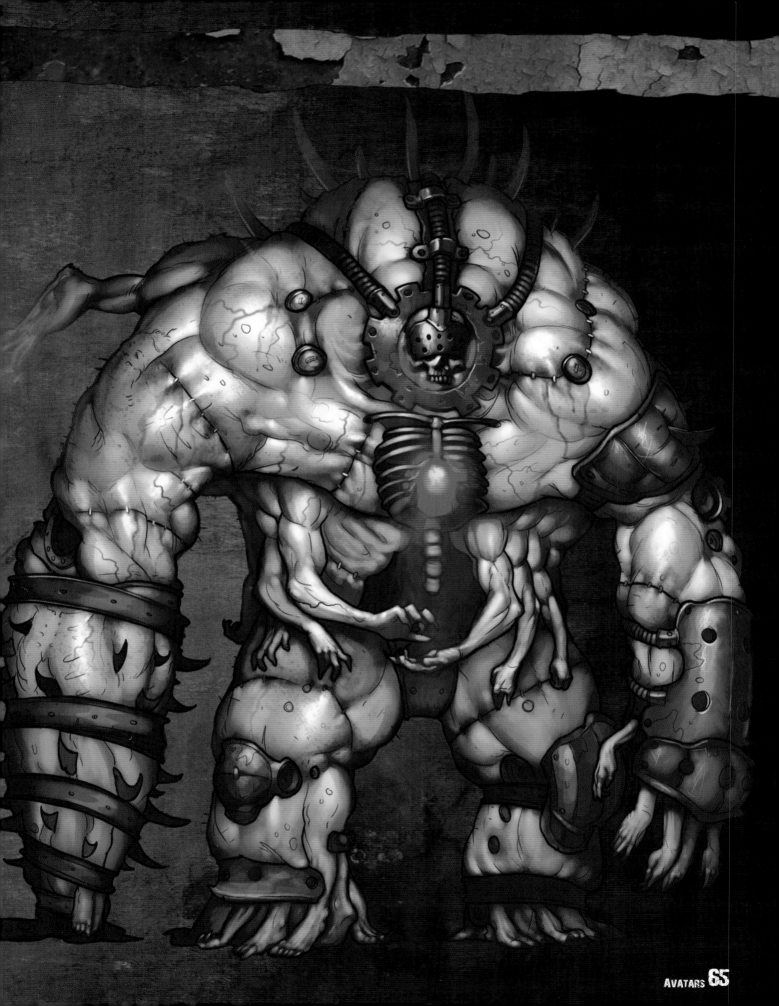

Nicodem, Avatar of Decay

The abandoned observatory, moments before the Event.

The observatory exploded behind Nicodem, sending timber and stone flying around him as he escaped out a secret back exit. Small fragments struck him like shrapnel, and he pulled the dark leather coat across his face to shield his flesh from the blast. It proved ineffectual as shards tore through the cloth and lacerated his face and shoulder. A larger stone struck his mechanical leg, bending the articulating piston, and steam whistled out of the hydraulic shaft as it depressurized, dropping him to the ground. He turned in his fall to see another large block propelling toward him, and he winced instinctively as time slowed to a crawl.

He saw, more than felt, the bones of his chest crushed. Not merely broken, but splintered into minute fragments which tore through internal organs even as they were smashed to paste. But at that same moment his mind was also infused with an otherworldly power he had never experience or imagined.

His body fell lifelessly to the ground, but he refused to rest. His broken body was of no further use to him. His will lashed out in frustration and he felt the rotting dead deep beneath the packed soil. He could always feel corpses at the fringe of his mind wherever he walked, but this was different.

He called to them effortlessly, promising them life, the ability to walk again. He pulled them from the earth, and they clamored to him. These were much older than he should be able to control, having spent too long detached from their souls, but he somehow was able to give them his will, and they rose. The zombie horde collected him from the wreckage of the observatory, bearing him aloft on a palanquin. *His* body twisted and turned, animated even in death by his unending command. He surveyed the army risen to obey his command. They cheered for him and vowed eternal allegiance. Thousands came, desperate to find him. They were more than the mindless creatures he had been capable of creating. These were *superior* undead, infused by the loose memories of the aetheric spirits that imbued them with new life.

The Event passed and the voices clamoring around him diminished.

He gasped, drawing air into his broken lungs. Below him, dozens of zombies, actual *expressions* of joy and hate on their faces, slowly slipped into a dull stupor as they became mindless once more. They lost their will and crumbled to dust, dropping him slowly to the ground as they fell.

He sat up with a sigh. Examining himself quickly, had his vision been dream or reality? He was surprised to find his wounds were gone, if he ever had any. They might have been nothing more than a fleeting glimpse of his future, of him at the fore of a great undead army that enthusiastically followed his every whim.

Nicodem could not be certain how he knew, but what had transpired was far more than any vision. He would command the very fabric of death, and the legions buried beneath Malifaux's hard ground would do his bidding - they had no choice.

NICODEM, AVATAR OF DECAY

50MM BASE

SOULSTONE COST: MANIFEST

AVATAR (NICODEM), GRAVEROBBER, UNDEAD

WK/CG	HT	WP	CA	DF	WD
4/-	3	8	7✘	3✘	12

RAVENOUS PALANQUIN

RG	⚔ 2
CB	4✘
DG	2/3/4

TALENTS:

Abilities

Borne by the Dead: This model receives +1 **Wk** during its activation for each Mindless Zombie it began the activation in base contact with. This model may move through Mindless Zombies with no penalty.

Hard to Wound 1

Mark of Decay: While within 10" of this model, Mindless Zombies lose the **Neutral**, **Mindless**, and **Walking Dead** Abilities and become friendly to this model's Crew. This model may ignore Mindless Zombies when determining LoS.

Restless Dead: After a non-Mindless Zombie Corpse Counter is placed on the table within 6" of this model, this model may Place a Mindless Zombie into base contact with the Corpse Counter and then discard the Counter.

Terrifying → 12

Zombie Fodder: When this model is hit by an attack, sacrifice a Mindless Zombie within 2" to cancel the hit.

Weapon

Ravenous Palanquin: Paired. Magical.

Actions

(+1) Casting Expert

(0) Mass Grave: This model's Controller flips a Card and Summons a number of Mindless Zombies based on the flip's value.

> **Black Joker:** zero
> **1-5:** one
> **6-10:** two
> **11-13:** three
> **Red Joker:** four

Triggers

Ca (✘📖) Putrefy: After damaging defender with **Decay**, defender must discard one Control Card. If that card is a 5 or less, this model's Controller draws one Control Card.

Cb (✘✘) Rot

Df (⚙✘) Dragged Down: After a non-Master attacker misses this model with a melee attack, that model performs a melee Weapon **Cb → 10** Duel. The Duel's TN is increased by +1 per Mindless Zombie within 3" of this model. Bury the attacker if it loses the Duel. Unbury the attacker within 6" of this model at the end of the Resolve Effects Step or immediately if this model leaves play.

SPELLS:

(0) Enhance the Dead
(CC: 15✘ / Rst: - / Rg: C) *AR: Discard one Card.* Sacrifice a number of friendly Mindless Zombies up to the number of ✘ in the casting total within 6" of this model. Summon one Punk Zombie into base contact with each sacrificed Mindless Zombie before it is removed from play.

(1) Decay
(CC: 14✘ / Rst: Wp / Rg: ⤴10) Dg 2/3♣/5♣. Friendly Undead models hit by this Spell or by any of its ♣ heal 2 **Wd** instead of suffering damage.

(1) Heed My Wishes
(CC: 16✘🐾 / Rst: - / Rg: (✘)10) Friendly Mindless Zombies' **Teeth** receive +2✘ **Cb** and +1 **Dg**.

(1) Rigor Mortis
(CC: 17✘ / Rst: Wp / Rg: 10) Target model receives **Paralyzed**.

MANIFEST REQUIREMENTS

1 - Nicodem kills two enemy models with the **Decay** Spell.
2 - Nicodem Summons three Mindless Zombies using the **Arise** Action.

When Nicodem performs the **Manifest** Action, follow the Manifest Steps in order.

MANIFEST STEPS

- Remove from the game all Totems attached to Nicodem.
- Discard all Tokens and end all effects on Nicodem.
- Replace Nicodem with Nicodem, Avatar of Decay.
- Nicodem, Avatar of Decay may immediately discard one Soulstone to perform a Healing Flip.
- Replace the Nicodem stat card and this card with the Nicodem, Avatar of Decay stat card for the remainder of the Encounter. Then continue Nicodem, Avatar of Decay's activation as normal for a Replaced model.

Seamus, Avatar of Dread

An anonymous alley, four months after the Event.

A woman's scream pierced the night's silence.

Seamus chuckled. He liked it when they screamed, gave him a bit of a thrill. This one had magnificent lungs. He was sure her cry had carried for blocks, giving the sleepers who heard it a good scare – maybe even stopped a heart or two.

"Come on love," he cooed to her as she backed deeper into the alley, his body blocking her only exit, "it won't hurt... much."

The woman's foot caught the hem of her dress as she retreated, spilling her onto the slick cobblestones. Her eyes searched for an escape, some sort of egress from the predicament she found herself in. Seamus wondered how any woman who plied her trade under the gaslamps could be as soft and weak as she was. It was pathetic. But, he decided, as her chest swelled impressively for another scream, she would make an excellent Belle. That would toughen her up a bit.

Footsteps scraped behind him, and suddenly the alley mouth was filled with shadows. "Halt, fiend!"

"And here comes the cavalry." Seamus winked at the woman, who had gathered her wits and petticoats and stood up, brushing an errant strand of hair out of her face.

"You are under arrest, monster," she growled, fishing a Constable's badge out of the dress's many folds.

"Ah. Live bait, I see, well done." He shifted the knife in his hand and broke into a slow, exaggerated clap. "I guess it's time to let the tiger out of its cage then. Here, hold *this*." The woman's smug grin turned into a little "oh" of surprise as Seamus lunged forward suddenly, burying the knife in her stomach.

He ignored the shouts of the Guardsmen at the alley mouth, instead drawing on their collective fear. He was the bogeyman to much of the City's police. The scary story they told the new recruits. He took that fear, wrapped it around the voices he'd had in his head for weeks, ever since that damned trip to the mountains, and channeled it through his body. They wanted a bogeyman? He would give them one.

He pushed the channel outward and felt it take hold. His body began to change, growing impossibly big, muscles expanding at a terrifying rate. He felt the sting of the Guild bullets as a few wild shots found their marks. His shirt, unable to contain his expanding physique, shredded as he grew, until it hung in tattered strips from his shoulders. *There, that's better.* He chomped down on the cigar in his mouth, settled the top hat – now ridiculously small on his oversized head – and glared at them. "Who's first?"

The Guardsmen fell back, terror gripping their hearts. Then the massive hulking shape of a Guild Peacekeeper stepped into the alleyway, its limbs tearing chunks of masonry from the walls on either side. Seamus grinned, smacking fist into open palm. "Yeah, you'll do, beastie."

He cast a glance back at the Constable now lying prone on the cobblestones. "Won't be but a minute, love," he said and then charged the Construct with a roar.

Seamus, Avatar of Dread

50mm Base

Soulstone Cost: Manifest

Avatar (Seamus), Graverobber

Wk/Cg	Ht	Wp	Ca	Df	Wd
4/7	3	5	6✗	3	12

Bludgeoning Fists

Rg	///// 3
Cb	6✗
Dg	3/4/5

Hurl Corpse

Rg	⌐8
Cb	4
Dg	1/2/3♠

Talents:

Abilities

Anathema: This model's **Terrifying** Ability affects all enemy models that do not have the **Anathema** Ability. This model's **Terrifying** Ability ignores any immunity to Morale Duels.

Feed on Fear: 🟊10. This model heals 1 **Wd** when a model within the 🟊 loses a Morale Duel.

Get Bloody: This model gains **Armor +2** while it is engaged with one or more enemy models.

Hard to Kill

Mark of Dread: While this model is in play, other friendly models with the **Terrifying** Ability increase their **Terrifying** by +1, while friendly models without the **Terrifying** Ability gain **Terrifying → 12**.

Regeneration 2

Stain of Damnation: This model is not considered a living model for game effects, but does drop Corpse Counters as normal when it is killed.

Terrifying → 13

Wicked

Weapons

Bludgeoning Fists: This Weapon ignores **Armor**.

Hurl Corpse: This model must discard a Corpse Counter it is carrying before declaring a **Strike** with this Weapon.

Actions

(+1) Fast

(0) Succumb to Darkness: This model receives -2 **Wp** and increases its **Terrifying** Ability by +2. This Action is cumulative and lasts until the end of the Encounter. This model cannot perform this Action if it would reduce its **Wp** below 1.

(1) Bellowing of the Big Bastard: (♪)4. Models perform a **Wp → 13** Morale Duel.

(1) Gorgon's Miasma: 🟊10. Enemy models receive -2 **Wp**. This Action ends at the start of the End Closing Phase.

Triggers

Cb (✗✗) Battered Skull [Bludgeoning Fists]: After damaging defender with this Weapon, defender must perform a **Terrifying → 11** Morale Duel.

Cb (🌀✗) Brutal Embrace [Bludgeoning Fists]: After damaging defender with this Weapon, defender must win a **Df → 12** Duel or receive **Paralyzed**. If the defender wins the Duel, it receives **Slow**.

Cb (✗) Splatterpunk [Hurl Corpse]: Models damaged by this Weapon perform a **Terrifying → 12** Morale Duel.

Spells:

(0) Gargantuan Growth
(CC: 14🌀✗ / Rst: - / Rg: C) This model's melee Weapons receive +1 **Rg**, +1 **Cb**, and ♠ to **Damage** Flips. This model also receives -1 **Wp**.

(1) Gorgon's Gaze
(CC: 14✗✗ / Rst: Wp / Rg: 8) Target model receives **Paralyzed**.

(1) Spontaneous Regeneration
(CC: 12🌀✗ / Rst: - / Rg: C) This model performs a Healing Flip.

Manifest Requirements

1 - Seamus successfully casts **The Face of Death** during two separate activations.

2 - Seamus uses the **Slit Jugular** Trigger against an enemy model in the same turn he **Charged** that model using the **No Escape** Action.

When Seamus performs the **Manifest** Action, follow the Manifest Steps in order.

Manifest Steps

- Remove from the game all Totems attached to Seamus.
- Discard all Tokens and end all effects on Seamus.
- Replace Seamus with Seamus, Avatar of Dread.
- Seamus, Avatar of Dread may immediately discard one Soulstone to perform a Healing Flip.
- Replace the Seamus stat card and this card with the Seamus, Avatar of Dread stat card for the remainder of the Encounter. Then continue Seamus, Avatar of Dread's activation as normal for a Replaced model.

COLETTE, AVATAR OF DECEPTION

Near the Star Theater, three weeks after the Event.

Sally screamed, and Colette couldn't really blame her. It wasn't every day one of her chorus line girls came face to face with an animated burlap bag stuffed with rotting body parts trying to kill her.

Sally disappeared in sections, as if she had been painted on a sheet of paper that just folded itself up into nothing. The nothingness unfolded, and there was Colette, with one flirtatious eyebrow raised in a silent, "Ta-da!" Sally's interrupted scream resumed from the other side of the courtyard where Colette had been standing moments before. "You like that?" Colette said, mentally bleaching herself for flirting with a diseased sack. "You'll love this."

A confetti of playing cards burst from her outstretched hands, shredding the nightmare creature into a spray of green and purple carrion. One of the playing cards flew back into Colette's palm. She passed a hand over it and there was a freshly glowing soulstone. "Money in the till!"

She ducked as Monday, one of her Mannequins, whizzed past, chased by a tiny imp with a big hat. The yard had gone from quiet rendezvous to a frantic affray of embattled showgirls and nightmare entities without a moment's notice. "Sally," Colette, shouted, "scream like that in Sweeney Todd and I'll put you center stage, girl! Lovely vocal work. Now shoot something! Cassandra — stop playing with that oversized teddy bear and help out Iris and Delia."

But there was no getting away from it — the ambush was turning against her. More and more of the creatures were seething out the drain covers or oozing out the walls. Her girls were in serious danger.

"Your new trick!" Cassandra shouted, pirouetting away from the ten foot bear and hacking one of the imps in half before it could reach Iris. "I think it's ready for an audience, dearest!"

It took only a moment — Colette had spent hours learning to control the energies needed, for was not the whole world a stage, and every day the performance of a lifetime?

Cassandra was about to hack again at the ten foot teddy bear when Colette embedded three glowing playing cards deep in its skull...

...when Colette shredded a boiling nightmare of whispering insanity with a rainbow stream of magic...

...when Colette swatted back a spell at one of the Stitched Together and it slopped in a putrid puddle on the cobbles.

In moments, the showgirls stood alone and victorious as the remaining horrors retreated.

Colette, Colette, and Colette gathered, while the others looked on in mute astonishment.

"I had no idea how good that hat makes me look," the first Colette said.

"I would put you center stage any day," replied another.

"Wouldn't you just," winked the third.

"Ahem," said Cassandra, arms folded and frowning. "When you're quite finished, darling."

The middle Colette took a bow, and like a mirror folding, the two on either side vanished. She wiggled her eyebrows, and then sighed. "Monday! Monday, they're all gone. That's a wall. Will someone put Monday's head back on?"

COLETTE, AVATAR OF DECEPTION

30MM BASE

AVATAR (COLETTE), M&SU MEMBER, SHOWGIRL

WK/CG	HT	WP	CA	DF	WD
4/-	2	6📖	7📖	6📖	8

FLOURISHED CARD

RG	➹10
CB	*
DG	1/1/2

TALENTS:

Abilities

Shell Game: Colette, Avatar of Deception is represented by three models: the Avatar and two Decoy models. At the start of the Activation Step, before any models are activated, this model's Controller secretly nominates one of these three models as the actual Colette, Avatar of Deception while the other two become Decoys. When these models activate the first time during the Activation Step, all three activate simultaneously. Only the model targeted with a **Reactivate** activates again.

The models may not spend more than a combined total of 6 general AP during their activations, but do not have to spend AP to **Pass** unless revealed as a Decoy. Reveal whether a model is the Avatar or a Decoy when it suffers **Dg** or **Wd**, is killed or sacrificed, or at the end of the End Closing Phase.

Spells cast by one Colette, Avatar of Deception model cannot be cast by the remaining Colette, Avatar of Deception models during their simultaneous activation.

Ramos' Gift: During their first activation in a turn, the first Soulstone discarded by either the Avatar of Deception or one of its Decoys is not deducted from its Crew's Soulstone Pool. This Soulstone may not be discarded to Summon a model.

Gunfighter [Flourished Card]

Something up My Sleeve: After all models have Cheated Fate during a Duel, this model may discard one Soulstone to replace its Cheated Fate Card with a Card from its Hand. This Ability may only be used once per activation.

Soulstone Augury: When this model discards a Soulstone to flip a Card, the flip receives 🔶.

The Show Must Go On: Once per Encounter, when flipping to determine if the Encounter ends, after seeing the result, this model's Controller can choose to have the flipping player re-flip.

Weapons

Flourished Card: Magical. Attacks made with this Weapon use **Ca → Df**.

Actions

(+1) Fast

(0) Mesmerizing: Target model within 6" performs a **Wp → Wp** Duel. If the target loses, it receives **Slow**.

(1) Card Tricks: This model's Controller looks at the top Card of another player's Deck. This model's Controller may then place it back on top of the Deck, or discard it if he or she first discards a Card from his or her own Hand.

(1) Mirror Dance: Place this model within 4" of a revealed friendly Decoy model.

(1) Pick a Card: This model's Controller randomly reveals a Card from an opponent's Hand. If that Card is a 📖 or a Joker, it is returned to its owner's Hand and this model's Controller must discard a card instead. If the revealed Card is any other suit, it is discarded. This Action may be taken once per turn per Crew.

Triggers

Ca (🦇) Bait and Switch [Flourished Card]: After damaging defender with this Weapon, cast **Bedazzle** on the defender ignoring **Bedazzle's** AR and **Shell Game's** Spell casting restriction.

Ca (📖📖) Surge

Ca (🔮🦇) Trigger Happy [Flourished Card]: After damaging defender with a **Strike** with this Weapon, immediately perform another **Strike** with this Weapon against the defender.

Df/Wp (🔮📖) Reflect Magic: After this model resists a Spell targeting it, the caster replaces this model as the target and suffers the Spell's effects. Use the difference in casting and resist totals if a difference is required. A reflected Spell has no effect if the original caster could not have been affected by it.

SPELLS:

(0) Sublime Performance
(CC: 14📖 / Rst: - / Rg: C) Gain +🦇 to **Ca** and **Cb**.

(1) Bedazzle
(CC: 14📖📖 / Rst: Wp / Rg: 10) *AR: Discard one Soulstone.* Each time target model Cheats Fate, it must do so randomly.

(1) Magician's Duel
(CC: 10📖 / Rst: Ca/ Rg: 〰 3) **Dg** 2/3/5. Targets with the **Use Soulstone** Ability receive -2 **Ca** when resisting this Spell. If the target is killed by this Spell, gain one Soulstone.

(2) Aetheric Subterfuge
(CC: 16📖 / Rst: - / Rg: C) *AR: Discard one Soulstone.* This model's Controller looks at the top three cards of an opposing player's Deck and top three of that player's Discard Pile. Discard any three of the Cards looked at and then place the other three in any order back on top of that player's Deck. This Spell may be cast once per turn per Crew.

Decoy - Minion

Soulstone Cost: Placed

Construct, Insignificant, M&SU Member, Showgirl

Wk/Cg	Ht	Wp	Ca	Df	Wd
4/-	2	6	7	5	*

Talents:

Abilities

Armor +1

Decoy: Until revealed as a Decoy, this model replaces its stat card with Colette, Avatar of Deception's stat card and may take Actions as if it was Colette, Avatar of Deception. While revealed, this model uses its own stat card, and may only take the **Walk** and **Pass** Actions, and cannot be **Reactivated**.

"Frustrating, Isn't it?": Discard all Tokens and end all effects affecting this model at the end of the End Closing Step. Remove this model from the game if a friendly Colette, Avatar of Deception is killed or sacrificed.

Nothing but Air: This model does not suffer **Dg** or **Wd**. Instead, when it would suffer **Dg** or **Wd**, inflict half the **Dg** or **Wd** on a friendly Colette, Avatar of Deception.

Manifest Requirements

1 - Colette performs the **Illusionist** Action three times. These Actions must take place over at least two separate activations.
2 - Colette kills one enemy model with the **Magician's Duel** Spell.

When Colette performs the **Manifest** Action, follow the Manifest Steps in order.

Manifest Steps

- Remove from the game all Totems attached to Colette Du Bois.
- Discard all Tokens and end all effects on Colette.
- Replace Colette with Colette, Avatar of Deception.
- Colette, Avatar of Deception may immediately discard a Soulstone to perform a Healing Flip.
- Place two additional Colette, Avatar of Deception models into play within 3" of the first.
- Using the **Shell Game** Ability, secretly nominate which model is Colette, Avatar of Deception and which models are the Decoys.
- Replace the Colette Du Bois stat card and this card with the Colette, Avatar of Deception stat card and the Decoy stat cards for the remainder of the Encounter. Then continue Colette, Avatar of Deception's activation as normal for a Replaced model.

Marcus, Avatar of Instinct

Somewhere in the Badlands, three months after the Event.

The purple wave had struck him as he pounced upon the three-spiked gazelle, explosively releasing all of the latent bestial potential stored within him. He became stronger than any man or animal. Faster, too. The Event didn't simply unlock the infused life-force of the animals he had integrated within himself; it changed him – physically, mentally. He was the primal beasts he admired. But he was not able to maintain it. He had no sooner completed his transformation and comprehended the vast depth of potential it suggested than it dwindled away as quickly as it had come.

That was months ago.

"Here are the 'stones you wanted," Myranda said from behind him. She tossed the sack upon his lap as he meditated and continued to their makeshift camp.

He closed his eyes once more. Soulstones were not the answer, he now understood. The quiet voices of the spirits released by the Event danced in and out of his mind like a dream upon waking. It was like a cat hunting dust motes while the mouse played at its feet. Still, he caught one wispy fragment, then another. Long and tedious was the process. Unlike the deliberate control of the hunt, he had to catch the aethereal strands by instinct, by focusing upon himself rather than the object of the hunt.

Then, nearly entranced, his instincts took a radical turn, twisting the numerous strands he had collected and weaving them throughout the minute fibers of his body, merging the very substance of his being with the animal essences he had experimentally blended with his own body. His chest heaved up and outward as the muscles thickened and bulged. His jaws cracked painfully, reshaping into a wide muzzle lined with long teeth and jutting fangs. A rack of horns broke through his skull and twisted up into points.

The life force of various animal stocks comingled with his own on an elemental level even he could not comprehend. He howled in pain as bones cracked audibly and his lower torso elongated into the powerful feline body of a Cerberus. All four wide paws dug into the soil to steady his shaking body as he metamorphosed. His shoulder blades erupted through the fur along his back, growing and stretching into wide bat-like wings. Even more painfully, the tail of the Cerberus became a venomous viper, writhing in confusion and anger behind him.

The transformation complete, he bent forward at the waist as far as his new form would permit as he gasped for air.

He waited for the influx of power to leave him in a rush as it had three months ago, waited to be reduced to mere human once again. This time, the power did not desert him. He was mastering his control over this manifestation. There, he stood, defiant and thrilled with power and vitality unimagined. His triumphant howl echoed through the forest.

Marcus, Avatar of Instinct

50mm Base

AVATAR (MARCUS), BEAST

Wk/Cg	Ht	Wp	Ca	Df	Wd
5/8	2	7	6📖	6	11

SHILLELAGH

Rg	⫽ 2
Cb	6🐾
Dg	1/2/4

CHIMERIC ASSAULT

Rg	⫽ 2
Cb	6
Dg	*/*/*

TALENTS:

Abilities

Flight

Mark of Instinct: While this model is in play, other friendly Beasts receive -1 to their **Wp** and +1 **Cb** to their melee Weapons. While within 6" of this model, friendly Beast models lose the **Ornery** Ability.

Regeneration 1

Rise of the Beasts: At the end of this model's activation, its Controller may nominate up to two friendly Beasts within 6". Those Beasts immediately activate simultaneously.

Weapons

Chimeric Assault: This model may discard a Control Card before making an Attack Flip with this Weapon. If it does not, this Weapon's **Dg** is 1/1/1. If it does, this Weapon gains one of the following effects for the duration of the **Strike** based on the suit discarded:

- 🐾: Dg 2/4/6
- ✗: Dg 2/2/3, **Poison 2**
- 📖: Dg 2/2/4, this Weapon ignores the **Armor** Ability. Models cannot use Df Triggers when attacked with this Weapon.
- 🦇: Dg 2/3/4, this model may Push defender damaged by this Weapon 2" away from this model after damage is inflicted.

Shillelagh: Magical.

Actions

(+1) Fast

(+1) Instinctual

(0) Smell Fear: When a model loses a Morale Duel within 6" of this model, but before the model performs a fall back move, this model may immediately **Charge** the model. Smell Fear ends when this model **Charges** this turn or at the Start Closing Phase.

(0) Dominance: Until the End Closing Phase, enemy non-Master Beasts receive ⊟ to all opposed Duels while this model is in their LoS.

(1) Give In To It: (Ӿ)8. Living and Undead models must win a Wp → 12 Duel or gain the Beast Characteristic.

(2) Diving Attack: This model **Charges** an enemy model ignoring LoS, terrain, and intervening models. If the **Charge** move ends without the target in melee range, end this model's activation.

Triggers

Cb (🐾🦇) Onslaught [Shillelagh]: After damaging defender with this Weapon, immediately make a **Strike** with this Weapon against the defender.

SPELLS:

(0) Evolutionary Confluence
(CC: 15🐾📖 / Rst: - / Rg: C) *AR: This model must discard one Soulstone. Until the end of this model's activation, replace Chimeric Assault's description with: "Dg 3/4/6, Poison 2. This model may Push a defender damaged by this Weapon 2" away after damage is inflicted."*

(0) Feral
(CC: 10📖 / Rst: Wp / Rg: 12) Target model receives the Beast Characteristic until the Start Closing Phase.

(1) Instinctive Behavior
(CC: 13🐾📖 / Rst: Wp / Rg: 8) Target non-Master model with the Beast Characteristic receives +0/+2 **Wk/Cg**, -2 **Df**, and its melee Attack and Damage Flips receive 🦇 until the start of the Start Closing Phase. Target then immediately performs a **(1)** Action or a **Charge** controlled by this model's Controller. The Action selected may not cause the model to be killed or sacrificed as part of the Action. This spell may be cast only once per activation by this model.

(1) Roar
(CC: 14📖📖 / Rst: Wp / Rg: (Ӿ)8) Living models Fall Back and it counts as losing a Morale Duel.

MANIFEST REQUIREMENTS

1 - Marcus gives two different enemy models the Beast Characteristic with the **Feral** Spell.

2 - Marcus gives an enemy model the Beast Characteristic with the **Primal Reaction** Trigger.

When Marcus performs the **Manifest** Action, follow the Manifest Steps in order.

MANIFEST STEPS

- Remove from the game all Totems attached to Marcus.
- Discard all Tokens and end all effects on Marcus.
- Replace Marcus with Marcus, Avatar of Instinct.
- Marcus, Avatar of Instinct may immediately discard a Soulstone to perform a Healing Flip.
- Replace the Marcus stat card and this card with the Marcus, Avatar of Instinct stat card for the remainder of the Encounter. Then continue Marcus, Avatar of Instinct's activation as normal for a Replaced model.

Ramos, Avatar of Invention

Hollow Marsh mines, two weeks after the Event.

Away from the miners' prying eyes, Viktor Ramos took stock of his situation. Recent events had forced him to reevaluate his plans, especially how the fall of the Red Cage could tip the balance of power he had carefully manipulated and put the Arcanists at risk.

Plots within schemes within machinations, he mused with a chuckle, *just another day in Malifaux.*

The situation with Hoffman and the Guild could wait. Instead, he centered himself, focusing on the faint whispers in the back of his mind. They were so insistent and forceful during the Event that he had all but succumbed to them, his mind lost in the whirlpool they created. Over time he had learned how to suppress them, push them aside and focus on the matters at hand. He also suspected that as time went along, distancing him from the Event, they would fade naturally, perhaps stop altogether. He had to listen to their message before that happened.

He released the voices, and they exploded in his mind — thousands demanding his attention. The voices whispered to him, sharing arcane secrets that had been lost for centuries. The secrets would have shattered a lesser man's psyche, but Ramos was not a lesser man. He endured and listened to what they had to say. Armed with this new knowledge, Ramos pushed the voices back into their sequester once again and focused.

He focused on progress, on innovation, on schematics for half-imagined Constructs he had yet to complete, mysteries their whispers gave him the answers to. The puzzle pieces clicked together, and he willed the concepts into reality. Four metallic spidery limbs appeared, punching through the sides of his coat, lifting him aloft.

With his arms extended in front of him, crackling electricity danced across his living fingers and up his forearm, arcing to his clockwork limb and then dancing back and forth between the meat and machine that was Viktor Ramos.

"Amazing," he whispered as the arcing light reflected on his glasses.

Moments later, the surge of energy dissipated, and he settled to the ground, slowly capturing his breath. Manifesting the power took quite a bit of strength, but with each attempt, it became a bit easier.

He wondered if the Event had imparted this expanded knowledge on others, if the Guild could comprehend the depth of what gifts it had left in its wake. Before he could consider this any further, the sounds of an argument brewing outside the office reached him. He could make out Johan's voice and the low rumble of the miners upset about something. Sighing, he shrugged out of the damaged coat and went outside to see what had created the disturbance.

There would be time for more experimenting later.

RAMOS, AVATAR OF INVENTION

50MM BASE

SOULSTONE COST: MANIFEST

AVATAR (RAMOS), CONSTRUCT, M&SU MEMBER, SCAVENGER

Wk/Cg	Ht	Wp	Ca	Df	Wd
5/8	2	6	8📖	5	11

CLOCKWORK FIST
Rg	⚔ 1
Cb	6
Dg	2/4/5

MECHANICAL LIMB
Rg	⚔ 2
Cb	5🐾
Dg	3/4/6

TALENTS:

Abilities
Arachnid

Armor +2

Immune to Influence

Learn from Mistakes: This model gains one Scrap Counter each time it suffers 1 or more **Wd** from an attack or effect generated by an enemy model.

Mark of Invention: Other friendly Constructs +1/+1 **Wk/Cg** while the Avatar of Invention is in play.

Perfect Machine: This model may choose to ignore any effects that targets Constructs.

Actions

(+1) Melee Expert

(0) Innovative Design: This model's Controller nominates one of the following effects and discards the number of Scrap Counters indicated. This Action may be taken once per turn.

- **Discard up to two Scrap Counters:** Armor +1 per Scrap Counter discarded until this model takes the **Innovative Design** Action again.
- **Discard one Scrap Counter:** This model makes a Healing Flip.
- **Discard one Scrap Counter:** This model's **Charge** Actions cost 1 AP until it takes the **Innovative Design** Action again.
- **Discard two Scrap Counters:** This model uses its **Cg** when taking **Walk** Actions until it takes the **Innovative Design** Action again.
- **Discard two Scrap Counters:** This model immediately takes two melee **Strikes** targeting the same defender.

(1) Hasty Assembly: This model may discard two Scrap Counters to Summon one non-Unique, non-Totem, Guild or Arcanist Construct with a Soulstone Cost of 5 or less that does not have the **Frozen Heart** or **Smoldering Heart** Ability. Inflict 2 **Wd** on the Construct when it enters play.

(1) Trash into Treasures: Gain one Scrap Counter.

Triggers

Cb (📖) Brutal [Clockwork Fist]: This Weapon inflicts +1 **Dg** for each 📖 in this model's Duel total.

Cb (🐾) Pin [Mechanical Limb]: A defender suffering **Wd** from this attack cannot move or be moved by movement effects.

Df (🐾) Electrocute: After a model inflicts Moderate or Severe damage on this model with a melee attack, that model suffers 1 **Dg**.

Df (✗) Pneumatic Grip: After attacker misses with a melee attack, attacker cannot perform melee attacks or block disengaging models for the rest of this turn.

SPELLS:

(0) Leap
(CC: 10🐾 / Rst: - / Rg: C) Move this model up to its **Cg**. This model receives **Flight** during the move. This Spell cannot be cast if this model is in melee.

(1) Electrical Creation
(CC: 15📖 / Rst: - / Rg: C) Summon one Electrical Creation.

(1) Electrical Fire
(CC: 14📖 / Rst: Df / Rg ↰12) **Dg** 2/3/4, ignoring **Armor**.

(2) Override
(CC: 15📖 / Rst: Wp / Rg: (✗)8) *AR: Discard one Soulstone.* This Spell ignores immunity to **Wp** Duels. All models, including this model, with the Construct Characteristic immediately perform a **(1)** Action or a **Charge** controlled by this model's Controller. The Action selected may not cause the models to be killed or sacrificed as part of the Action. This model's Controller declares the order in which the Constructs take their Actions before resolving the first Action. This Spell may be cast once per turn.

MANIFEST REQUIREMENTS

1 - Ramos successfully casts **Electrical Creation** and/or **Construct Spider** twice.
2 - Ramos inflicts 8 **Wd** on enemy models with the **Electrical Fire** Spell.

When Ramos performs the **Manifest** Action, follow the Manifest Steps in order.

MANIFEST STEPS

- Remove from the game all Totems attached to Ramos.
- Discard all Tokens and end all effects on Ramos.
- Replace Ramos with Ramos, Avatar of Invention.
- Ramos, Avatar of Invention may immediately discard a Soulstone to perform a Healing Flip.
- Replace the Ramos stat card and this card with the Ramos, Avatar of Invention stat card for the remainder of the Encounter. Then continue Ramos, Avatar of Invention's activation as normal for a Replaced model.

RASPUTINA, AVATAR OF FAMINE

Somewhere in the Eastern Mountains, five months after the Event.

Rasputina knelt in the ice and snow just outside the temple entrance. Her skirt was cut above her knees leaving her skin exposed to the cold that would have frozen any ordinary person. She didn't notice. Icy-blue veins were clearly visible in winding paths up her chest and neck, just below the skin. They pulsed a bright, luminescent blue, pumping the frozen blue blood throughout her cold body, glowing in the dark night.

The pale winter sun had set some long hours before, and the twin moons could not break through the dense clouds amassed above her. She meditated in the darkness, silent save the whistling wind, blowing her cape to her side. Even the two Silent Ones behind her remained motionless and silent in body as well as speech.

The world had changed since her arrival in Malifaux. The Event flooded the world with unprecedented spiritual power. Her body remained famished, thirsty, yet she refused to eat. It made it easier to consume the gossamer fragments of that loosened power, and she drew the energy within her ravenously.

Her blue veins throbbed brighter and quicker as her anticipation rose. Overlooking the steep descent aside the mountain, she cast out her will, gathering the cold about her like a cloak of frost. It settled on her chest and shoulders first, then gathered across the rest of her body, jagged shards tearing through the leather and fabric with ease. Ice erupted from the rocks and snow beneath her as powerful long legs and icy arms grew from the cold sheath surrounding her.

Where she had stood moments before, a towering creature of ice now stood. Encased at its heart, Rasputina controlled its movements as if they were her own. She stood upon the ledge and surveyed the sheer drop to a narrow trail below. She turned her new form to look back to the cave that led to December's Temple and sneered.

Under her silent command, the icy sheath moved in fluid grace. Where its wide feet struck the ground, it tore the leg away below the bend of a knee, leaving behind a jagged block of ice. It stepped forward and ice burst forth from the ground to meet it, forming the full leg once again. At its every move ice splintered and fell in dagger-like shards. The cracking of the thick ice echoed across the mountainside at each shifting of its form, only to freeze together once more as the wind descended upon it, as if desperate to reach Rasputina cradled within its chest.

Her new body struck the side of the mountain with a resounding crash as Rasputina willed it to descend. The sheer face could not provide a trail for it to follow, and it slid across the inhospitable surface like an avalanche, crashing and breaking along the way. Snow and ice tumbled around her. As rock tore blocks of ice away, the tumbling snow around her was drawn into the voids hammered into her body, rebuilding her as she quickly traversed the dangerous slope, fearing nothing in the dark.

She had been brought to Malifaux as a criminal for actions she could not fully recall. But crimes had been committed against her, and those transgressions needed atonement... she hungered for it.

RASPUTINA, AVATAR OF FAMINE

50MM BASE

AVATAR (RASPUTINA), GRAVEROBBER

WK/CG	HT	WP	CA	DF	WD
4/6	3	8	7✗ / 📖	4	10

ICE BLADE	
RG	///// 2
CB	5✗
DG	3/3/5

ICE SHARDS	
RG	⌐8
CB	5
DG	1/2♟/3♟♟

TALENTS:

Abilities

Adaptive Mind [Ca]: When this model uses this stat, it can add either of the stat's suits to the total, but not both.

December's Pawn: When this model flips or plays the Black Joker, immediately draw two Control Cards.

Encased in Ice: Armor +2. This model may ignore damage inflicted by (✗), (♦), or one or more ♟.

Frozen Heart: This model is immune to Morale Duels.

Hard to Kill

Ice Sculptures: Models within 3" of this model gain "**Shatter 2**: (✗)2, **Dg** 2 when this model is killed." This Ability does not affect models that already have **Shatter**.

Icy Brethren: Friendly Ice Golems receive +1 **Wk** while this model is in play.

Mark of Famine: Friendly models gain the **Frozen Heart** Ability while this model is in play.

Ravenous Vengeance: This model's **Charge** Actions cost 1 AP when declaring a **Charge** targeting a model that has inflicted 1 or more **Wd** on it this turn. If this model does not end the move with an enemy model in melee range, its Activation immediately ends.

Winter Walks With Her: ♦3. Severe terrain for models without the **Frozen Heart** Ability. Models without the **Frozen Heart** Ability must win a **Df →12** Duel after resolving a melee attack targeting this model or receive **Slow**.

Weapon

Icy Claw: Models hit by this Weapon lose the **Armor** Ability until the Start Closing Phase.

Actions

(+1) Casting Expert

(0) Eat Your Fill: This model may immediately use this Action after it kills a model with a melee attack. Heal all wounds suffered by this model and immediately end its activation.

(0) Freeze Over: Target a terrain piece within 6". Models without **Frozen Heart** currently touching the terrain piece cannot move or be Pushed until the End Closing Phase.

Triggers

Ca (▢▢▢) Surge

Cb (✗ 📖) Shattering Storm [Ice Blade]: When this Weapon kills an enemy model, increase the damage that model's **Shatter** Ability inflicts to 4.

Cb (📖) Chills [Ice Blade/Ice Shards]: After damaging defender, that model receives **Slow**.

SPELLS:

(0) Frigid Offspring
(CC: 14▢▢▢ / Rst: - / Rg: C) *AR: Discard one Corpse Counter within 6".* Summon one Ice Gamin.

(0) Instill Cravings
(CC: 13✗✗ / Rst: Wp / Rg: 8) Target model suffers 1 **Wd** at the end of its activation if it did not inflict 1 or more **Wd** with a melee attack during its activation. This effect lasts until the end of the Encounter.

(1) December's Maw
(CC: 15✗ 📖 / Rst: Df / Rg: ///// 2) Sacrifice target **Ht** 1 or 2 non-Master model that has suffered at least 1 **Wd**. Enemy models within 6" and LoS of the sacrificed model must perform a **Wp → 13** Morale Duel. This model then makes a Healing Flip.

(1) Hungry Winds
(CC: 15✗ 📖 / Rst: Df / Rg: (✗)8) All enemy models losing the Resist Duel suffer 1 **Dg** per ✗ in the casting total. A model may prevent this **Dg** by discarding one Control Card.

MANIFEST REQUIREMENTS

1 - Rasputina reduces an enemy model to 1 **Wd** with the **Biting Chill** Spell.
2 - Rasputina kills two enemy models with a single casting of the **December's Curse** Spell.

When Rasputina performs the **Manifest** Action, follow the Manifest Steps in order.

MANIFEST STEPS

- Remove from the game all Totems attached to Rasputina.
- Discard all Tokens and end all effects on Rasputina.
- Replace Rasputina with Rasputina, Avatar of Famine.
- Rasputina, Avatar of Famine may immediately discard a Soulstone to perform a Healing Flip.
- Replace the Rasputina stat card and this card with the Rasputina, Avatar of Famine stat card for the remainder of the Encounter. Then continue Rasputina, Avatar of Famine's activation as normal for a Replaced model.

The Dreamer, Avatar of Imagination

Gutter Street, one month after the Event.

The veil between reality and fantasy parted, slowly opening like a theater curtain drawing out the show's start for an enraptured audience. Two horrible claws reached out, gripped the sides of the tear and pushed wider, the void swirling with motes of impossible colors. Late night revelers, heading home after one too many libations, halted and watched the spectacle with growing dread. They held a collective breath as something exited the tear, wondering what fresh horror had come to Malifaux. Hearts beat like trapped birds within their chests as first one and then another bedpost appeared...*bedposts*?

Breaths held in terror gave way to nervous laughter as the length of a child's bed exited the tear, bedclothes in disarray. Everyone wondered who the trickster was, where was this master illusionist hiding? Then the point of a wooden toy sword exited, the weapon held *en charge* by a little boy standing with all the seriousness of a general leading his troops. It was too much; the gathering crowd erupted with good-natured mirth.

The Dreamer surveyed his playthings, they were laughing at him. This simply would not do. They should have been bowing to him, or at the very least silent. No, this would not do at all. "Chompy!"

Laughter turned to screams of terror as a second body exited the tear. It was no child at play in its bed. It was a thing of nightmares, of the deepest terrors that haunt sleeping men. It belonged to the claws pushing the tear open, a second pair of limbs carrying the boy's bed before it like some noble's litter. Its bony-ridged head reared back, bellowing a challenge which carried far more weight than the boy's. "That's better," the Dreamer grinned.

"Now, what shall we play this evening?" Pirates? No, he was bored of pirates. Cops and robbers or knights and dragon? No. His playthings seemed to be making the choice for him, fleeing the terrible duo as the tear mended itself behind them with a pop. *Hide and go seek!* What an excellent idea! They hadn't played that for oh so long, Chompy would love it!

The boy thought about how for months his nighttime companion couldn't play with him like he wanted to, neither of them could be in the same place at the same time. But then that strange night, when the wall of purple had danced so merrily through him, he had heard the voices of a thousand thousand playmates in his head, and they told both of them such secrets. Secrets which included how to...what did they call it...cross over *simatennislee*?

After that, every night since had been a playtime he would have never dreamed possible. It didn't matter where they were or who was around, he and Chompy always found playmates to participate in his favorite games. Even if they weren't in the best place for hide and seek, or playing pirates and making the mutineers walk the plank, he could change the dream with a wave of his toy sword. With just a thought he could create enough hiding places, or stretch how far down the dirty mutineers would fall after their trip down the plank. It was GREAT!

A few of tonight's playmates looked to be cheating, trying to run off and hide where he and Chompy couldn't find them. Not fair. He waved the toy sword high, pointed it in their direction and shouted.

"Lord Chompy Bits, CHAAAAAAARGE!"

The Dreamer, Avatar of Imagination

50MM BASE   SOULSTONE COST: MANIFEST

AVATAR (THE DREAMER), NIGHTMARE

WK/CG	HT	WP	CA	DF	WD
4/-	4	8	7🐾	5	12

TOY SWORD

RG	///// 2
CB	5
DG	1/2/4

TALENTS:

Abilities

Anathema: This model's **Terrifying** Ability affects all enemy models that do not have the **Anathema** Ability. This model's **Terrifying** Ability ignores any immunity to Morale Duels.

Mark of Imagination: When this model **Manifests**, nominate one of the following effects. That effect remains in play until the end of the Encounter. If this model is removed from the game, the effect ends.

> **Cops and Robbers:** Friendly Nightmare models gain the **Hunter** Ability. Enemy models gain the **Scout** Ability.
> **Hide and Seek:** Ranged attacks targeting friendly Nightmare models receive ⊟ to the Casting or Attack Flip. Melee attacks targeting friendly Nightmare models receive ⊞ to the Casting or Attack Flip.
> **Pirates:** When a friendly Nightmare model kills an enemy model with a melee attack, draw one Card. When a friendly Nightmare is killed by an enemy model's melee attack, that model's Controller draws one Card.
> **Slay the Dragon!:** Friendly Nightmare models gain the **Terrifying → 12** Ability. Enemy models receive **Armor +1**.

My Teddy Bear: A Crew containing this Master ignores the **Rare 1** limitation on Teddy. Teddy models hired by a Crew containing this model gain the Nightmare Characteristic.

Parting the Veil: At the start of each of the Activation Phases, this model's Controller may nominate one of the following Special Events/Terrain to occur for the remainder of the turn: **Caustic Gas, Dead Zone, Dim Lighting,** or **Hanging Tree**. This is in addition to any other Special Event that will occur. If a Terrain effect is selected, it may not be placed within 1" of any other model or terrain piece and is removed from play at the end of the turn. The same Special Event/Terrain cannot be nominated two turns in a row.

Release Nightmares: When this model is killed or sacrificed, you may Place any number of friendly buried Nightmares within 6" of this model before it is removed from play.

Shapeless: This model may perform two **(0)** Actions during its activation.

Terrifying → 13

Weapon

Toy Sword: Magical. After final Duel totals are determined, but before Triggers are declared, this model may add any one suit to its Duel total.

Actions

(+1) Casting Expert

(0) Consume Dream: Target **Paralyzed** model within 8" suffers 2 **Wd**. This model heals 2 **Wd**.

(0) Dream Walker: Switch this model with one friendly Nightmare within 12".

Triggers

Ca (🐾) All My Friends [Frightening Dreams]: This model's Controller may place any number of friendly buried Nightmares within 6" of this model.

Cb (✗ 🐾) Chompy's Turn! [Toy Sword]: After resolving this **Strike**, this model performs another **Strike** targeting the defender. That **Strike** is resolved using **Cb** 5 and **Dg** 2/4/6 and cannot declare Triggers.

Cb (📖) "Take That!" [Toy Sword]: A defender wounded by this Weapon cannot discard a Soulstone to prevent the **Wd** from this **Strike**.

Df (🐾) "No Fair!": After this model suffers Moderate or Severe damage from a melee attack, bury the attacking model once the attack is resolved. The attacking model is unburied within 6" of this model at the end of the Resolve Effects Step, or immediately if this model is removed from play.

SPELLS:

(0) Daydreaming
(CC: 17🐾 / Rst: - / Rg: C) *AR: Discard two Soulstones.* Summon one Daydream.

(0) Falling Dream
(CC: 13📖 / Rst: Wp / Rg: ↰8) Target Minion receives **Paralyzed**. At the start of the Resolve Effects Step, the target's Controller must discard two Cards or target is killed.

(1) Frightening Dream
(CC: 10🐾 / Rst: - / Rg: C) Place one friendly buried Nightmare within 6" of this model.

(1) "This Can't be Real!?"
(CC: 14🐾 / Rst: Wp / Rg: 12) Target model receives **Slow**. After the end of its next activation, it performs a **Wp → Wp** Duel with this model. If the target model loses the Duel, it receives **Paralyzed**.

(1) Trapped Your Own Nightmare
(CC: 15🐾 / Rst: Wp / Rg: 10) Target model loses the **Terrifying** Ability and treats all other models in play as having **Terrifying → 12**.

MANIFEST REQUIREMENTS

1 - The Dreamer inflicts 5 **Wd** on enemy models with Twist Reality **Strikes**.
2 - Lord Chompy Bits successfully uses its **All Done** Trigger while attacking an enemy model.

This Action may only be taken if both The Dreamer and Lord Chompy Bits are still in the game. When The Dreamer/Lord Chompy Bits performs the **Manifest** Action, follow the Manifest Steps in order.

MANIFEST STEPS

- Remove from the game all Totems attached to The Dreamer/Lord Chompy Bits.
- Discard all Tokens and end all effects on The Dreamer/Lord Chompy Bits.
- Replace the model taking this Action with The Dreamer, Avatar of Imagination and remove the other Master model from the game. Apply all **Wd** suffered by The Dreamer and Lord Chompy Bits to The Dreamer, Avatar of Imagination.
- The Dreamer, Avatar of Imagination may immediately discard a Soulstone to perform a Healing Flip.
- Nominate one **Mark of Imagination** effect.
- Replace The Dreamer and Lord Chompy Bits stat cards and this card with The Dreamer, Avatar of Imagination stat card for the remainder of the Encounter. Then continue The Dreamer, Avatar of Imagination's activation as normal for a Replaced model.

Lilith, Avatar of Nature's Malevolence

Somewhere deep within the knotwoods, moments before the Event.

The Ortegas were not the only group of intrepid men and women that took up arms against the indigenous Neverborn threatening the "good" people of Malifaux. Led by a Exorcist operating slightly beyond sanctioned regulation, the small group of men hunting Nephilim deep in the knotwoods did not look like much. Yet they were outdoorsmen and battle-hardened.

"She be here," Barnabus Shyre, the Exorcist said with lips drawn in a perpetual scowl.

Micajah, called "Cage" by the others, set the heavy sack upon the dry forest floor. Blood from the numerous severed Nephilim heads it contained painted the burlap a glistening black. He cocked the Colt in one hand and drew his narrow sword. He smiled.

Behind him, Bartholomew "Big Bart" Lichman was neither so sure nor cocky. "How you know, Barnabus?" he asked. "This ain't a spirit. Ain't a zombie, neither."

The Exorcist did not turn to face the doubter. His voice was low and even as he said, "No, this is not my normal prey. But I know she's here." He studied the trees and thorny brush before him. He couldn't see her, but knew she was there.

Lilith stared right back at him through the dense foliage, regaining her strength. They had doggedly pursued her the previous day and all through the night. They never rested. She could hold her own against four at the least. Seven of their number remained, and the loss of their comrades had no visible impact upon these men. They had left them unceremoniously in the dirt as they pursued her trail. It was oddly abnormal for a human. She disliked their unpredictability.

Now she was near the coven yet not close enough to get reinforcements. If any of these men discovered it and survived, well, the forest might be overrun by Guild hunters.

Sword in hand, she lunged forward, and the flora moved aside at her passage as if deferring to her authority over the land, itself. Her plan was to repeat her previous tactic of picking off one or two before disappearing into the brush to strike again later. It would work again, unless they overwhelmed her. That was a possibility she hardly acknowledged.

As she leapt forward, however, crackling purple energy enveloped them all, and they gasped, clutching their heads. Barnabus dropped his crossbow and sharply inhaled as the sinews along his neck went taut. Lilith was struck painfully and her chest heaved. Her sword fell from her hand, and she clutched her arms tightly around herself. Cage somehow quickly shook of the strange shock of the Event that passed through everyone. He aimed and fired at the incapacitated Lilith in the same quick movement.

As he squeezed the trigger, the vines and brush surrounding Lilith reached out, wrapping themselves around her torso and arms. She was yanked back so quickly the brush shook and the bullet seemed to pass through only leaves. She was gone.

Barnabus took longer than the others to right himself. The pain was severe. He staggered away from the others in confusion. As his eyes cleared and he looked back, he saw a woman, beautiful and fierce, erupt from the foliage beside the men. His eyes must have been deceiving him still for he thought she did not leap from behind the bushes, but from *within* them! As she slashed through the side of one man with long claws of thorn, she would disappear back into the forest, melding with the trunks only to leap out of another tree many yards away. It was bedlam. She was everywhere and nowhere, the forest a living thing under her command.

He ran then, still dazed from the pain of the Event, before Lilith could find him. He thought he had eluded her, too, until she found him cowering beneath a clump of ferns half a mile away and gave him to the forest.

Lilith, Avatar of Nature's Malevolence

50MM BASE

AVATAR (LILITH), NEPHILIM

WK/CG	HT	WP	CA	DF	WD
6/9	3	6	6🐾	6🐾	10

CLAWS	
RG	///2
CB	7🐾
DG	2/4/5

THORNY VINES	
RG	⌐8
CB	6🐾
DG	1/2/3

TALENTS:

Abilities

Armor +1

Black Blood

Bloodthirsty Foliage: When a living or Undead model within 8" of this model and in base contact with a woods terrain piece is killed, this model gains one Blood Token.

Haunted Forest: While this model is in base contact with a woods terrain piece, its Claw Strikes can target models anywhere within 2" of that woods terrain piece.

Hungry Trees: While this model is in base contact with a woods terrain piece, its Thorny Vines Strikes can target models anywhere within 8" of that woods terrain piece or 4" of any woods terrain piece.

Mark of Nature's Malevolence: Friendly non-Unique Nephilim gain the **Wicked** Ability while this model is in play.

Master of Malifaux: This model ignores the hazardous, severe, and water terrain traits when moving. This model ignores terrain when drawing LoS.

Rush of Magic: Draw one additional Card when drawing Cards in the Draw Phase, then discard down to your Crew's Maximum Hand Size.

Wicked: This model's Strikes against disengaging models deal damage in addition to ending the Action.

Weapon

Claws: Paired.

Actions

(+1) Fast

(0) Drain Blood: This model may immediately use this Action after killing a living or Undead model. This model gains one Blood Token.

(1) Blood from Stone: Discard any number of Soulstones. This model gains one Blood Counter for every two Soulstones discarded.

(1) Erupting Underbrush: This model discards a Blood Token. This model then performs a Claws Strike against every other model within a woods terrain piece this model is touching. After resolving the attacks in an order of this model's Controller's choosing, Place this model in a new location touching the same woods terrain piece.

(1) Lost in the Woods: Target enemy model completely within a woods terrain piece and within 12" of this model must win a Wp → Wp Duel with this model or suffer 2 Dg. If the target loses the Duel, the target cannot move or be moved by movement or placement effects.

Triggers

Cb (✗🐾) Beset by Nature [Thorny Vines]: If defender is damaged by this Weapon, it is Pushed 4" toward this model, ignoring the severe terrain trait.

Cb (🐾🐾) Bloody Fate [Claws]: After damaging defender with a Strike, draw one Control Card. Discard one Control Card if the defender was not killed by the Strike.

Df (🐾) Elusive: When this model is missed by melee Strike, Push this model up to 3" ignoring terrain.

SPELLS:

(1) Earthquake
(CC: 12🐾 / Rst: Df / Rg: (✗)12) Nominate a direction. Push all models 2" in that direction.

(1) Sanguine Proliferation
(CC: 15🐾 / Rst: - / Rg: 10) AR: This model or a friendly model within 6" discards one Blood Token. Place a 3" diameter circle of woods terrain completely within range touching target woods terrain piece. This terrain piece stays in play until the end of the Encounter.

(1) Wooded Path
(CC: 12🐾 / Rst: Wp / Rg: 10) Nominate two other models in base contact with two woods terrain pieces in range when casting this Spell. If both models lose their Resist Duels, Switch the two target models.

(2) Nature's Revenge
(CC: 15🐾 / Rst: -/ Rg: 6) AR: Discard one Blood Token. Target a woods terrain piece. Enemy models within 2" of the terrain piece must win a Df → 15 Duel or suffer 2 Wd. This model gains a Blood Token for each living or Undead model killed by this Spell.

MANIFEST REQUIREMENTS

1 - Lilith inflicts 10 **Wd** on enemy models while those models are in base contact with a woods terrain piece.

2 - Lilith successfully casts **Illusionary Forest** during two different turns.

When Lilith performs the **Manifest** Action, follow the Manifest Steps in order.

MANIFEST STEPS

- Remove from the game all Totems attached to Lilith, Mother of Monsters.
- Discard all Tokens and end all effects on Lilith.
- Replace Lilith with Lilith, Avatar of Nature's Malevolence.
- Lilith, Avatar of Nature's Malevolence may immediately discard a Soulstone to perform a Healing Flip.
- Place three 3" diameter circle woods terrain pieces completely within 12" of Lilith, Avatar of Nature's Malevolence.
- Replace the Lilith stat card and this card with the Lilith, Avatar of Nature's Malevolence stat card for the remainder of the Encounter. Then continue Lilith, Avatar of Nature's Malevolence's activation as normal for a Replaced model.

Pandora, Avatar of Insanity

Anderson Street, two weeks after the Event.

The sun had fallen behind the row of buildings silhouetted in the west, and people withdrew to their homes to secure themselves against the darker shadows that slinked in the night. So when a cry rose from the twisting alleys several blocks away, shouting, "She went this way! Toward Anderson Street!" breaking the evening's silence, trepid eyes peeked around barely parted drapes and shutters.

Pandora rounded the corner, breathing heavily, and ran as fast as she could with her dark box tight against her side. Hiding behind a shipping crate, she struggled to catch her breath. The mob came around the corner, the orange glow of their torches stretching beyond her hiding place.

"She's down there," one said. "Go check it out, Nigel."

"Like hell! She's a witch! We go together."

A third muttered, "You all better be tellin' the truth. I soiled my britches once over your stories of this girl."

"You'll know when you see her. Don't hesitate, but be ready! She can twist your thoughts against you, remember? I seen what she did to poor Ned!"

They approached cautiously; their words were filled with hatred. She had no remaining soulstones and she was exhausted and wounded from their initial beating and her narrow escape. The alley was blocked to her right, offering no escape.

The gossamer voices fluttered along the edge of her mind, but she dismissed them as the distracting voices of the woes that whispered to her incessantly. These voices were different, she realized after a moment. Not long after the Event she learned how to embrace the tiny spark of that aethereal energy that tickled her spine. Once before, during the Event, she had drawn in hundreds, embracing them. They changed her. Allowed her to look into the box and command what was there.

"Well, lookee here," a voice above her said as its shadow crossed over her hiding place, breaking her concentration. "Don't look so tough after all! Gonna cry, little witch?"

Another member of the mob dragged her to her feet and spun her to face the others. They held weapons, knives, and torches. They meant to kill her. Too tired to fight or run, the mob may have succeeded with whatever it had in store for Pandora if not for Nigel's next action.

No longer afraid of the seemingly weak young girl before him, he backhanded the box she carried out of her arms. It struck the ground with the resounding ring of a brass gong, the top open to the sky. Gaseous tendrils enveloped Pandora's legs, darkening as they lifted her into the air. Each member of the mob then realized the girl they had persecuted was not the one dying tonight, *they were*. Her head thrust back and brilliant energy erupted from her wide eyes.

The small mob, bent on killing her moments ago, now stared only at the box. Their minds were filled with nightmarish visions of suffering – their own suffering. Some went mad, clawing at their own eyes. Others wept at the base inhumanity the box showed them. Still others refused to accept what they saw, thinking the gift of deception was one of the girl's tricks. Some refused to accept it, that is, until thick tentacles reached out from the small box, wrapping tightly around them. Then they knew the awful truth and the screaming truly began.

Those few smart enough to turn tail and run as the box hit the ground slid to a stop as a lithe young woman detached herself from the shadows. The mob members froze, caught between the woman's brazen saunter and the horrible sounds behind them.

"Uh uh uh, where do you think you're going? We haven't had time to play yet," Candy hissed at them as something sharp filled her hands.

Pandora, Avatar of Insanity

40MM BASE

AVATAR (PANDORA)

Wk/Cg	Ht	Wp	Ca	Df	Wd
-/-	4	7	7🐾	4	10

TENTACLES OF MADNESS

Rg	3
Cb	4🐾
Dg	2/2/3

WRETCHED GAZE

Rg	10
Cb	4🐾
Dg	1/2/3

TALENTS:

Abilities

Anathema: This model's **Terrifying** Ability affects all enemy models that do not have the **Anathema** Ability. This model's **Terrifying** Ability ignores any immunity to Morale Duels.

Bond (Candy, Petulant Youth): This model may simultaneously activate with any friendly Candy, the Petulant Youth regardless of distance between the models.

Destinies Entwined: You may allow any effect that affects this model to affect a friendly Candy, the Petulant Youth in play. Any time this model suffers **Wd**, the total must be divided equally between this model and Candy, the Petulant Youth. Any remaining **Wd** are suffered by this model.

Emotional Trauma: When an enemy model loses a **Wp** Duel while within 12" of this model, that model suffers 1 **Wd**.

Expose Fears: Enemy models attempting to target this model must first win a **Wp → Wp** Duel or the Action immediately ends.

Immobile: This model's position in play may not be changed by movement effects or placement effects. This model cannot be buried.

Mark of Insanity: Friendly Sorrows receive the **Hard to Wound 1** Ability and lose the **Insignificant** Characteristic while this model is in play.

Martyr: When this model is hit by an attack, but before applying the Duel's result, its Controller may nominate a friendly Woe in base contact. The Woe is now the target of the attack.

Terrifying → 13

The Box Opens: Models within 12" of this model lose any immunities to **Wp** Duels.

Unhealthy Relationship: Friendly Woes in base contact with this model receive +1 **Wp**, receive the effect of any Spells affecting it, and may use its (0) Actions as if they were their own.

Weapon

Wretched Gaze: Attack Duels with this Weapon use **Cb → Wp**. This Weapon ignores **Armor**.

Actions

(+1) Casting Expert

(0) Pacify: Target enemy model unaffected by **Incite** or **Pacify** within 12" performs a **Wp → Wp** Duel with this model. If the target model loses, it must activate after any other model in its Crew which has not been affected by **Pacify**. If this model wins the **Wp** Duel, it may choose to perform the **Pacify** Action again this activation.

(1) "Suffer!": (❂)6. All non-Woe models must immediately perform a **Wp → 12** Duel. If a model loses the Duel, it receives **Slow**. This Action may be performed once per turn per Crew.

Triggers

Ca (✗ 🐾) Mental Torture [Self-Destruction]: A defender losing the Resist Duel also receives **Paralyzed**.

Cb (🐾) Crushed Ego [Wretched Gaze]: After damaging defender, immediately Cast **Self-Destruction** on defender.

Cb (🐾) Ensnared in Lunacy [Tentacles of Madness]: After damaging defender, the defender's location in play may not be changed by movement effects or placement effects and the defender cannot be buried. This effect lasts until Resolve Effects Step.

SPELLS:

(1) Self-Destruction
(CC: 14🐾 / Rst: Wp / Rg: 8) Select one of the target model's basic melee Weapons. Target suffers a Damage Flip with that Weapon. This Damage Flip cannot be Cheated.

(2) Mass Hysteria
(CC: 17🐾 / Rst: Wp / Rg: (❂)12) This model's Controller may Push enemy models that fail to resist this Spell up to 2".

(*) Hollows of Despair
(CC: 12🐾 / Rst: - / Rg: 12) This model spends up to two AP when casting this Spell. Place one 50mm Marker (**Ht** 5, obscuring) per AP spent after this Spell is successfully cast. A Marker cannot be placed within 1" of a model. Models moving onto a Hollow of Despair Marker must perform a **Wp → 13** Duel. Models losing the **Wp** Duel are immediately buried and are returned to play within 1" of the Marker they were affected by during the Resolve Effects Step or if the Marker is removed from play. These Markers remain in play until this Spell is cast again. This Spell may only be cast once per turn per Crew.

MANIFEST REQUIREMENTS

1 - Pandora inflicts 10 **Wd** on enemy models with the **Emotional Trauma** Ability and/or **Self-Loathing** Spell.
2 - The same enemy model must lose the **Wp** Duel caused by the **Dementia** Spell twice.

When Pandora performs the **Manifest** Action, follow the Manifest Steps in order.

MANIFEST STEPS

- Remove from the game all Totems attached to Pandora.
- Discard all Tokens and end all effects on Pandora.
- Replace Pandora with Pandora, Avatar of Insanity.
- Pandora, Avatar of Insanity may immediately discard a Soulstone to perform a Healing Flip.
- Remove a friendly Candy from the game and Replace it with Candy, the Petulant Youth in base contact with Pandora, Avatar of Insanity. Candy, the Petulant Youth enters play with a maximum **Wd** stat of 8.
  - **OR**
- If a friendly Candy is not in the game, Place Candy, the Petulant Youth in base contact with Pandora, Avatar of Insanity. Candy, the Petulant Youth enters play with a maximum **Wd** stat of 6.
- Replace the Pandora stat card and this card with the Pandora, Avatar of Insanity stat card for the remainder of the Encounter. Then continue Pandora, Avatar of Insanity's activation as normal for a Replaced model.
- Replace the Candy stat card with the Candy, the Petulant Youth stat card for the remainder of the Encounter.

Candy, the Petulant Youth

30MM BASE

SOULSTONE COST: PLACED

AVATAR (CANDY), WOE

WK/CG	HT	WP	CA	DF	WD
5/7	2	6	5 🐾	7 🐾	8/6*

SHARPS

RG	🔪 1
CB	5 🐾
DG	1/3/5

TALENTS:

Abilities

Bond (Pandora, Avatar of Insanity): This model may simultaneously activate with any friendly Pandora, Avatar of Insanity regardless of distance between the models.

Cracked Psyche: This model is immune to Morale Duels and receives +2 **Wp** when defending in a **Wp** Duel. This Ability is not affected by **The Box Opens**.

Destinies Entwined: You may allow any effect that affects this model to affect a friendly Pandora, Avatar of Insanity in play. Any time this model suffers **Wd**, the total must be divided equally between this model and a friendly Pandora, Avatar of Insanity. Any remaining **Wd** are suffered by this model.

Her Eyes: A friendly Pandora, Avatar of Insanity may draw LoS and range from this model when casting Spells. These Spells use this model's **Ca**. Spells with the 🗡 icon may not be cast through a model in melee using **Her Eyes**.

Irresistible: Enemy models must win a **Wp →** 12 Duel when targeting this model with an attack or the Action fails. This may not be ignored by any Talent.

Martyr: When this model is hit by an attack, but before applying the Duel's result, its Controller may nominate a friendly Woe in base contact. The Woe is now the target of the attack.

Weapon

Sharps: Poison 2

Actions

(+1) Casting Expert

(0) Incite: Target enemy model unaffected by **Incite** or **Pacify** within 12" performs a **Wp→Wp** Duel with this model. If the target model loses, it must activate before any other model in its Crew which has not been affected by **Incite**. If this model wins the **Wp** Duel, it may choose to perform the **Incite** Action again this activation.

(0) Sweets: Target friendly model within 2" performs a Healing Flip. This does not cause this model to lose **Harmless**.

Triggers

Ca (👁🐾) Shame [Unveil Guilt]: Add +2 **Dg** to the damage of the first of the two Damage Flips.

Cb (✗🐾) "Snip Snip!" [Sharps]: After damaging defender, select one of defender's basic melee Weapons. During defender's next activation, it must discard a Card when it declares a **Strike** with that Weapon or the **Strike** immediately ends.

Df (🐾) Regret: After inflicting Moderate or Severe damage on this model, the attacker may not attack this model again for the remainder of the turn.

SPELLS:

(1) "I Know What I'm Doing!"
(CC: 12🐾 / Rst: - / Rg: C) Push this model up to 6" in any direction ignoring hazardous, severe, and water effects. This Push may not end closer to Pandora, Avatar of Insanity than it began.

(1) Unnerving Presence
(CC: 13🐾 / Rst: - / Rg: ⊛4) Enemy models must first discard a Control Card before Cheating Fate. An enemy model that cannot discard a Control Card cannot Cheat Fate.

(1) Unveil Guilt
(CC:12🐾 / Rst: Wp / Rg: 8) Target enemy model suffers two Damage Flips with its Bash Weapon. The Damage Flips cannot be Cheated.

Zoraida, Avatar of Fate

Somewhere in the Bayou, four months after the Event.

Twigs and leaves cracked beneath her bare feet, gnarled and calloused to the point where she could not feel the layer of frost covering the Bayou. The sun would soon burn it off, and the lizards, amphibians, and other bayou animals startled by the anomaly would shake off their instinctual terror and soon forget it ever occurred. But Zoraida would not. It was no freak occurrence. December's influence continued to mount. The death of His physical body at Kythera was just the beginning; the aetheric tear caused by the falling Cage only accelerated the coming end.

All of the Tyrants now stirred. If any were to ascend, it would mean the end of their world.

She felt responsible for the Breach, for her part in twisting Malifaux's fate and destiny. Those two cosmic forces did not react well to manipulation and were now recoiling and lashing back in punishment.

She could not unravel the knot they had made. Humans and the Neverborn alike, reweaving the strands of Fate as they liked. Standing in the cool muck that rose above her ankles, Zoraida concentrated on the throbbing pulse of life that beat beneath her. Most of Malifaux had been laid barren in that war so long ago, but the Bayou still throbbed with life.

She could hear whispered voices carried on the wind seeking refuge against the pain and confusion of their displacement. She wanted to take them in, absorb and bind them to her own spirituality like a soulstone. They were so frail. But they were everywhere. How could she gather so many?

She had grown old, far beyond nature's intention, and set in her ways. *When I was young, first escaping to the Bayou,* she thought, *I had the youthful optimism and elasticity of spirit to solve this.* That thought was a revelation.

She drew in a tenuous ribbon of the residual energy and pressed it down deep against her own life force. Where the power should have been contained within a soulstone, or forced to power a spell as she would normally do with the aether, this spiritual energy was different. It did not manipulate external forces. Instead, the energy spilling out of the aether manipulated an *individual*.

She drew in more and more of the tenuous wisps floating along the edge of her perception. Needing the flexibility and vitality of youth, her body slowly straightened, losing the haggard bent posture of age. Her skin softened and grew taut, stretching away wrinkles as warm color returned. Muscles in her thighs, chest, and arms grew firm and strong as raven black returned to her hair, washing away the white in a wave. She released the leftover energy she had absorbed, letting it levitate her into the air as it slowly dissipated.

Zoraida floated above the Bayou, glowing with the vitality of youth. She, alone, understood what had to be done and now knew how to do it. But it would require the sacrifice of many. It was a price she could accept.

Zoraida, Avatar of Fate

50MM BASE

SOULSTONE COST: MANIFEST

AVATAR (ZORAIDA)

WK/CG	HT	WP	CA	DF	WD
4/6	2	8	7🐾	6	11

WITHERING TOUCH

RG	〰 1
CB	5🐾
DG	1/2/6

TALENTS:

Abilities

Bayou Two-Card: Once per turn, this model may play the top Card of the discard pile instead of flipping a Fate Card during a Duel.

I Saw This In the Cards: This Crew's Initiative Flips receive 🔶.

Irresistible: Enemy models must win a **Wp →** 12 Duel when targeting this model with an attack or the Action fails. This may not be ignored by any Talent.

Mark of Fate: One friendly model may use this model's **Bayou Two-Card** ability once per turn. This counts as the Ability's once per turn use.

Weapon

Withering Touch: Magical. This Weapon ignores **Armor**.

Actions

(+2) Casting Master

(0) Empowered by Fate: Discard a Control Card. This model performs a Healing Flip. This model's Controller declares whether this model heals the **Wd** indicated or draws an equal number of Cards up to its Crew's maximum Hand size. If the flip was the Red Joker, draw up to its Crew's maximum Hand size.

(1) Reading the Cards: 🎯6. Each time an enemy model in the 🎯 Cheats Fate and/or discards a Soulstone during an opposed Duel with a friendly model, or when Resisting a Spell cast by a friendly model, this model's Controller may discard one Fate Card and then draw one Fate Card.

(2) Create Voodoo Doll: Summon one Voodoo Doll Totem. Immediately sacrifice any other Voodoo Doll Totems attached to this model.

Triggers

Ca (🐾🐾) Consume Fate [Pins and Needles]: This model draws one Card for each wound suffered by the defender.

Ca (🐾🐾) Master of Manipulation [Obey]: After defender fails to resist **Obey**, completely resolve the Spell, then cast **Obey** on the same target. This Trigger may be used once per activation.

Cb (✗🐾) Ravaged by Time [Withering Touch]: After hitting a defender with this Weapon, do no damage. Instead, reduce defender's **Wd** stat by 2 until the end of the Encounter. Multiple **Ravaged by Times** are cumulative.

Df (🐾) A Servant's Rage: When this model is damaged by a melee **Strike**, after the attack is completely resolved, immediately select a friendly model with the Beast, Construct, and/or Doll Characteristic within 4" that has LoS to the model inflicting the damage. The friendly model may Push up to its **Wk** and perform one melee **Strike** targeting the model that inflicted the damage. This Trigger may be used once per turn.

SPELLS:

(0) Tangled Threads
(CC: 15🐾 / Rst: Wp / Rg: 8) Target model must discard one Control Card immediately after declaring an Action other than **Pass** and spending AP or the Action immediately ends.

(1) Obey
(CC: 14🐾 / Rst: - / Rg: 12) Target non-Master model immediately performs a **(1)** Action or **Charge** controlled by you. The Action selected may not cause the model to be killed or sacrificed as part of the Action. This Spell may be cast once per activation.

(1) Pins and Needles
(CC: 12🐾 / Rst: Df / Rg: 8) **Dg** 1/2/5, **Poison 2**.

(1) Scrying
(CC: 16🐾 / Rst: - / Rg: C) This model's Controller nominates another player and looks at one Card plus one additional Card per 🐾 in the casting total in that player's Hand.

(2) Suppressed Destiny
(CC: 16🐾 / Rst: - / Rg: 🎯6) Enemy models ignore suits in their Duel totals unless those suits are associated with a stat or on a Fate Card flipped using a Soulstone.

MANIFEST REQUIREMENTS

1 - Zoraida successfully casts **Crystal Ball** two times.
2 - Use a model controlled by **Obey** cast by Zoraida to kill an enemy model.

When Zoraida performs the **Manifest** Action, follow the Manifest Steps in order.

MANIFEST STEPS

- Remove from the game all Totems attached to Zoraida.
- Discard all Tokens and end all effects on Zoraida.
- Replace Zoraida with Zoraida, Avatar of Fate.
- Zoraida, Avatar of Fate may immediately discard a Soulstone to perform a Healing Flip.
- Replace the Zoraida stat card and this card with the Zoraida, Avatar of Fate stat card for the remainder of the Encounter. Then continue Zoraida, Avatar of Fate's activation as normal for a Replaced model.

Hamelin, Avatar of Contagion

Throughout the City, five months after the Event.

The unholy union of Hamelin the Piper and the sinister Tyrant referred to only as the Plagued came to a sudden and violent end at the hand of that girl's vengeful spirit unleashed upon him. His body had been shattered, obliterated against a wall, scattering the carrion and skittering creatures writhing within him across the floor of the observatory, just as he finished the ritual that would unlock all the power necessary for his final ascension.

With that dissolution of his form came an equally dissipated awareness and will as the creatures that comprised him crawled away. Still, he was a Tyrant and that was no small thing. He fought to call them together again, to recreate himself. The *device* was still salvageable, and with the release of the Fire Tyrant, a hole had been made into the aether. He had little time, but his will was severe and stronger than any other might imagine.

He should have been lost. *They* had thought that too, the Neverborn, when they sealed him in that prison in the Necropolis.

Even though his body had exploded with the observatory, nothing was more enduring than a virus and the creatures that carried it. Some of the insects escaped the fiery turmoil, worming beneath the timber and rubble. Just a few. But they carried not only the disease of the Plagued, but His very will.

It should have taken years, centuries, or even eons as it had before. The Event had come and gone, and the *device* that would open the gateway into the aether, allowing him to ascend and dominate that world saturated in magical energy, was gone with it.

His body was gone. His will was greatly reduced. His mind, too, was nearly broken. But he was angry. Angry beyond measure. Even more than when the Neverborn broke him and confined him centuries earlier.

Slowly he spread the original contagion in those few surviving dark insects to others of their kind, calling more and more from the sewers once again until there were enough to hold him again. With each new crawling bug added to the reconvened mass, his awareness grew as well, until he was ready to walk again. He pulled them together within the flesh of a freshly fallen human victim of their deadly disease. They rebuilt that flesh to the more comfortable and familiar body of Hamelin, the man that first released Him.

It took months. The Event was gone. But he could feel the prickling energy that still danced about this world from the inundation of the wave. It was nothing for him to take bit after bit of that energy within him, gorging upon it desperately.

"Now," he growled, a centipede crawling out of his drooping lips. "Now, they will pay." Water dripped upon him from a sewer grate above, and he looked up at the light spilling down. The insignificant creatures that did his bidding would not be considered insignificant for much longer. He would unleash upon them a contagion that would destroy them all.

HAMELIN, AVATAR OF CONTAGION

50MM BASE

AVATAR (HAMELIN THE PLAGUED), SOULLESS

WK/CG	HT	WP	CA	DF	WD
4/6	2	9	7✗ / 🐀	5	12

CONTAGIOUS TOUCH	
RG	⫻ 1
CB	6✗
DG	2/3/5

PIPES	
RG	⌐10
CB	7🐀
DG	1/3/3*

TALENTS:

Abilities

Adaptive Mind [Ca]: When this model uses this stat, it can add either of the stat's suits to the total, but not both.

Contagious Eruption: While Hamelin, Avatar of Contagion is in play, when a model with one or more Blight Tokens is killed, all models within (ϗ)2 of the killed model gain one Blight Token.

Crippling Plague: Enemy non-leader models in play gain Insignificant while they have one or more Blight Tokens.

Nihilism: While this model is in play, friendly models lose Insignificant. If this model is in play at the end of the Encounter, no friendly models count as Insignificant.

Mark of Contagion: All Malifaux Rats entering play gain one Blight Token.

Poxed Servants: Enemy models damaged by a friendly model with one or more Blight Tokens gain one Blight Token.

Weapons

Contagious Touch: This Weapon's Damage Flips receive ➕ when damaging a target with one or more Blight Tokens.

Pipes: After this Weapon inflicts Severe damage on a non-Master model with **Wp** 5 or less, that model takes a **(1)** Action or a **Charge** controlled by this model's Controller.

Actions

(+1) Fast

(0) Pestilent Miasma: ⚫2. Models with one or more Blight Tokens receive ⊟ to their Attack and Damage Flips.

(1) Frenzied Piping: ⚫10. Friendly Vermin may inflict 1 **Wd** on themselves when inflicting damage on a model with a melee attack to increase the **Dg** inflicted by +1.

(1) The Gift of Contagion: ⚫3. Friendly models gain one Blight Token.

Triggers

Cb (✗🐀) Coughing Fit [Contagious Touch/Pipes]: After damaging a defender with one or more Blight Tokens, the defender receives **Slow**.

Cb (✗) Spread Like Wildfire [Contagious Touch]: After damaging defender with this Weapon, the defender gains one Blight Token.

Df (✗) The Ague: Attacker receives **Slow** after resolving a melee attack against this model.

SPELLS:

(all) A Tyrant's Judgment
(CC: 17✗🐀 / Rst: Wp / Rg: (ϗ)10) Enemy models without a Blight Token losing their Resist Duel gain one Blight Token. Enemy models with Blight Tokens losing their Resist Duels suffer 1 **Wd** per Blight Token they have.

(0) Bask in the Plague
(CC: 13✗🐀 / Rst: - / Rg: (ϗ)8) Discard one Blight Token from each model in range. This model heals 1 **Wd** per Blight Token discarded.

(0) Piper's Swarm
(CC: 14✗🐀 / Rst: - / Rg: C) Discard up to three Cards. Summon one Malifaux Rat per Card discarded.

(1) Leprous Dance
(CC: 13🐀🐀 / Rst: - / Rg: (ϗ)10) *AR: This model must discard a Soulstone.* Enemy models with one or more Blight Tokens immediately take a **Charge** or **(1)** Action controlled by this model's Controller in an order of his or her choosing. A model may choose to perform a **Wp → 14** Duel to ignore the effects of this Spell. This Spell may only be cast once per turn per Crew.

(1) Piper's Lure
(CC: 14🐀 / Rst: Wp / Rg: 18) Push target model 4" toward the closest table edge. If the target is pushed into contact with the table edge, kill target and draw two Cards.

MANIFEST REQUIREMENTS

1 - Hamelin the Plagued must kill an enemy model with a model controlled by the Pipes Weapon.

2 - Hamelin the Plagued must give three enemy models the Insignificant Characteristic with the **Understand the Soulless** Spell.

When Hamelin the Plagued performs the **Manifest** Action, follow the Manifest Steps in order.

MANIFEST STEPS

- Remove from the game all Totems attached to Hamelin the Plagued.
- Discard all Tokens and end all effects on Hamelin the Plagued.
- Replace Hamelin the Plagued with Hamelin, Avatar of Contagion.
- Hamelin, Avatar of Contagion may immediately discard a Soulstone to make a Healing Flip.
- All Malifaux Rats in play gain one Blight Token.
- Replace the Hamelin the Plagued stat card and this card with the Hamelin, Avatar of Contagion stat card for the remainder of the Encounter. Then continue Hamelin, Avatar of Contagion's activation as normal for a Replaced model.

LEVETICUS, AVATAR OF ENTROPY

Deep within the Bayou, five months after the Event.

Weeks had passed, he and Zoraida had spent literally every waking moment – hers, his spirit form did not need sleep – learning how to put their newfound talents to use. They had no Tyrants to fight, no way to directly test their knowledge except to spar against each other. Already today they had spent hours manipulating magic, probing each other's weaknesses, and experimenting with new spells. It was taking its toll. Zoraida broke off her current assault, unable to focus on the task at hand.

"Again," he encouraged Zoraida as she sat down on a root, exhaustion drawn across her face.

"In a moment. I may be younger now, but my endurance is not limitless," she gasped. Leveticus could hear a note of jealousy in her voice.

"Very well." While he waited for her to recover, he strode around the small clearing they had chosen for today's work. The Bayou's beauty had never stirred him the way it did Zoraida. All he saw was miles and miles of tangled plants and murky water, what an awful place.

His musings on the subject were interrupted by a blinding pain that washed through his disembodied spirit. "Not again," he gasped. He knew better than to fight against it, instead focusing in an effort to draw out the vision it heralded. The first two times this occurred he had misunderstood their purpose, but since then he had witnessed four visions, each longer and more involved than the last.

He saw himself and the four Riders, rushing across the hardpan toward an unseen destination. He was at the fore of the group, his spirit made manifest, riding a powerful ghostly steed, something more and less than real. He recognized three of the four Riders as the same beings he had encountered under the Hanging Tree. The fourth was new to the dream. Clearly a female, her long hair swept back by the wind, she wielded a spear, which she leveled toward their invisible foe as a jousting knight would his lance. Her horse, unlike his spectral mount, was a blending of meat and machine, but more machine than horse, unlike the decaying creatures ridden by the Hooded Rider and Dead Rider.

What he could only assume were explosions began to pepper the hardpan around the imposing group, but they rode through it, oblivious to the danger. He watched as at least one explosion erupted in a bloom of dirt and flame directly below the horse. He cringed mentally, and then was amazed to see himself still riding, completely unscathed by the attack. Then he shouted orders to the four Riders, and they fanned out as they came alongside him. The frequency of the explosions and sounds of gunfire intensified as each of them encouraged their mounts to faster speeds. They were at the enemy's line, but Leveticus could still not make out just *what* this enemy was. It was then that the pain vacated him in a rush, taking with it the vision just as the enemy was coming into view.

The experience left him drained of energy as the previous ones had. Zoraida was watching him from her perch. "Another vision?"

"Yes," he replied. He summarized what he had seen for her, leaving no detail out of the retelling.

She listened. Once he had finished, she had a single question for him: "But where was I?"

LEVETICUS, AVATAR OF ENTROPY

50MM BASE

AVATAR (LEVETICUS), RIDER, SOULLESS, SPIRIT

WK/CG	HT	WP	CA	DF	WD
6/10	3	8	7*	4	10

DEATH TOUCH		
RG	////	1
CB		5
DG		0/1/12

TALENTS:

Abilities

Destructive Infusing: This model makes a Healing Flip when a friendly Rider model kills an enemy model with a melee attack.

Fate's Master: This model may discard any number of Control Cards at the start of its activation. For each Card discarded, this model's **Ca** receives the suit from the discarded Card until the end of its activation.

Hard to Kill

Mark of Entropy: ⊗10. Enemy models taking the **Charge** Action suffer 1 **Wd** after resolving the Action.

The Fifth Rider: If this model is killed or sacrificed during the turn, at the end of the Closing Phase its Controller may Place a Leveticus, Avatar of Entropy in base contact with a friendly model with the Rider Characteristic in play. Both models immediately suffer 2 **Dg**.

The Ground Trembles: While this model's Crew has one or more of the following models in play, this model gains the following effect listed for that model:

Dead Rider: Regeneration 1
Hooded Rider: Wreathed in Flames: Models hitting this model with a melee attack suffer 2 **Dg**.
Mechanical Rider: (+1) Melee Expert, +1 Df
Pale Rider: Cb receives +✕.

Slow Dissipation: If this model has more than 1 **Wd** at the end of the Resolve Effects Step, it suffers 1 **Wd**.

"To Me!": While this model is in play, friendly Dead Riders, Hooded Riders, Mechanical Riders, and Pale Riders in play or entering play gain the Rider Characteristic until the end of the Encounter.

Unfathomed Purpose: At the end of the Draw Step, once per turn, this model's Controller may discard any number of Cards from his or her Hand and then draw an equal number of Cards. This model suffers 1 **Wd** for each Card drawn using this Ability.

Actions

(0) Arcane Understanding: Inflict any number of **Wd** upon this model to draw an equal number of Cards.

(1) Rejuvenating Knowledge: This model discards two Control Cards. This model makes a Healing Flip.

Triggers

Cb (✕) The Face of Death: After successfully hitting defender with a Death Touch **Strike**, discard up to three Control Cards. The Damage Flip receives ✚ for each Card discarded.

SPELLS:

(1) Necrotic Unmaking
(CC: 16✕ / Rst: Df / Rg: 10) This model suffers 1 **Wd**. Target enemy model suffers 3 **Wd**. If target is killed by this Spell, it does not generate any Counters. Summon one Steampunk Abomination into base contact before it is removed from play.

(1) Soul Harvest
(CC: 14✕ 🦇 / Rst: - / Rg: ⊗5) When a living model within range is killed or sacrificed, this model gains one Soulstone.

(1) The Foretelling
(CC: 15📖 / Rst: - / Rg: (I)8) Other friendly Riders may immediately resolve their **(0)** Spell as if they had successfully cast it.

(2) Bring Forth a Rider
(CC: 20🦇* / Rst: - / Rg: C) Before the Casting Flip, this model declares a Rider to Summon. The second suit required for this Spell is based on the Rider being Summoned: Pale Rider: ♣, Dead Rider: ✕, Mechanical Rider: 📖, Hooded Rider: 🦇.
AR: Discard one Soulstone and sacrifice another friendly Construct within 6". Summon the declared Rider. This Spell may be successfully cast only once per Crew per Encounter.

MANIFEST REQUIREMENTS

1 - Leveticus must have been killed or sacrificed twice.
2 - Leveticus must Summon two Steampunk Abominations with the **Necrotic Unmaking** Spell.

When Leveticus performs the **Manifest** Action, follow the Manifest Steps in order.

MANIFEST STEPS

- Remove from the game all Totems attached to Leveticus.
- Discard all Tokens and end all effects on Leveticus.
- Replace Leveticus with Leveticus, Avatar of Entropy
- Leveticus, Avatar of Entropy may immediately discard a Soulstone to make a Healing Flip.
- Friendly Riders in play may immediately resolve their **(0)** Spell as if they had successfully cast it.
- Replace the Leveticus stat card and this card with the Leveticus, Avatar of Entropy stat card for the remainder of the Encounter. Then continue Leveticus, Avatar of Entropy's activation as normal for a Replaced model.

SOM'ER AND PEACHES, AVATARS OF INDULGENCE

Somewhere in the Bayou, three weeks after the Event.

Som'er Teeth was in a downright sour mood. No amount of piglet and youngin' kicking seemed to lift his spirits, and even his pet 'skeeters gave Jones a wide berth, sensing he had something downright powerful on his mind. He certainly did, and that was the trouble.

Ever since the purple light show had danced around him... no *through* him...and the voices with the big words had filled his head, he could do nothing else but think. Think about the Bayou, about what would he do if it was suddenly gone, about what would his kin do to survive, about how he could stop what was coming, and why wouldn't he embrace the gifts the voices had given him? He hated thinking too much, it made the Big Hat shrink and his head hurt.

Sighing, he rubbed and punched at his temples with gloved fists, trying to reject the thoughts swimming in his green head. Sitting down by the water's edge he was sure none of the other Gremlins could see his distress. He hoped so. The last time he had been vulnerable was that day while he stood frozen with his head cocked, listening to the purple voices. One of his boys had tried to grab the Big Hat off his head, if a gremlin could believe it. *His Big Hat, while he was wearing it!* The poor Gremlin's arm had paused as it reached for the Big Hat, eyes wide with surprise that Som'er was himself again. Shooting Klem was a damn shame. But without a Big Hat, he couldn't be much of a boss. What else could he do? Damned heavy the Big Hat had become. It was all a very heavy weight on his mind. His thoughts turned to...

...Snorting and the clank and jangle of metal on metal at his shoulder. A massive shadow fell across him, blotting out his own. He looked over his shoulder and there she stood, loyal as a mangy dog and twice as mean. "Peaches," he cooed as he walked over to the sow's massive bulk.

The still balanced on her back gurgled merrily at his arrival. He poured a healthy slug into a beaten tin cup and knocked it back in one gulp, eyes tearing as the fire tore down his throat and lit the furnace in his belly. The voices quieted down some, and the urge to think wasn't quite as pressing on his brain. "Girl, you always know the right thing to say. A few more sips an' I'll be right as rain."

"Gents, I's done some heavy thinkin'!"

Som'er sat astride Peaches, the tin cup and its sloshing contents in one hand, a half-eaten leg of some sort of Bayou critter in the other as he shouted at the Gremlins within earshot. She had carried him back from the water's edge — his sense of balance lost somewhere between cupfuls five and six of the 'shine. Where he had acquired a bucket of food was a mystery.

"It's been a good long time since we've gone on a hoot and holler. I'm thinkin' it's time we did. Pay them humans some visits like they've been payin' us? What do ya say? Eh boys? Let's have the best travelin' shindig the Bayou's ever seen!"

Excited murmurs rolled through the growing crowd at the prospect of a good old fashioned traveling ruckus. Som'er thought that if the world was going to end he and his kin might as well go out celebrating like there was no tomorrow, since there would quite possibly be none. He took another swig from the tin cup and grinned like a fool.

"Now, who wants a drink?!" The whoops, hollers, and crack of boomsticks shot into the sky were his answer.

SOM'ER AND PEACHES, AVATARS OF INDULGENCE

50MM BASE

SOULSTONE COST: MANIFEST

AVATAR (SOM'ER TEETH JONES), GREMLIN, PIG

WK/CG	HT	WP	CA	DF	WD
4/7	3	6	5 ✗	4	10

DRUMSTICKIN'		GORE	
RG	⚔ 1	RG	⚔ 1
CB	6 👆	CB	5 👆
DG	2/3/4	DG	2/5/6

TALENTS:

Abilities

BIG Momma: Friendly Pig models affected by **Stampede** may end **Stampede** when they end an Action within 6" of this model.

Blubber: Armor +1. This model ignores damage inflicted by ♠.

Companion (Bayou Gremlin)

Hard to Wound 1

Mark of Indulgence: Other friendly Gremlin models receive +1 **Wp** while this model is in play.

Survival of the Fittest: When a friendly Gremlin is killed or sacrificed within 6" of this model, draw two Control Cards. When two or more models with **Survival of the Fittest** are in range of the Gremlin, the closest model draws Cards.

The BIG Hat: Other friendly Gremlins receive ♣ in **Wp** Duels while within 6" of this model.

Used to It: When this model would be damaged by the **"Woops!"** Ability, the Damage Flip becomes 0/0/1.

Weapons

Drumstickin': A defender wounded by this Weapon performs a **Df → 12** Duel. If the defender loses the Duel, it must discard one Control Card or receive **Paralyzed**.

Gore: Damage Flips during this model's **Charge** Actions inflict +1 **Dg**.

Actions

(+1) Reckless: This model may suffer 1 **Wd** to receive **Fast**.

(0) '"Shine Pig!": Nominate one of the following effects. All friendly Gremlin models within (✗)6, including this model, gain the effect, but receive **Slow** at the start of their next activation.
- Make a Healing Flip.
- The model's **Wp** flips receive ♣.
- Gain the **Hard to Kill** Ability.

(0) Sooeet Nothin's: Target Pig within 8" makes a Healing Flip. End target's **Stampede**.

(1) "Protect the Hooch!": (✗)10. Push friendly Gremlin models 3" toward this model.

Triggers

Ca (✗ 📖) "She Ain't Fat!" [Swamp Gas]: Summon one Piglet after resolving this Spell.

Cb (👆) "Atta Girl!": After this model resolves a hit with one of its melee **Strikes**, it may discard a Control Card to take another melee **Strike** using a different melee Weapon. This Trigger may only be used twice during this model's activation.

Df (✗) B.Y.O.G.: After suffering damage from an enemy attack, this model Summons one Bayou Gremlin.

SPELLS:

(1) Reckless Frenzy
(CC: 15 ✗ / Rst: - / Rg: ⊗12) Friendly Gremlins, including this model, do not suffer a **Wd** when they use the **Reckless** Ability. This Spell may be cast once per turn.

(1) "Sooey!"
(CC: 10 / Rst: - / Rg: (✗)18) Friendly Pigs may Push up to their **Cg** toward this model. All Pig models in range **Charge** this model if it loses the Casting Duel.

(1) Swamp Gas
(CC: 15 ✗ / Rst: Df / Rg: (✗)6) Models without the Gremlin or Pig Characteristics suffer 2 **Wd** and are then Pushed 3" directly away from this model.

MANIFEST REQUIREMENTS

1 - Som'er Teeth Jones must take the **Take a Swig** Action three times and heal one or more friendly Gremlin models at least one **Wd** each each time the Action is taken.

2 - Som'er Teeth Jones must inflict 4 **Dg** on enemy models with the **"Pull My Finger"** Spell.

When Som'er Teeth Jones performs the **Manifest** Action, follow the Manifest Steps in order.

MANIFEST STEPS

- Remove each Totem attached to Som'er from the game. Som'er's Controller may discard two Cards per Totem to prevent it from being removed.
- Discard all Tokens and end all effects on Som'er.
- Replace Som'er with Som'er and Peaches, Avatars of Indulgence.
- Som'er and Peaches, Avatars of Indulgence may immediately discard a Soulstone to make a Healing Flip.
- Replace the Som'er Teeth Jones stat card and this card with the Som'er and Peaches, Avatars of Indulgence stat card for the remainder of the Encounter. Then continue Som'er and Peaches, Avatars of Indulgence's activation as normal for a Replaced model.

VIKTORIAS, AVATARS OF SLAUGHTER

Ten miles Northwest of Ridley Station, during the Event.

A wall of crackling purple energy washed across Viktoria as she and her crew fought against the fleeing group of escaped prisoners they had finally caught up with, freezing her in place. Her twin gasped in agony as the wave passed through her, dual swords stopped in mid-strike. The convict before her blinked in astonishment as the crackling energy pricked his skin and temporarily blinded him. It took a moment for him to shake off the stunned confusion, thanking his luck the swords had halted their descent. His assailant, however, shook in pain, gasping and gurgling. Chuckling, he raised his hand to strike her, ignoring the departure of the strange wall of energy moving across the countryside.

A Ronin knocked into him from the side before he could drive his knife into the Swordmistress, and the two fought away from her as she fell, writhing in pain upon the rocky ground.

The other Viktoria, frozen in place with her pistol outstretched before her, suffered none of the torturous agony incapacitating her sibling in spirit. *Her* target didn't care why she didn't fire upon him and lunged at her as well. She saw the assault coming as if slowed, moving through a pool of molasses, yet she could not move to either dodge or deflect the coming blow. Another of their Ronin prodigy slashed into his side, and they tumbled away as Viktoria looked on, unmoving in the grip of the wave's power.

But the remaining convicts saw the Viktorias' strange hesitation and turned from running away madly to take on the two Ronin, dispatching them quickly. The men ascended the hill together toward the bounty hunter and her twin, intending to kill the two women with ease. As the lead man stepped near them, he stopped dead in his tracks. The sword held loosely in Viktoria's left hand suddenly rang out like a hammer striking an anvil. The convicts recoiled in pain, clutching their ears until the sound subsided to a low hum. Viktoria rose slowly behind her gun-wielding sibling, her twin swords elongating and curving like the venomous fangs of a Razorspine. Both women glared at the men, eyes burning with a terrifying bloodlust.

What disturbed the men most was the single humming Masamune. It elongated before their eyes, curving wickedly and widening as it grew. A creature's head formed in the metal at the base of the blade, its eyes blinked open to stare at the convicts while its long metallic tongue, which spread up along the blade, seemed to absorb the blood spattered on the metal.

The sword hummed thrillingly, as if excited about the bloodletting to come. The Viktorias looked upon the men as beasts for their slaughter, willed to kill by the Masamune sword's magic. They broke into smiles that chilled each man to his soul and charged the group.

It was the last thing any of the men saw before a blur of whirling death descended upon them.

VIKTORIAS, AVATARS OF SLAUGHTER

50MM BASE

AVATAR (VIKTORIA), MERCENARY

WK/CG	HT	WP	CA	DF	WD
-/8	2	6	6 🐾	5	12

AWAKENED MASAMUNE

RG	⚔ 2
CB	8 🌀 🐾
DG	3/4/6

TALENTS:

Abilities

Bloodlust of the Masamune: When this model activates, its first Action must be a melee **Strike** Action targeting a model in its melee range or, if there is no model in this model's melee range, a **Charge** Action targeting the nearest enemy model. If this model does not take one of these two Actions first during its activation, it suffers 2 **Wd**.

Bulletproof 2

Called to Slaughter: This model's **Charge** Actions cost 1 AP. If the **Charge** movement ends without the target in this model's melee range, this model's activation immediately ends.

Draw of the Masamune Nihonto: Whenever a model within 8" of this model is killed by a melee **Strike**, Push this model 5" towards the model before it is removed from play.

Mark of Slaughter: When a friendly model activates while this model is in play, that model nominates one of its basic melee Weapons to gain the "**Cb (🌀) Critical Strike [the nominated Weapon]**" Trigger until the end of its activation.

Two Faces of Fate: When this model flips or plays the Black or Red Joker, look through its Controller's Discard Pile for a Joker and shuffle the first Joker found into the Controller's Fate Deck.

Weapons

Awakened Masamune: Magical. Paired. This Weapon's Damage Flips receive 🔼. This model draws one Control Card each time it kills an enemy model with this Weapon.

Actions

(+2) Melee Master

Triggers

Cb (✗ 🗡) Compelled to Kill: After killing a model with a melee **Strike**, do not draw a Card. Immediately **Charge** the nearest model.

Cb (🌀) Critical Strike [Awakened Masamune]

Cb (🗡 🗡) Whirlwind [Awakened Masamune]: After damaging defender with an Awakened Masamune **Strike**, immediately make an Awakened Masamune **Strike** against another target in melee range.

SPELLS:

(0) First Strike

(CC: 14 🗡 / Rst: - / Rg: C) This model may immediately make a melee **Strike** targeting a model after it enters this model's melee range. Resolve this **Strike** completely before resolving any Duels initiated by the moving model. This model uses **Cb** 6 🌀 when making these **Strikes**.

(0) "OUR KILL!"

(CC: 13 ✗ 🗡 / Rst: - / Rg: C) Switch this model with target friendly model engaged in melee with an enemy model.

(1) Compelled by the Masamune

(CC: 14 🗡 / Rst: Wp / Rg: 10) Reduce target's **Wk** to -. Target gains the Action: "**(1) Serpent Strike:** This model **Charges** the closest enemy model. If this model does not end the move with an enemy model in its melee range, its activation immediately ends."

MANIFEST REQUIREMENTS

1 - One Viktoria must kill a model with a melee **Strike** during a turn in which it is under the effect of the **Sisters in Battle: Fury** Spell cast by another friendly Viktoria.

2 - Two different Viktoria models must have used their **Whirlwind** Trigger on enemy models.

A Viktoria cannot take the **Manifest** Action unless both Viktorias are still in the game. When Viktoria performs the **Manifest** Action, follow the Manifest Steps in order.

MANIFEST STEPS

- Remove from the game all Totems attached to both Viktorias.
- Discard all Tokens and end all effects on both Viktorias.
- Replace one Viktoria with Viktorias, Avatars of Slaughter. Remove the other Viktoria from the game. Apply all **Wd** suffered by both Viktorias to Viktorias, Avatars of Slaughter. If this reduces Viktorias, Avatars of Slaughter to less than 2 **Wd**, it enters play with 2 **Wd** remaining.
- Viktorias, Avatars of Slaughter may immediately discard a Soulstone to make a Healing Flip.
- Replace the Viktoria stat cards and this card with the Viktorias, Avatars of Slaughter stat card for the remainder of the Encounter. Then continue Viktorias, Avatars of Slaughter's activation as normal for a Replaced model.

Balancing the Books

October 15

Hoffman hadn't left the Guild compound at the end of the day, and the fire in the coal furnace on the floor beneath him had diminished so that little heat radiated from the iron grills in the floorboards. Even the wick in his kerosene lamp flickered as if struggling against the encroaching cold. The wind outside blew strong from out of the north, and everyone that talked about it said it was unnatural. As it was his first autumn in Malifaux, he wouldn't know. Everything in Malifaux seemed uncomfortable to him.

He pushed the case files across his desk and rubbed his upper arms to increase circulation. He had read the same sentence perhaps a dozen times in the last hour but couldn't really focus on the meaning of the text. He looked across the room at the grotesque form of his brother standing almost motionless, save the rising and falling of his chest, silently staring at him. He had been like that since he had come wandering into the Guild compound unannounced, frightening even seasoned Guardsmen and deputized marshals who had gathered around him. Although hulking and well-armed, he made no threatening gesture, even when shackled. Only when he was led to the holding cells below the compound did he resist, easily breaking his bonds, and he strode directly to his younger brother's workrooms.

The guards escorting him, though puzzled and alert, were somehow unthreatened and followed him all the way to Hoffman where he simply stood, much more like a construct awaiting instructions than a freethinking man.

That was weeks ago.

Ryle stood where Hoffman instructed him to, unmoving for hours, even if Hoffman left to attend other business. If Hoffman didn't return by dusk, Ryle would then go stomping down the halls, drawn to him, his boots ringing on the wood with all the resounding commotion of a horse trotting through the halls.

"Mr. Hoffman," the Governor General's Secretary, Lucius, said from behind him, "Working late?"

Hoffman jumped, believing he was alone in the investigator's room, if not the entire commissioned officer's offices. He twisted as best he could to see Lucius who remained directly behind him, as if purposely beyond Hoffman's ability to get him in his sight. "Yes," he said, as casually as he could muster. "Just trying to get my head around some things that have been puzzling me."

He fidgeted in the wooden chair, pulling at the brass rod of his body brace digging into his side. He hoped Lucius would not take notice of the files on Henry the mining Steamborg, Nicodem the Undertaker, Colonel Mathews, and others in Malifaux with self-articulated mechanical prosthetics. It was his charge to investigate each of them for possible ties to growing rebellious groups rumored to practice the darkest and most illegal activities, as decreed by highest law. Of course, much of that was recent supposition on the part of Hoffman. He had been charged with stamping out all illegal practices of bio-mechanical grafting, but almost all of the men he and his deputies apprehended had been quickly released after a brief interrogation by Guild lawyers that answered not to him, but directly to Lucius. Lucius and the bevy of lawyers regularly inquired about Ramos, of course. *His* file was on Hoffman's desk, too, thick but buried beneath the others. So much evidence pointed to him, but he somehow always had some alibi or excuse to explain all of his activities. Even his work in bio-engineering mechanical grafting was conducted on grants from Old World universities, always on men destined for death unless he intervened last minute to save them in desperation, and always accompanied Guild regulations on registering the work. In the case of Ryle, Hoffman suspected he was commanded by Ramos to go to his brother, creating quite a blatant slap in their face.

Hoffman now wondered if the accident that consumed Ryle was not entirely an accident. So much of the events now confronting him and other officers made it difficult to pursue Ramos. It was so perfectly packaged.

As if reading his thoughts, Lucius said, "I see your poor brother still watches over you. Or does he look to you for help? To bring him back into the light of normal men?" An odd thing for him to say, Hoffman thought, since he had never seen the Secretary fully in the light, either.

"I wouldn't know," he said. "You, of all people, know how I feel about the grafted."

"Yes. Of course. I can only imagine the pain he must cause you: a constant reminder to what you have lost." He didn't believe Lucius could empathize with any of those things, true though they were. "A shame he must only stand about like that. He is well-armored, I notice. Quite a gift. Just handed to us, too."

Hoffman said nothing.

"I'll see if we can get some use out of him," Lucius said. Odd, Hoffman thought, again, that it was a declaration rather than a request.

"Be my guest. But he seems to only obey me."

"I wouldn't worry about that. I'm sure he'll follow my commands." He let the thought linger. Breaking the awkward silence, he then said, "In the meantime, I have some new material for you to examine," as he dropped a book on the desk before him. It was larger than a typical text, and the edges were peeling and worn. "From Sonnia Criid's collection," he said loudly. More loudly than necessary, Hoffman thought, given the solitary environment. "One of the few left intact from the excavation of the temple at Nythalm."

"Nythalm? South of Kythera, right?"

"Yes. Beyond the bayou."

"What does this have to do with me, sir?"

"It has notes of particular interest to you, actually. Your charter."

"Grafting? Bio-mechanical grafting? But the book looks – old."

"Yes. Very. It's Neverborn, of course. Criid and her staff have translated much of it, though the science and schematics will likely make more sense to you."

Hoffman nodded. "You want me to continue translating?"

Lucius inhaled sharply. "Yes. And report to me, immediately, any indication of where the Neverborn might have conducted these experiments. Criid has a fascination with it, apparently. We'd like to track her down, too." Thumbing through the tome quickly, he saw drawings of bodies, human looking, with many cross section images of mechanika that made little sense to him and the way he had come to understand the connective techniques by which the nervous system linked to the machinery. Criid's handwritten notes in the margins would be interesting, but his heart leapt as he neared the end of the book. The connective imagery might have been ancient to the Neverborn, but to him, it was revolutionary. Even progressive, blending abstract sister sciences in a way he hadn't imagined possible.

He was about to say something about it when he saw a strange symbol drawn on the inside of a corpse near the arcane interface at the base of its spine. It stopped his heart and time, too, seemed to freeze. He recognized the symbol as a signature, and although it was refined and included a new line and a curve, it was a symbol he had seen before.

He closed the book with a snap, and in his excitement, he nearly fell out of his chair.

"Interesting?" Lucius asked, clearly aware of its importance.

Hoffman said nothing, his mind racing with hundreds of questions. Lucius left him and walked to Ryle, speaking to the hulking husk of a man in low tones that didn't carry across the room. Hoffman pressed himself up from his chair and locked his brace at the knees. He hobbled quickly from the room. Ryle didn't follow and wouldn't. Lucius gave Hoffman a sidelong glance as he quickly departed, and he sneered.

The book remained on his desk, but he moved as quickly as he could to his own lab to look through other books similarly unearthed on the topic of grafting, though much less specific.

He nearly stumbled in the hall, such was his haste.

The symbol marked in that ancient book was almost identical to the one Ramos used on his own grafted works.

As Hoffman stumbled into his lab to frantically find evidence collected to verify his newfound supposition, across the street in the Guild Sanitarium, Lady Justice struggled to regain consciousness for the first time since the observatory had exploded and collapsed upon her almost two months prior while she fought against hundreds of walking dead and Plagued victims.

She drifted in and out of near wakefulness throughout the night. As the first of the sun's rays broke the eastern horizon, her eyes snapped open revealing twin, milky-white orbs, looking remarkably like infused soulstones. She blinked unseeingly, forever in darkness despite the yellow light spilling into her room. She tried to sit and her breath caught in her chest as if knocked from her. She coughed reflexively and it led to a violent wracking that shook her as thick mucus and dried blood came up. She couldn't reclaim her breath, and she blacked out once more, still wheezing and choking.

When she awakened again, it was mid-morning. She took longer to evaluate her surroundings and state of health. Her right arm was strapped to her side, and her breath came in desperate shallow gasps. Her clothing had long been replaced by a short gown. She reached out with her left hand, groping not only for her sword and pistol belt, but, most importantly, the black bandana she wore over her eyes. Without these tools she felt weak and exposed.

When she swung her legs over the edge of the bed, she was again wracked with a cough that threatened to incapacitate her. Wet and phlegmatic, she coughed painfully and reeled. Her feet were unsteady, and she could not focus the strange images in her mind that allowed her to walk, blind, through the unfamiliar building. She groped helplessly before her and around the corner of the doorframe and staggered weakly into the hall. Several nurses were quickly upon her, urging her to return to bed. She refused around choking gasps. Doctor Carl Morrow, too, was summoned, but she batted his pressing hands away somewhat ineffectually.

"Back to your bed, now," he said.

She struggled to speak, but her words came below the rattling cough as she said, "I am Lady Justice!" in a wheeze.

"Yes, yes," he said patronizingly. Attempting to push her back into her room, though, was met with a slap against his shoulder that might have been meant for his face.

He stepped away from it easily, which further bewildered her. She shoved past him, but he caught her around the waist and started to struggle as she fell against him, too weak from the cough to continue. "There, there," Morrow said, gently stroking her thick hair, somewhat knotted from months of bedrest. "That's my good girl," he crooned.

"Let her be, doctor," a commanding voice said behind him.

She recognized the voice as that of one of the Ortega boys, but she didn't know Santiago or Francisco well enough to discern which. They were both there, she knew, but she could only vaguely perceive them in her mind. The doctor stood, releasing her and turned to face the men. "Officer Francisco. We'll not have any trouble out of you today--"

"So long as you don't get disagreeable," Francisco said, cutting him off.

"She needs to be back in bed. Her injuries--"

"Are beyond you. She's Lady Justice. If she wants to go on a stroll, we'll let her."

As he spoke, Santiago had approached her and put her groping hand upon his shoulder. Her lower lip actually trembled, and she looked broken, even scared. It was an image neither man would ever forget. She coughed up blood, and her head rolled against him as she fell against his protective bulk. He regretted the bandana around his neck was filthy with his sweat and the dust of the trail, but they had been back and forth from Latigo to the City numerous times in the past months and his hygiene was never a priority. He pulled it from his neck and wrapped the gingham fabric over her eyes, knowing the blue checkered pattern was far from what she would prefer. As soon as he pulled the knot tight, Justice righted herself, standing free of him. Her coughing grew steady, and finally she controlled it so that it was nothing more than a nuisance. Her bare feet were planted firmly, too, and she rose, standing as tall as either brother. Exposed, wearing no more than the gauzy gown and a dirty rag over her eyes, she regained the inspiring confidence that few could withstand. It was her unflinching, unseeing judgment of the truth. It gave her unparalleled strength. The binding over her eyes gave her clarity and purpose.

She could see the truth and knew her purpose again.

Santiago turned to smile at Francisco. They may have both wished it was Perdita standing there before them, but seeing Justice standing tall and proud gave them hope. Her breath was still shallow, but she spoke quietly and evenly when she asked, "Where's my Judge?"

Francisco said, "Down the hall. He's in worse shape than you, though. Still in a coma."

"The Quarantine Zone? The — whatever that was; the wave?"

"They call it 'The Event'. No one knows. Laid out Perdita, too. She's up a floor. But the building you were fightin' in came down, blown up by whoever took up residence there."

"Resurrectionist."

"Prob'ly. But speculation on some plagued fella, too. Not Res."

She nodded, putting the pieces of her memory back into place.

"Why do I keep thinking of Ramos? Dr. Ramos? Was he there, in the Zone? I cannot get him out of my head."

The brothers looked at one another uncomfortably. The doctor and nurses withdrew, silently attending other matters of their station. At least, that's what they pretended. "What?" she asked.

Francisco stepped toward her. "Lady," he said, his voice low. "Your injuries — they were *fatal*." She coughed, though more gently than before, more in control. "You're not going to like this. Your whole side was crushed. Your ribs. A lung. You were dying."

The thought of that man replacing part of her with something unnatural was more than repulsive. It was akin to damnation. She was unsure how, but she had the recurring image of him wielding great magics and conducting horrific experiments upon the flesh. *Her* flesh. The images plagued her, going deep into her memory, back to the attack at the observatory in the Quarantine Zone. They had danced through her mind while she remained comatose. "Ramos." She sighed and shook her head, feeling despair pressing down upon her. She could barely stand, and her breath came in raspy gasps. Her arm was limp in the sling and could not grasp a darning needle much less her greatsword. For once,

she was uncertain of her fate and her purpose. She needed her sword. The weight upon her shoulder would make her feel like herself. "Where are my weapons?" she asked, weak, more as an afterthought.

"And your clothes, I suppose," Santiago suggested, although he appreciated the thought of her walking about bare legged.

She didn't seem to care. The three rather quickly found her weapons and the dirt-stained and torn attire she had worn in combat those several months earlier. Justice walked right to the locked chest that contained them, striding past confused and protesting doctors and aides into a back room. The boys spun away from her when she pulled the gown over her head, showing little concern for modesty. Buckling the last buckle on her boot, high on her calf, she said, "Will you men ride with me?"

"Of course," Francisco said without hesitation. "Where?"

"A visit to Viktor Ramos. Help me with my sword."

Santiago helped sling it over her good shoulder. "But your arm?" he said. "Can you wield it?"

She gnashed her teeth, feeling impotent. "I can still fire a gun. But I need my sword."

"Are we arresting him?" Francisco asked of Ramos.

"I'm not sure he'll come along willingly. Killing him may be in order."

📖📖📖

It was high noon when they crested the small hill overlooking the Miners and Steamfitter's Union offices near the Hollow Marsh Excavation site. Justice rode with Santiago, reluctantly acknowledging her reliance upon him given her weakened state. He was proud at first to carry her but grew quickly uncomfortable. He had no good way to ride, not wanting to put his arms around her and grasp the saddle horn or reins, though she was silent and stoic no matter what he did. He almost wished she would simply chastise him and tell him exactly what to do. Typically so full of bravado himself, he wasn't easily intimidated. Never by a woman.

Despite the mounting tension, Francisco saw his brother's discomfort, squirming on the saddle behind her, and he reveled in it, winking at Santiago every time his younger brother looked over at him.

The sun stood high in the sky, casting a pale light, but it offered little warmth. The October wind blew cold out of the north. Santiago pulled his duster around Justice who refused a coat of her own. She neither reacted to the cold nor had a reaction to Santiago trying to keep her warm.

They were all surprised to find Hoffman standing on the trail before them, strapped to a mechanical armature, a feline-like construct standing beside him, and a bird-like one gliding above. He just stood there, looking down the hill at the office building. He wore his finest clothes, including a silk vest, a gold chain dangling from the watch in his breast pocket, and an expensive gentleman's bowler resting upon his bald head. The coat he wore was a thick woolen gentleman's coat, imported from his far away home near London.

Francisco had heard of the relationship between Hoffman and Ramos. As they rode up beside him he said, "Don't get in our way, Hoffman." It was bold of him to address the higher ranking officer so, but he was emboldened by Lady Justice, speaking for her. "We intend to confront Viktor Ramos." Francisco was unsure exactly why they were, but such was the silent power of Justice's command.

"I'm not here to stop you, Mr. Ortega. I'm here for the same thing."

"To bring him in?" Francisco asked.

"To kill him?" Santiago offered more hopefully. He had nothing against the Union boss. He was just itching for the opportunity to do what he did best.

It was Justice who answered. She said, "To ask questions. To get answers."

Hoffman nodded. "I'm not expecting this to be easy. He has at least one bodyguard near him always. The big Indigena, Joss, for one. But more, the miners will be loyal, even to their death. And he has an arsenal of constructs that even I cannot duplicate."

Santiago said, "But if you can get him alone, no bodyguards–"

Justice sat upright in the saddle before him and said, "He's more than he seems, isn't he, Hoffman?"

The frail man merely nodded. The Ortegas understood at once.

They walked down the trail in a line, their horses left behind, lashed to a branch. Hoffman's mechanical attendant allowed him to walk in step beside Justice, his Hunter construct clicking alongside him. Miners outside the tunnels ceased their labors to regard the high-ranking Guild officers striding down the hill toward them. It wouldn't be the first time one of their ranks had been arrested by the Guild. But these were a different sort than the common Guild Guardsmen that carried out a basic arrest. Everyone had a heroic idolatry of the Ortegas, men familiar to all people in Malifaux for their steadfast vigilance against the Neverborn that threatened them. Lady Justice, too, was well known to the miners. Her thick mane billowed in the cold wind even after she had haphazardly cut so much of the knotted locks away. It flowed over the sword dangling loosely from her shoulder at her lower back.

Still, the presence of the Guild descending upon them was met with unease. One bulky steamfitter, his arms bulging beneath a dark sweater, took up his mighty mallet and rested it upon his shoulder, showing no sign of returning to work. His name was Johan, and the steamfitters near him, tightening thick screws along a failing seam that released a torrent of bright steam, lifted their tools as well, all heavy weapons in their meaty hands.

It was Hoffman, surprisingly, that spoke in a commanding tone, his voice carrying throughout the camp. "At ease, men!" His militant tone belied his small frame and the crippled demeanor vanished as if an illusion. "Return to your work. Johan," he said to the lead steamfitter, "get your men back on that tank. The drill won't work if it can't hold the pressure." He smiled and winked at the bulky man who continued to regard them coldly. Turning to a group of miners gathering at the main cave entrance, he said, "Mr. Creedy. Back to work. All of you, back to work!" Santiago was impressed. All but Johan did as instructed. He stood resolute, staring at them, unafraid and undaunted. At a small side-mine, Hank the spidery Steamborg strode from the dark depths, the sharp metal points of his great legs striking the rocks with resounding cracks. Like Johan, he stood at the entrance, unmoving but vigilant.

They hoped to confront Ramos inside his office, a wooden building every bit as large as a frontier home. As if expecting them, however, he stepped out of the office to confront them from the wooden rail of the small porch.

"Cold day," Ramos said to them by way of greeting. "Perhaps I can fetch you some tea? Coffee?"

The Ortegas naturally deferred to Lady Justice to lead them, but Hoffman again surprised them by stepping forward. "We should speak within, Professor. Not in front of all of these men."

Ramos smiled falsely. "No. I think we can conduct our business here, beneath the sun."

"Very well," Justice said. Her left hand rested upon the gun at her hip. The Ortegas, too, had their hands upon their holstered Peacebringers. It was a formidable line, and almost any man in Malifaux would crumble in fear against such a group. Ramos remained too confident, almost too prepared for the encounter. It set them on edge to confront a man that didn't naturally bend to their intimidating presence. "What did you do to me, Ramos?" she demanded of him.

"Saved you," he replied without hesitation.

"Or damned me. Why?"

"Why? Your life was endangered. Our good man, Mister Hoffman, here, convinced me of your valor. Your importance." He emphasized the last word strangely, whether sarcastically or in sincere acknowledgement of Justice's worth, the Ortegas could not be sure.

"I don't think so," she said. "Not without personal gain. Did you think it would absolve you of crimes against Guild statutes?"

"Yes," he said matter-of-factly. He continued, saying, "Isn't it interesting that I'm confronted by Lady Justice, head of the Death Marshal division, and two Ortegas, not just family heads, but among the highest ranking officers of the Monster-Hunter division, chartered with protecting the good people here from various Neverborn threats. No Witch Hunters among you? Do you not see this as providence?"

"You forgot me," Hoffman said sternly. "A mistake I thought you wouldn't make again."

Ramos, always in control, briefly revealed his agitation at Hoffman's reference to something the others didn't know about. He masked his feelings quickly. "No, Mr. Hoffman. I shan't overlook you. But your charter is a bit more obscure than the others. I'm sure you've taken your time looking over all the pertinent data regarding my work. Everything is, no doubt, in order and according to Guild requirements of legality?"

"Not why I'm here."

Ramos was more curious than concerned when he said, "Pray; why are you here, then?"

"It's about the symbol you use on your work. The unique work like Hank over there. And," he paused, not wishing to say it, "Ryle. Not mere prosthetics. That's just what the Guild used to get me to toe the line." Speaking so frankly, openly criticizing the Guild, Francisco was shocked and nearly reprimanded him before remembering Hoffman's authority. Santiago and Ramos were equally impressed. Only Justice remained characteristically stoic.

She did say, "And me, Ramos? Did you brand me?"

"You, Lady Justice? Like I said, you were dying. Actually, I'd not have been able to help at all if not for the work I previously did on Ryle. Delving so deeply into the flesh has never been my true interest. How's your breathing, by the way? And the arm?" She said nothing. "Hard to catch your breath? Tingling in the fingers?" He lifted his mechanical arm and the quick gesture nearly had Santiago draw his guns in response. He was itching for a fight. Ramos held a milky white soulstone between metal finger and thumb, the swirling eddies within visible even at the distance between them. The stone was pure and valuable, they could tell. He tossed it to Justice. Though blind, she snatched it easily out of the air. It was warm and comfortable in her palm. "A construct cannot be healed," he said, clearly implying that she should use it to heal herself. "Things are not always what they seem. Not so black and white, good or evil."

She pocketed the stone but was anxious to use it. If she could wrap the gossamer fabric of the spiritually charged energy within it about her own damaged form and repair her failing internal organs and, she prayed, her arm, it would support Ramos' claim that she was still her natural self, unaugmented by the artificial armature she found so deplorable. Still, she suspected

Ramos of hiding something from her, of withholding an important tool he might use against her sometime in the future. He was correct: the scales teetered erratically and she could not immediately discern the truth. "Our actions tip the scales from side to side, Ramos. Law must be met."

Ramos seemed to know exactly how to play her. He said, "Who's law? *Natural* law or that handed down from a man in power? Am I criminal for saving your brother's life, Hoffman? Or yours, Justice? By using the knowledge and skills I've acquired *naturally*?" He was wise to accentuate the word. It had a strong effect upon Lady Justice.

She said nothing. Her conflict with Resurrectionists and their animated puppets left little room to doubt her purpose and actions. Ramos, however, challenged her absolute vision of right and wrong. As he said, he was a man, using his innate gifts and abilities. If it was true that he did not unnaturally replace her organs, and clearly didn't replace her arm with a mechanical prosthetic, perhaps he spoke truthfully after all. Still, her arm tingled, and she couldn't shake the buzzing in the base of her skull that felt as though it originated deep within her torso. She had to reluctantly acquiesce and take him on his word that he did nothing to her physically to make her less than natural, less than human. Why images of him floated in and out of her memory like a dream, quickly dissipating, perplexed her.

Hoffman stepped beside her. He spoke as confidently as Ramos. "Perhaps you are right, Dr. Ramos. Your crimes, though a concern to the Guild, is specifically for the lawyers and judges of the Witch Hunter charter to determine, as you suggest. In pursuit of interests to *my* charter, I have unearthed a tome with a symbol familiar to you. Unless I can determine its unique design, I'm afraid it has rather serious implications regarding your innocence. If Lady Justice and I might sit with you, in private, you can help convince us how we might proceed."

Ramos regarded them for a long moment. His mind worked quickly. He knew there could be only one symbol Hoffman referred to, and he sought, in his memory, for some mistake he might have made – some grafted device he couldn't account for. Finally, he had to reluctantly say, "Yes. Perhaps it is best we spoke in private. No need to detain Ms. Justice, though. I believe she has what she's come for."

Justice said, "Actually, it would do me well to sit. Need to catch my breath. Can you extend me that hospitality, Doctor?"

He had to reluctantly agree.

When they were seated within his makeshift office, warm but still uncomfortable, Hoffman revealed the symbol he had discovered in an ancient and forgotten Neverborn text.

Ramos tried to dismiss it as coincidence and even pointed out the symbol's differences with his own design. He confessed that he had possibly seen the symbol in some text he had, himself, collected and inadvertently adopted it as his own mark.

None of them were convinced, least of all Ramos, who looked quite perplexed.

He gave Hoffman several books from his collection, which he promised might aid in uncovering the truth. All of them would speculate upon the puzzling ramifications of Ramos' symbol, buried deep within a book written long ago, by a people that had not yet heard of humans.

Lucid Dreaming

November 28

Pandora was not herself. She couldn't explain it, exactly, but knew something was askew as she sat upright in her bed and heard her *mother* fussing beyond her bedroom door, working in the kitchen, preparing a breakfast of semolina.

The air was heavy with the smoke from the night's coal fires, but the rising sun cut feebly through the veil. It was a weak winter sun that was ineffective against the morning chill which clung stubbornly to the shadows and within the cracks of the cobblestones. She yawned, stretched, and pulled the quilted nightcloak about her shoulders, trying to keep warm. The thought that June should have brought with it a warm morning to greet her was dismissed as nonsense. Every day was winter.

"Mother?" Pandora called as she left her room. No one was there to greet her, but a fire still burned in the potbelly at the center of the house, and embers glowed with dark orange flickers from the hearth in the main room. "Mother?" she called more loudly. Her bowl was upon the table, in its usual place, but there was nothing within it. Their home was small, and she quickly checked every room. There was no sign of her mother anywhere.

Pandora was old enough to fend for herself, but the feeling of isolation fell upon her stronger than she could have imagined, and the anxiety was stupefying. *She's gone to find some food. Some water,* she said to herself. *She'll return shortly.* Still, the feeling of abandonment was strong and filled her with a sense of dread.

She sought to rid herself of such nonsensical feelings as she thought her mother might – by busying herself and working the time away until she would return. So, she grabbed a burgundy shawl and wrapped it over her shoulders and head, slipped her cold feet into a pair of slippers, and grabbed a bucket from the back stoop. She stepped out into the brisk morning air and strode to the communal water pump in the alley between buildings. It wasn't the cold that caused her more discomfort, but the silence. Only halfway to the pump did she realize that none of her neighbors were about, nor were there people traveling on the street in front of their house. She dropped the bucket and, despite her nightly attire, ran around the house to confirm her fear. The street was bare. The people were gone.

"No," she said in a gasp as her lower lip quivered. "Mother!" she called, needing that familiar and comforting presence to calm her and assure her that everything was as it should be.

It's what we've always wanted, she thought. *No more people. The place to ourselves.*

"We have?" she asked aloud, answering her own inner voice.

Of course. Think about it. How we loathed them!

"We did? I do not believe we did. Why would we?"

Her inner voice spoke but was interrupted by a crash behind their home that sounded like metal cans being knocked aside. "Hello!" she called. "Anyone?" She wanted an answer and the silence that greeted her was stifling. She shivered, but not from the cold. The fear of isolation felt heavy within her and she felt she was being watched, which paradoxically compounded her fear. It was irrational, she thought, that she was growing so desperate to see someone else there, to assure herself that she was not alone, but the thought that someone was watching her made her even more uncomfortable. She looked around at the adjoining buildings, spinning madly, faster and faster, looking at each for a familiar face. The opaque blackness of each window was all she could see.

The voice in her mind was so quiet and muffled, as if far away, but she heard it say, *Who?*

"The people here," she said around a cry. "The people!"

Quieter, still, and far away, the voice said, *Who?* It wanted a name, she realized. She thought to say their names, to appease her inner fear, but when she began to speak the names of her neighbors, nothing came to her.

At the door of a neighbor's house, she shook the handle, but it was locked. She pulled herself up to look through the front window, but the interior was so dark that she could see nothing but shadows. After she had dropped back to the ground below did she realize that the other windows, clearly visible from the outside of the house, offered no light into it when she looked through that front window.

Her stomach growled and her lips were cracked. Her fingers and toes were numb in the frigid air. Still, she pulled herself back to look into that window, more intently examining the inner space. Deep shadows were all she could see. The dim gray light of the morning could not penetrate the darkness on the other side of that window, and her reflection was the only thing visible. Against the darkness, her own image was too strong to make out any of the furniture or other contents of the home. If there were no people, perhaps they would, at the least, have a small store of food or water and that would be a treasure, indeed, in these difficult times where both were in such short supply. She moved to her left, trying to find a better angle where her reflection wouldn't block her view, and thinking that if she looked at a more oblique angle into the room instead of through her reflection, she might better see something therein. But her reflection didn't follow her as she moved. When it cocked its head, a movement she didn't make, and seemed to look at her inquisitively, she yelped and fell to the ground below, landing full on her backside. She screamed as her own dim reflection remained there in the window, looking down on her before pulling away and turning to walk into the darkness of the house.

She couldn't help herself as the terror mounted and she ran to the back of her home and in through the back door. She slammed the door and bolted the lock and then fell to the cold worn planks, crying inconsolably. Reaching out to a nearby rug, she pulled it over herself, hiding her face within its dusty folds, rolling herself into a ball. Only a few minutes passed that way, but in her fear, it seemed like forever.

Against the wall beyond the potbelly stove rested the small axe they used to chop the timber for their fires. She snatched it up and was hacking at the front door of the next door neighbors whom she could not remember. The head barely sank into the wood as she struck, for it was heavy and thick and she was weak. But each strike brought with it more anger and determination. The strange darkness beyond, and her living reflection horrified her, but she needed to know what was within.

An hour or more passed before she had a splintered hole, narrow and ragged, cut into its face. She dropped the axe beside her to thrust her bare arm through the small hole she had carved, cutting herself as her arm and hand scraped against the jagged wood. She groped for the handle, and if she thought the cold outside was severe, the strange feeling that struck her lacerated arm made her think all the heat within her was being drawn out. When the door swung inward, the light behind her could only penetrate the shadows several feet in. She was ready for that, however, having grabbed a kerosene lamp kept over the mantle before leaving her house. She lit it quickly, and its light, too, could barely penetrate the ashen gray darkness.

She stepped into the house, disturbed that she could only see a few feet before her but determined to continue. She followed the edge of the rug, deep burgundy and gold, she guessed, though it was like looking through a fog in the depth of night, even though it was literally right at her feet. The wall nearest her was just beyond her reach, but it was even more lost in the shadows and she could barely make out the darker lines of the wainscoting and ornate frame of a picture above it upon pale wallpaper with elaborate filigreed columns. When she had taken several more steps and the faint outline of another frame , seemingly identical in size and shape to the first, came into her view, she turned, holding her lamp outstretched to examine the first she had passed, but the wall was barren save the faint swirls of the floral print of the wallpaper. The light of the door was faint and far away, just a pinhole, even though she had taken only several steps into the room.

She couldn't help herself. Going no further in that wretchedly cold room, Pandora ran as fast as she could toward the pinhole of light that was the door, so far away. She ran and she ran but could get no closer to it, even though, by her reckoning, it should have been only six feet away, at the most. Running gained her no ground toward the door, and as she came to a stop, the small doorway in the great distance slowly narrowed, as if the door might be swinging shut, but it continued to shine, as a beacon behind her.

The floor, she found, was the same – wooden planks with that thick rug upon it. The walls, too, were marked with the vertical lines of the wainscoting. Turning to resume her trek, the frame of the picture loomed before her, exactly where it was before she had run from it.

She walked as if carrying a great weight, step after step, but it did not seem to get any further into the house. She wished to weep again but had no energy, and the dehydration left her tearless. Crying was the only thing that made sense to her.

She walked past the picture and tried to examine the image upon it, but the face upon the canvas was a muddy, indistinct shape, like a shadow within a shadow.

She continued on, following the line of the carpet, afraid to deviate from the path. As the picture frame disappeared in the darkness behind her, another came into view immediately before her. As she feared, it was the same indistinct shape of a person without form, identical to the last. She intended to pull the picture from the wall and nearly set her lamp down but thought better of releasing the light and held it firmly as she pulled the large framed painting from the wall. It fell, and she hurled it into the room toward the opposite wall. Knowing the outside dimensions of the house, she knew the wall should be only eight feet away at the very furthest. The frame neither struck the wall, nor made any noise at all if it fell to the floor. It was simply consumed silently by the gray darkness.

Turning to resume her trek, as that was the only recourse, the picture was there ahead of her again.

She collapsed against the wall, holding her head perfectly still at the exact space between those damnable pictures. The one behind her was just gone, and the one before was not yet in sight. A movement one way or the other would return a frame into vague perception.

The wall was there as it should have been, but the light from that faraway door now loomed ahead of her, in a strange reversal. She turned back, and the dim gray was all that was there, but the wall was on her left now. It was a minor change but disoriented her greatly. She took a step forward, in the same direction she had been going with the wall on her right and carpet on her left, now toward the light. She hesitated. It was a trick. Her eyes could not be trusted. Not in that place.

Turning, Pandora walked away from the light and into the depth of darkness. "Hello?" she called loudly, and her voice echoed back as if she were in a great cave. She called out again and again until she realized something was off. Where she called "hello?" with an inflection of a question, the echoed voice was more of an acknowledging statement. "Hello?" she called again, over-emphasizing the upward lilt at the end. In equal emphasis, her echo was a firm statement, different than her own. She tried it again with the same result. But when she tried it with eyes open, the echo was the same fading tone as her own intonation.

She realized that nothing was as it seemed. Reality had little meaning, and her eyes were the least to be trusted. Eyes closed, then, she reached out her hand. It struck the solid surface of the painting that had showed up over and over. She looked at it now, with her fingers touching the edge of the frame. Strangely, the small light in the distance was now behind her, although she faced the wall and the painting directly, as if it were all in reflection.

She leaned closer to examine the painting, holding her lamp close to her face and its surface. The image thereupon was indistinct and amorphous – just a blob of shape in the center. "It's Mother," she said, recognizing the figure there although it was so indistinct. "But that's not right. How could it be? There's no sense in that. This isn't even our home." The gray void pulsed in that low rumbling growl. The thought of her mother irritated her for some reason. She leaned close to the picture again. She came to recognize the familiar colors of her own hair, flesh, and burgundy around the lower mass of colors that resembled the burgundy shawl wrapped over her shoulders. She gasped and stepped back. The image, indistinct though it seemed, was of *her*.

The void behind her growled again. She had no means of defending herself against whatever might be out there.

She returned to the image, more anxious and determined. "It's a mirror," she said. Using her sleeve, she rubbed vigorously at the thick grime coating it, making it difficult to see. Sure enough, the oily coating slowly rubbed away to reveal her own reflection, smiling in faint triumph at the discovery.

As she turned her head and shifted in place, examining the mirror, she could not help but jump, shrieking briefly as something moved in the dark depth behind her reflection. She spun, assuming it was behind her, but the void was undisturbed. Pandora turned back to the mirror and jumped again. She stood off-center, slightly to the left of the mirror. Her reflection stared back at her, but at an angle from her right.

She couldn't take much more of the torment and sank to her knees. *It's a game,* she said to herself.

Heart beating and exhausted from the emotional trauma, she didn't even know what that statement meant. "What game?" she asked.

Figure it out.

The thought of her Mother embracing her entered her mind. It might have been a comforting thought of protection. Instead, it made her feel helpless and impotent needing to rely upon another. That was the key, she suddenly realized: the image of her mother in her mind was as vague and formless as the smudged reflection of the mirror.

She stood, staring at her reflection. "There is no Mother," she said resolutely. "It's a lie. I am alone." She had no fear of that isolation but took pride in it. She closed her eyes, fingers reaching out to touch the surface of the mirror. She thought of it breaking. She could not run from the mirror, and she could not discard it into the surrounding void, either. But as she focused upon the mirror shattering, thinking of the shards of glass in her mind with clarity, the mirror split in a fracture down the center. She opened her eyes, though she regarded her reflection with a fierce and angry expression. She was on one side of the crack in the mirror, her reflection on the other. "It's not real," she said. "This is all a lie." She stared at herself in the mirror that began to tremble, vibrating on the wall. "*I* am not real. It is a dream."

The mirror shattered, sending shards of glass flying through the air. As the first jagged piece struck her arm, her flesh shattered, too, as if she were the mirror. Her arm, torso, all of her fractured just as the vague images of the rug and wall broke. The pieces flew off to be consumed by the gray void.

Pandora, the reflection, stood with her arm outstretched, touching the epicenter of the broken glass where her other self had just been. Her reflection had carried the kerosene lamp in the right hand, but it now held the arcane box that contained her sorrows. She remembered most of the experience that led her into that abandoned house in Malifaux, with a winter that lingered into June, but smaller details were already dissipating, as dreams typically do.

A heavy footfall behind her made her jump as it struck the ground like a great hammer upon stone. She spun to face a towering creature that came out of the foggy darkness that surrounded her. The Beast towered over her, standing at least eight feet tall with its head hung down below its bulky shoulders. Although its deeply-muscled arms and torso were similar to that of a giant man, snapping jaws with dagger-like teeth were inset within its torso, chomping at the flesh of its arm as it leaned forward. Its head was a stretched and fur-covered parody of some goat-like animal. Long and conical, almost rabbit-like, ears hung back and down around its neck just behind two thick horns that curved down toward its jaw. Its eyes were extremely large, even for its already massive skull, and completely black, but small, pinprick dots sparkled within like the reflection of a night sky. Its snout was long, wide, and bony with short-bristled gray hair, but its thin black lips were pulled up and back, exposing its quickly chattering teeth, every one of them long, wide, and flat. It stepped forward again, into the brightness of the circle of light in which Pandora stood, and its leg was powerfully thick. Its thigh alone took as much space as three of the girls, and it bent back at the knee and then came down again, like the hind leg of a mighty stallion. Its large-hoofed foot struck down into the carved slate ground with a crack, and it snorted through flared nostrils. This was the great and ancient creature that had many names, but she knew him as Nytmare. His appearance had changed since last she had seen him, now more fur covered and less plated with bony armor. He was always different, forever changing, like the horrible dreams he brought.

She should fear him, as almost all things did, but she understood him better than most and stepped toward him unafraid. "I came looking for you. I thought I'd catch you, but it was I who was caught. How did you do that?" She should be furious with him for tormenting her within the nightmare. Instead, she was impressed, perhaps envious of the power he possessed over one so strong as her.

It chattered, clicking noises in its throat or clacking its large teeth in a kind of speech that she didn't at first understand. It spoke again, and she began to understand as images formed in her mind that seemed quite clearly not hers. She understood it to say, *'I did nothing.'*

"The dream was mine? Yes, the dream is always the dreamer's. But you manipulate it. Twist it. For the fear it instills. Thoughts of a mother? That's how I broke your illusion."

He chattered and clicked and she understood him to say, *'Are you sure that's part of my twisting? Did you think of her tormenting you or bringing you comfort?'*

The anxiety returned as he spoke of such things. "I loathe them," she said firmly.

'Of course.' His foot struck the large slate slab upon which they now stood as he stepped toward her. *'Don't we all loathe them?'* But the images he conveyed had a hint of mockery, as if to suggest that they did not loathe the humans but somehow envied them. She dismissed it as further torment. Tormenting her with thoughts of *them*. However, she was once again impressed by his ability to twist a person's fears against them as she was so many years before when she had first discovered the depth of her abilities and how similar she and the Beast were.

But she was no longer young and lacking a will of her own. "We need your assistance," she said as commandingly as possible. He stood further upright, stretching tall above her. "There's no more time for us to follow our own agendas."

He snorted, his breath washing down upon her warm and foul. *'You have put aside your own agenda Pandora?'* It was odd how he accentuated the first syllable of her name. *'You think you can hide your thoughts from me? Here, in this place?'* The box at her side struck a high, long chord of sound as if responding to him. When it finally dissipated, the Beast leaned forward to regard her more closely. *'You serve their needs? Lilith and the hag? The Box? Do you hear it, yet? Do you hear it speaking to you Pandora? Do you know which is the master, you or the Box?'*

She did not hear it speak, as he suggested, and thought it was another of his tricks to sow confusion and doubt. Her box was a tool, and she controlled it, she thought firmly. "What about you? Who do you serve? The boy?"

'My servitude is to a higher need. As is yours.' He continued to look at the dark box held at her side, which perplexed and agitated her. True that it possessed strange abilities that augmented her own, but she found it strange that he might suggest it was more.

She sought to refocus the discussion. In this dream-world, he was too strong, too manipulative, even against one such as her. "We've come to you for help. Our need is dire. We must stop the Tyrant Entities as our ancestors once sought to do. Where they failed, we must succeed."

'Stop?'

"We must end them. Finally. They stir again, gathering their strength and their form. They once again interfere with the tangible world. December is known and nearly rose again during the Event. Zoraida thought he might have been killed by the Otherworlder. The girl with the Masamune. Its power was foretold to disrupt the connection they have between the aether realm and our own."

'Killed? There is no killed. Not of a Tyrant.'

Then how can they be stopped? They mean to ascend. It will destroy us. It will destroy everything."

'That has always been the intent of a Tyrant. They cannot be stopped. But they draw power from the aether as ones such as you and some of the humans. They may channel their power as you do through a totem linked to your will. As they exist more in that world, they need a vessel of this world.'

"Like you and the boy?" Nytmare stood abruptly, genuinely surprised at the reference. Pandora said, "Are *you* a Tyrant?" He was clearly taken aback, having never considered such a thing.

The Beast paused and looked down upon her from high above. Its teeth gnashed audibly and she felt it was both vehement and proud. It looked back to the box which hummed now with a resonating chord as though from a single long string on a harp. The Beast said, *'I am Nytmare. I am Agreus. I am Nomios. I am Phobos. I am Divergence. I am Ahriman and Angra Mainyu. I am Nihil. I am the Light upon the Dark.'*

Reciting his many names made little sense to her, though he spoke as if it were the appropriate answer to her question. "You said we serve a higher purpose. If we cannot kill a Tyrant, what of the vessel? The girl December has chosen. If she is killed, will He–"

'He would choose another.'

"But the Cage has fallen. It has torn through the fabric between this world and the aether. Released great power. They gather it, growing too quickly. How can we stop them if they rise again, like December, like Plague?

Now the Tyrant Cherufe is free from the prison. Who might stop It if It chooses a vessel?"

His great head drew close to hers. *'It has already chosen. It chose a vessel while still imprisoned. One of the first to cross through the Breach. But we can use the power flooding this world, too,'* he chattered. A great nail protruding from his forefinger struck the box, nearly knocking it from her. *'To trap them. To keep them from the physical.'*

She jerked the box away from his striking finger, scowling at him. "It is not one of them," she said. He huffed several times, each in quick snorts. It may have been laughter. Did he know something, or was this more of his trickery?

She looked down upon it, cradled against her hip. Faint diaphanous tendrils escaped from the closed lid, snaking around her waist and down her leg in gossamer arms of green, blue, and purple. But they were faint, and she could not feel them. "What is *it*?" she asked him of the box.

The box struck a higher, longer chord. As the lingering sound slowly dissipated he said more uncertainly, *'It is of all. Material. Spiritual. Ethereal. Astral. It breached the barrier between. It is Pandimensional. It is Panthereal. It is Pandemonium.'* The vaporous tendrils flared with more intense color as the Beast intonated the last three strange words. A sharp pulse of sound emanated from within it, trembling now in her hands. The sound was so high that it caused her to wince. When she opened her eyes, the gray void was gone, and she stood in the middle of the room that she inhabited within the heart of Malifaux.

She looked out the window, and it was cold, with frost on the ground, as it was in her dream. Her heart beat with the lingering anxiety of that nightmare, but she knew it was November. Still, as she left the room, her heart quickened yet again, so afraid was she that she did have a mother and that woman would be waiting for her. As her hand turned the cold knob of the door, releasing it from the latch, she told herself that it was a vile thought. Still, she had the lingering hope that an aging woman might be there.

Aircars

As the population spread across the City, the need for quick and safe transport became apparent. To facilitate this, Guild engineers developed "aircars," cable-guided gondolas that transport individuals and supplies in relative safety and comfort across dangerous areas of the Slums and Quarantine Zones.

A blend of railcar and Zeppelin's rigid airships, aircars range in size from small cabs approximating a stagecoach to massive aerial beasts pulling several floating stockcars. Aircars are slowly pulled along the lines by steam-driven engines and are well-armed and armored to ensure that this valuable Guild asset remains in Guild hands. The dockmast stations support the thick metallic cable high above the city streets. These heavily-armored dockmasts, beginning with Dockmast One at Guild Headquarters, are the fruit of an ambitious project to incorporate Malifaux's taller buildings into this new transportation system, restoring towers as well as constructing new spires.

Different routes have names tying them to terminus, such as Sourbreak, Deadfall, and Riverview. The Guardsmen who man the cars and dockmasts have taken to drawing straws to determine assignments. Manning any of the few dockmasts in the Quarantine Zone can be a death sentence.

Despite the dangers for those stationed at certain outposts, the aircars have seen great success in supporting Guild operations by rapidly moving resources. Because the fusion of Zeppelin and armored railcar work well together, suggestions for using Zeppelins for scouting and transportation outside Malifaux have reached the Governor General. His advisors caution patience with such an ambitious project, however. Even within the City's borders, the smaller cable-guided aircars meet with attacks from the ground   and sometimes air. The last controlled flight of an airship outside the City ended in disaster when a group of gremlins opened fire on the ship above the bayou. An errant shot managed to ignite the airship's hydrogen gas, sending it flaming headlong into the swamp. Doctor Viktor Ramos has been consulted and is currently working with Guild engineers on a less combustible form of lighter-than-air gas derived from soulstone. Until the compound is perfected, the Governor General has decided it is simply too dangerous to attempt flights outside the City.

Cold Hearted

December 2

Joss looked up the side of the mountain, now fully vertical as he neared the last stage of his ascension. He was buried to his waist in heavy snow, just loose enough that it could not support his great bulk. If there was a trail still beneath his feet, he could surely no longer tell.

He loosened the heavy leather anorak enough to reach behind him and dialed up the energy level of the dynamic generator mounted to his back, fumbling for a minute to feel the correct knob beneath the heavy mitten he refused to remove. A blast of wind bit into him, drawing the remainder of the heat from his chest at once, and he cursed, quickly refastening the buttons to tighten the coat again, to rebuild whatever heat the generator might create. He was afraid it would catch the heavy coat on fire, but he had the same fear the previous three times he had overpowered it. As he had vowed each of those times, he was sure this had to be the very last time he throttled up the power. It brought little additional warmth, anyway. Maybe if he caught on fire it might actually help, he wondered, pondering if flame could freeze.

His mountain guide had convinced him to take this longer trek that wound further back and forth across the mountain's face because it was much easier to traverse. For the first leg of their expedition, three days earlier, he may have been right as the group walked virtually unimpeded across rocky but manageable trails. They had camped without incident upon a flat landing where even the two pack mules showed no discomfort, and the extra men he had brought to test their mettle remained in good spirit, dismissing the rumors of the mountain's sinister brutality from the comfort of the campfire while they downed bitter but hot coffee. They remained in good spirit despite the cold rolling down upon them, and the coffee gave way to long draws on icy flasks of whisky, which they were sure still warmed their bones. They had slept restfully beneath thick flannel, convinced that those rumors of the mountain were exaggerated tales told by others to sound tough in the taverns of Malifaux. Or, as they now laughed, were told by men weaker than them, which made Joss' men sound tough and brave, too. He, alone, remained silent and aloof, knowing better than the others that their expedition would not remain as uneventful.

It was the next day, while hiking and continuing the joke at the expense of those previous mountaineers, clearly weaker than them, that they pressed into a tangible wall of cold that chilled them instantly, freezing their flesh and spirits. Their guide, a grizzled and robust man himself, caused the sense of panic to mount as he stepped through the physical barrier, grew wide-eyed and quickly stepped backward, out of the cold, hesitating. He pressed his hand against it, moving it through the wall. "Dropped twenty-five, thirty degrees," he muttered. "T'ain't nat'ral," he said, his voice a coarse whisper against the wind that cut through their anoraks like knives.

It was the first time Joss had dialed up the dynamic generator beneath his coat. He had looked down upon the men hesitating on the path, the wind carrying thin flakes of snow before them as an ominous portent of what was to come. Joss adjusted his goggles, tightening them against his face, and turned silently from the men and pressed on. They looked from one to the other, each unsure of what to do, but no man intended to disappoint the bulky northwestern tribesman steadfastly striding above them.

The cold and wind had sapped their will, leaving the lighthearted joviality of the previous night a vague and mocking memory. They silently followed one after the other, eyes downcast upon the tread of Joss' boots imprinted in the thickening snow. The last thing they had said to one another was a brief discussion about "The Cold Heart of the Mountains," which became the name of that particular mountain for many years to come, although no one was ever sure any one member of that expedition survived this trek. Still, rumor of the Cold Heart spread to every man, woman, and child in Malifaux.

The lead man, ominously named "Mister Graves", stopped abruptly, and they followed his gaze up the trail to see Joss momentarily double over, bracing against another blast of wind. They could see it strike him, cold and gray. It was the second time Joss throttled up the dynamic generator, although his hand was a sickly pale blue as he withdrew it from his coat, struggling to put the thick lined mitten back upon it. Graves, too, determined to prove his worth, steeled himself against the raging elements and strode forward. His choked scream reached Joss who turned to see him topple, frozen like a man carved from stone.

The others withdrew, but a mule and one more Mountaineer perished before they could retreat to slightly more favorable conditions. Only the hired guide could continue with Joss and that because of the extra coat he managed to pull from Graves. The last words he said to Joss was, "They'll never make it back!" above the gale. They had forged on in silence, struggling through drifts and slipping on ice that was all but invisible beneath a layer of snow, fighting the wind that seemed to blow directly upon them.

By mid-day, Joss had to admit that he could no longer tell if they were still on the trail that had gradually narrowed as they ascended, and he labored over more frequent and larger stones that blocked the way. He turned to the guide for reassurance, but he was not there. Joss could not be sure when he lost the man, or whether he had fled in judicious retreat, fallen from the edge of their path, or merely froze to his death. Joss couldn't have heard him above the ferocious howling of the wind, even if the guide had screamed for help directly beside him.

Joss had continued, of course, climbing despite the lack of sensation in his hands and feet; most of his body, in fact. Now, however, Joss had come to a true impasse. He no longer doubted that he had been forced off the trail, and he traversed the mountainside as best he could, but the way before him was blocked by several great rocks, each consumed by jagged vertical pillars of ice. Looking up, he knew his destination was only perhaps a hundred feet above him. It was not the apex of the mountain, for the peak was vaguely visible through the blinding blizzard beyond the ledge he sought. But above the mountain he could see the thick roiling black clouds swirling in a great circle for many miles, like a hurricane held in place. The eye of that raging storm was a gaping hole of absolute blackness, clearly visible even through the snow. That black spot loomed directly above the ledge, not the mountain peak, and arms of lightning occasionally flashed from the dark center of the circling cloud to strike that flat ledge of his destination. He could not hear its thunder above the wind but could feel it vibrate through him less than a second after the brilliant flash of light illuminated the rocks and ice around him.

Joss was a man that rarely felt fear, but not for the first time on the arduous climb did he reluctantly admit to himself that he truly doubted he would ever leave it alive.

He shook out his hands, ineffectually trying to get some feeling back into them. He pulled the twin axes from his back, the static electricity snapping about the intricately engraved blades as the energy from the dynamic generator powered them through the thick cables that extended beneath his anorak to the ends of the metal shafts. He doubted his ability to climb the absolute vertical surface but knew he could not continue winding his way back and forth looking for whatever might be left of a trail, even if he did cut through the rocks and pillars of ice before him.

He had little strength remaining, but the electrically charged heads sheared through the rock with fortunate ease. He pulled himself up and sank the second axe into the rock, and he climbed, painfully and with each muscle stinging in protest. He pulled himself up, the axes like claws, dragging himself along the mountainside. He thought he could go no further and looked down to realize he hadn't even traversed half the distance to the ledge above. Dropping would kill him. He pressed on, and the wind impossibly intensified as he drew to the final stretch of the wall, driving against him like a steam engine. He could barely hold on, let alone complete the climb. Somehow, the great barrier of wind gave for a moment, releasing him, and he propelled himself upward, grasped the edge, and pulled himself from the rocky face, his axes dangling behind him by their power cords. The wind and snow raged on, just beyond the ledge, battering the axes against the cliff but barely blew against him as he rolled to his back, face toward the ominous black eye directly above.

He blinked twice, and when he closed his eyes against a bolt of lightning that lit the sky above him, he succumbed to the exhaustion and passed out.

📖 📖 📖

He had no way of knowing how long he might have been unconscious because the sun was blocked by those swirling clouds.

A pair of hands was upon him, pulling him upright, pouring a warm fluid into his mouth. His vision was blurred, and he could not taste it, only vaguely felt the hot liquid dribble down his chin.

The image of a young man's face was before him, blurry and pulling away as he slipped back into unconsciousness. "Rasputina," Joss said. "Must get to Rasputina."

The boy's eyes grew wide, and he looked quickly from the left to his right. "Shh!" he commanded. In a hoarse whisper he said, "Do not speak!"

Joss was out again.

📖 📖 📖

He awoke next as if from a Sunday afternoon nap in the warm orange glow of a fire burning low in the alcove beyond the foot of his bed. The narrow apartment was sparse but warm, and his covers were drawn merely to his waist, leaving his bare torso exposed but comfortable. He was propped to his side because of the generator mounted to his back. He could feel none of the familiar tingling of added power injected into his nervous system, however, and knew at once that it had been powered down completely. After a quick check he confirmed that the acolytes had even tried to remove it. Fools were lucky it didn't kill him. Or that they didn't accidentally discharge it and kill themselves. His axes, however, were disconnected, and their removal caused him to sit upright in a panic. They leaned against the wall, neither damaged nor tampered with.

He had never been there but knew he was in the heart of the mountain within one of many rooms built to accommodate those who strangely worshipped the ancient December as a god.

The acolytes practiced their own esoteric magics and had fallen against the judgment of the Guild, their abilities something lost between the elemental and the more macabre views the Resurrectionists held regarding life. Ramos had befriended them quickly, of course, finding an ally in the acolytes who shared his Arcanist principles regarding the freedom to explore their own powers and abilities.

The storm he had traversed could not have been the priestess, Rasputina's, doing, nor could it have been natural. Rumors of December's death at Kythera, then, were another exaggeration, as Ramos had suspected. The colossal cloud above the temple and the powerful cold and wind he had gone through demonstrated the power of the Tyrant, still gathering. Joss had all the information he wanted and would happily descend to deliver his findings to Ramos as he had been charged. He needed supplies and a quick conversation with Rasputina to deliver the boss's message, and he would depart from the quiet subterranean temple of December's acolytes.

Fully dressed and his axes reconnected and held to the dynamic generator magnetically, he set out to find her, not at all predicting that his ordeal on Cold Heart was about to become remarkably more difficult.

Exiting into the dimly lit corridors beyond his room, he was met by a small man in layered icy-blue robes whose upper face was enshrouded by the cowl that fell over his eyes. He approached from the hall extending to the right. No natural light could reach them, but lanterns hung at intervals along the walls casting a red glow upon plastered walls that made the hall and chambers temporarily dispel the reality they were in caverns carved into a mountain.

As the acolyte neared him, Joss said, "I need to see Rasputina." The acolyte's eyes grew wide beneath his hood, reflecting strangely crimson in the light. Joss realized the light was unnatural, a luminous rock placed within the lantern's chamber. "It is urgent," he said, and the acolyte jumped toward him with palms pressing forward unthreateningly.

"Shh!" he motioned emphatically. "You mustn't speak! Not so loud!" His eyes darted back and forth conspiratorially.

"What's this about?" Joss asked as quietly as he could. He was a man that could not easily lower his voice.

The acolyte winced. "Come," was all he said, and this no louder than a breath as if compensating for Joss' volume.

"I'll need supplies, too," he said and the acolyte seemed to duck his head as he led the way before him.

The shadow of someone approaching from an adjoining corridor stretched into the hall before them, and the acolyte first froze, motionlessly intent upon the shadow of the person approaching. Presently, he jumped to the wall, his back pressed tight to it. He motioned for Joss to do the same. Instead, he stood firm and reached for the handles of the axes upon his back. The acolyte grabbed his arm to stop him, which would normally have elicited a somewhat unrestrained reaction. Something in the fearful urgency of the man's youthful face stayed his hand. Reluctantly, he, too, backed against the wall just as the figure emerged from the hall into his view. Although dressed in ceremonial robes similar to the acolyte, it could not hide the more curvaceous figure of a woman who merely regarded the two men emotionlessly. The acolyte stared at the opposite wall, remaining as motionless as possible. She might have been beautiful, Joss thought, regarding the even grace of her movement as she turned and walked toward them. But her red hair was unkempt and oily, and her flesh bore small scars from her neck and up her cheek near her ears. As she drew closer, he realized they were bite marks made in the familiar row of what must be human teeth. Her eyes conveyed her loathing of both men.

She intended to pass, but Joss realized he was simply too broad to allow even her petite frame to easily get by in the narrow corridor. He pressed against the wall as tightly as he could, but the dynamic generator on his back prevented it.

She looked up at him, clearly with disdain and impatience. He pushed her shoulder so that he might help her squeeze past, but his hand upon her elicited a startling reaction. Her nails, sharp as claws, slashed his forearm, and her cracked lips pulled away from her teeth, and she hissed. Though seething, enraged that he might put a hand upon her, she managed to move past him.

Even in the darkness he had seen the emptiness of her mouth. She was still within earshot when he asked, "What happened to her tongue?" The acolyte's expression was one mixed of fear and anger at this stranger's insolence. Joss was not hired for his intellect, but he was shrewd and quick-witted. He quickly suspected something foul had befallen the women inadvertently brought into the Cult of December's ranks.

"Ignore it," the acolyte said and motioned for Joss to follow him.

Something about the passion that burned within the girl, so full of pain and anger, enraged Joss, though he rarely felt emotionally attached to anyone's problems, much less a stranger's. As they traversed the narrow corridors and up through the levels of the temple, he saw more and more women turning from his sight, hiding their own faces in the shadows, or quickly turning down another corridor. When any one of them could look him in the face, it was with unbridled hatred and defiance. All of them looked upon the young acolyte with seething hatred although, as they did with Joss, most simply averted their gaze and slinked away.

He saw more acolytes as they walked, all of them young, some of them whispering quietly to themselves in a faint whisper that never traveled beyond their own ears as they bent close to one another. If a female ever neared them, especially one standing tall, looking still strong and angry, they snapped silent and often stood rigid against the walls to allow her to pass, looking more terrified than any of the other females slinking silently in the dark corners of the complex.

At one such encounter, Joss had seen enough and pulled his acolyte aside. He thought he had understood the fear and anger of the girls — that they had endured something horrible here upon the side of the mountain. But the men's attitude of fear and their own compulsion for silence made little sense to him. Without even trying to lower his voice Joss said, "What happened here? Tell me."

"Be silent!" the young man said in a hoarse whisper.

Joss was not silent. He did not raise his voice but it still resounded from the rock walls for all to hear. "What did you do to the girls?" Acolytes and Silent Ones stopped and turned toward them. "Where are the priests?"

"You fool!" the acolyte accused. He backed away from Joss, advancing confidently and angrily toward him. "It has nothing to do with us! It's December. The prophecy."

"I've heard the prophecy," he said.

"Silent Ones," he said nodding to a girl partially obscured by the deep shadows of protruding arches along the wall. "December needs a voice. He must find the frozen heart, and through her He must incant the invocation." It was gibberish to Joss. "A voice!" the acolyte said. "She must have a voice. The girls must not speak. Or December could consume all. The frozen heart and a voice for Him to speak. We're trying to save the world."

Something in the acolyte's demeanor told Joss that he didn't fully believe it himself. That the story was only partially true or that there was more left unsaid. A female peered around the corner of another corridor meeting theirs, clearly meek; she cowered when his gaze fell upon her. She trembled when she looked back at him to see he still looked at her, and he knew the signs of a person frozen in fear. He had seen it in many of his enemies. He looked back over his shoulder and saw the first girl he had seen in the corridors below, now clearly following them, and she turned to regard him, full of contempt but confused at his own hostility toward the boy. Joss stepped close to the boy and actually tried to whisper. It still carried over the stillness. "And the bite marks? The submission? The anger? What caused that? Those were part of a plan to thwart December?" It was an accusation. Joss didn't understand the fervent following of this Tyrant Entity by other humans, but he understood how men in power could use their power for all of the wrong reasons. Using strength against the weak was something he had seen plenty of.

A hand fell upon the thickly flexing muscles of his forearm. He turned to see the girl he had first witnessed when he had left his room. Hostile and loathsome to touch him, she pulled her hand from his arm with a look of disgust at having to place her fingers upon his skin. The look of contempt she shot at the acolyte was worse. Looking back to Joss, she pointed at the young man and shook her head. She pointed up, through the ceiling of the corridor and motioned something, clenching her fists before her and pantomiming rage with her teeth. "*Not the boy,*" he understood, and nodded.

The acolyte said, "The priests." He looked away, ashamed and afraid once again. "She means the priests are to blame. Not us, the acolytes." The boy slid along the wall, away, looking considerably more afraid of the Silent One than of Joss, which perplexed him.

She pointed up, through the ceiling, again.

Joss turned to the acolyte. "Take me up," he commanded, though his voice was even. "Take me up." He was sure it would get him out of the temple's living quarters at the least, and would likely provide a means for his exit as well. Following the unspoken command of the Silent One, he suspected he'd get the answers to his question as well.

They didn't speak as they traversed the narrow corridors of December's temple. Joss saw other young men, acolytes, as well as the girls, each averting their eyes from him, but all as full of hostility or fear as the next. One girl even stared hatefully at the boy, causing him to go rigid and silent, before noticing Joss. Once she did, her facial features relaxed, and she quickly walked on, and the boy resumed his quiet stride as well. Many of the women were more afraid than angry, cowering and trembling at the sight of him. What he did not see were the older, more mature men that he was accustomed to seeing in all the dealings Ramos had in the past. They were the supposed leaders of the faith, and they were noticeably absent.

Joss said, "She blamed the priests. Where are they?" They boy would not speak even after Joss repeated the question more menacingly. When he said, "Maybe I should speak to these priests, myself," the boy bowed his head once more.

He said in a sad whisper, "I don't think it will be necessary."

Joss was led through a series of elevations and chambers of the temple. He saw elaborate and beautiful decorations and architectural brilliance in vast cavernous chambers, illuminated with many thousands of the luminescent crystals that reflected all light like mirrors, to fill each room with a rainbow of colors. Other rooms, whether spacious or small, were ascetic, void of ornamentation or comfort, and often with just enough light to make out the area.

Presently, the steps and walls became rough, and more natural. They came to the top of the stairs and the boy halted at the twin doors of heavy timber. "I'll go no further," he said to Joss. "She's out there." The boy trembled, and his lower lip quivered.

"Rasputina?" At the word, his eyes grew wide, and he could no longer stand there at the landing before the great doors. He stepped down, first slowly, uncertain, and then nearly ran.

Joss opened the great doors, striding confidently into the wide and rough-hewn cave that opened to the side of the mountain at the far end, glaring brightly though he knew it was dark beneath the storm that raged. He strode to Rasputina, angry enough at whatever tragedy had befallen the women here at the hands of the elder men that he would help right those wrongs. But the sickly sweet smell of blood and decaying flesh filled his nostrils, and he heard her harsh and angry words, conveying her conflict, before he could see her. Pillars of ice rose from the floor, and frozen stalactites dropped from the ceiling, making him feel as if he walked into the mouth of December, Himself. Stepping around those icy teeth, he was shocked by what he saw. Rasputina, unconcerned by the cold, wore only a skirt, cut on one leg nearly to her hip, leaving her legs bare above leather boots. She had no coat, and her arms were bare, pale but covered in blood from her hands to elbows. Those icy teeth, he realized, were exactly that; before her was a man, one of the cult's elder priests that Joss had expected to find in the temple. But he was held off the ground by one of those jagged ice spikes, pierced from beneath, and another from above that cut down through his shoulder, thick blood seeping from the laceration and flowing across his body and pooling beneath him. The priest's eyes were rolling up into his head, and Joss knew he was on the edge of death. He had seen this fight many times, as a man's will dies moments before his body follows. He knew this man would soon expire as his head lolled against the ice that held him aloft.

Standing there, between those icy teeth, he realized that other men, now merely corpses, were frozen within them, sometimes above, sometimes near the ground. He recoiled, more in surprise than at the visceral state of the remains; each had large areas of flesh and muscle torn away as if devoured by a creature before they could be fully frozen within the ice.

He gasped, looking at all of the corpses frozen into each icy fang around him.

She turned, and he recoiled again, for dark blood covered her lower face and dripped down the front of her tight bodice and upon the skin of her shoulders and upper chest.

"Rasputina?" He was at a loss, and that was not a common occurrence for a man known for his ability to predict any horrible event and react to it evenly and quickly.

"Ah, Ramos' right-hand man. What do they call you, again?"

"Joss." Her eyes were wild. She smiled, and the macabre gore around her mouth made the gesture horrible and sinister. He had no coat, no supplies, but he looked to the mouth of the cave, gathering his wits and formulating a plan of escape should this encounter go badly. So far, he began to understand, there was no good way the day was going to end.

"Yes, Joss. Good of you to visit. Where's your boss? Frozen on the path up?" He said nothing. "No. Of course not. Cozy down in his apartments in the city. Comfortable, isn't he? No one aware of what he's up to as he plots and schemes and devours the Guild right there within them."

"Rasputina," Joss began, slowly and more gently than he had spoken to another person in many years. "What are you doing here?" The robes of the priest before her had been torn away from the wound caused by the jutting spike from above, and a large patch of his flesh along his ribs was gone, removed to the bone. Killing the priests might have been justified for the full extent of their crimes, but she had crossed a line even he couldn't understand.

"Doing here?" she asked, and her eyes gleamed. She almost laughed, but her expression was mocking. "I'm in education now, Joss. A school marm. Teaching wayward children."

"You're killing them. The priests."

"Oh, I don't see it that way." He wanted to say something, but could not. "They want to know power, Joss. They *really* want to know power. They need to know what it's like to have power. Something you already know, don't you?" Still he said nothing. "What brings you up here, Joss? Want to join the religion?" She sneered, clearly angry at the notion of a religion devoted to the worship of one she despised. "The initiation doesn't take that long." She tried to smile but it, too, was false. He was cold and stoic, having very little normal emotion, himself. Rasputina, however, was something different. Almost devoid of any human emotion, he realized. It made her considerably more dangerous than last he had seen her. She had killed now and had gone far beyond the first kills that left a normal person full of confusion, doubt, and guilt. She could kill without hesitation, without mercy, now.

He thought he might change the subject, to speak to her normally so that it might ground her in something real. "Ramos suspected the rumors of December's death at Kythera were false. The miners that were lost are of no consequence."

"Miners? Is this about miners?" She grew angry. "While he's down there, living out his life in comfort, designing an intricate plan for his future, I'm up here--" She cut herself off. At least she had some emotion left. Unfortunately, it seemed that anger was the only thing she could still feel. She regained her composure, burying the anger beneath that inner sheath of ice.

"No," Joss said. Of course Ramos had sent him here to partially chastise her for killing those men, tools of his organization. However, Joss knew he'd need to change tactics with her now, fully aware that something strange had befallen Rasputina. "Not about any miners. Ramos doesn't care about the miners. Only you. He wants you to come down to the city. He can protect you."

"Protect? Me?" Her eyes were piercing daggers. "Me?" she spat. "Ramos doesn't know nearly as much as he thinks he does. He is another child stumbling about, thinking the world revolves around him." Something in what she said seemed to strike a memory that caused her to pause, looking less angry, more regretful as she looked past him, almost longingly.

"He'll do what he can to help you," Joss said. "And the women here."

"Put us in one of his shows?" she asked absently. "Pretty showgirls to be fawned over?" Her voice was quiet. Joss suspected that once Rasputina likely longed to be normal. Perhaps even a dancer as she now suggested in sarcastic jest.

Her eyes suddenly fastened upon him, and her thin brows drew down in renewed anger. Her lips, too, drew back in a sneer, the blood around her mouth gleaming in the light from the mouth of the cave. "I have a message for you to deliver to your boss," she said. "You let him know that I'm tired of dealing with his messenger. I want to talk to him. You tell him to come up for a visit. You know what? Let's send him a message he'll really understand, so that there's no doubt about my sentiment." Her arm whipped from her side in a flashing arc and a wind emanated from her with such violent force that he was knocked from his feet and thrown against the far wall with enough force to stun him. Before he could fall to the floor, her other arm had snapped from above to her side, and ice shot up from the floor of the cave and from his back, holding him in place, frozen to the wall. It had him by the torso, from around his neck all the way down to his thighs, leaving his limbs struggling futilely. She walked toward him

casually while he struggled against the ice, pressing against it and striking it with his fists, all to no avail.

"Ah, Joss. Ramos' right-hand man. You'd do anything for him, wouldn't you? It's not the money, I bet. It's being so close to all that power. Control. Isn't that right?" He continued to struggle. She reached out to grab him around the wrist of his right arm. It was so frigid that he lost all sensation in the arm, and it went limp and numb. She pulled it out straight and placed his hand to the wall, freezing it in place, the arm extended.

"Rasputina," he pleaded. "We want to help! We want to help you!"

She left him hanging there for a moment, standing before him emotionlessly. His arm was numb, but he looked on in horror as it turned blue, freezing from within as the biting chill of her touch solidified his blood and tissues. Gathering his wits, he renewed his struggle to free himself from the ice but knew it was in vain. Of all the ways he had imagined he would die, always at the hands of another, this was far from anything he could have predicted. Never would he have imagined he might die without a fight, helpless while his adversary took her time.

Minutes passed, though it stretched longer in his mind as she stood before him, concentrating on the cold that devoured his arm. Joss had to focus for his mind had begun to retreat from the reality of his impending death.

She was interrupted by the mute groaning of a girl beside her. Rasputina's eyes fluttered open, glowing pale blue before returning to normal.

The girl wore tight black leather, strapped around her legs by narrow buckles. Like Rasputina, she wore only a small bodice to cover her upper body, leaving her shoulders and arms bare, but she, too, seemed oblivious to the cold. Still, she fastened a long cape, just the pelt remains of a fur-covered mountain creature that fell over her shoulders and to the ground. She motioned to Joss and shook her head, but it was more of an appeal to Rasputina than a command. Turning so that he could see her, he recognized her long red hair and defiant expression as the girl he had first encountered deep within the heart of the temple, though she no longer wore the ceremonial robes.

"Mara!" Rasputina said with renewed anger at the girl that stood between her and Joss. "What do you think you're doing?"

She pointed at him again and then toward the mouth of the cave. She meant, "He should go." Rasputina regarded the girl who stood her ground and shook her head again. She pointed at him again, and then toward the mouth of the cave. She held his anorak in the other hand at her side.

"Is that right?" Rasputina said around a sneer. "Sorry, Joss. But the message will still be delivered." Her arm shot forward again, and her open palm slapped his shoulder. Like a hammer striking ice, the shoulder shattered, sending shards that were recently his flesh flying about them. She waved her hand dismissively, and the ice holding him in place withered away in a second, dropping him to the cold rock below.

On his knees, he looked up at his arm, still frozen to the wall, and blood flowed freely from his shoulder, a great torrent resulting from the sudden severing of flesh.

Rasputina was upon him, lifting him by the back of his shirt, stronger than he imagined she could be. When he struggled to his feet, his head swimming and dizzy, she released him and waved toward the cave entrance. The cold wind she commanded struck him again, and he was thrown bodily toward it and out of the cave, rolling on the snowy ledge beneath the dark eye of the storm once more. He had no strength and could not hope to survive the mountain as he was, wounded and exposed. His blood pooled beneath him, freezing quickly to his side. "Do you see now, Joss?" she questioned angrily, motioning to the clouds swirling above him. "Do you see? Tell Ramos that the storm is mounting! Tell him that! You want to be like him, Joss! Tell him you need a new right hand just like his. Tell him that if he sends his 'Right-hand man' back as an errand boy, I'll rip it right off! Tell him!" He struggled to his knees, confused and unsure what he might do next, vaguely and instinctively fighting against the inevitable. She kicked him in the stomach hard enough to throw him over the edge of the ledge where he had climbed with his axes, exhausted.

The wall of wind hit him, buffeting him against the side of the cliff, knocking him about as it propelled him to the snow-covered rocks dozens of feet below. The blanket of snow softened his fall, but the jagged cliff had further torn his flesh and broken several of his bones, including a number of his ribs, making his breathing painful and laborious. The cold numbed him at once, and he knew it would race against his blood loss to kill him. He suspected the cold would kill him first. He didn't fight against it, knowing that if the cold had its way, he would drift off to sleep and die rather gently.

The Silent One, Mara, fell beside him, having leapt from the cliff above. She landed on her feet in a crouch, her hair flowing from her fall and the wind that raged. The fur hide billowed behind her, leaving very little protection against the elements. She didn't need it, he realized. He thought for a moment she might have descended upon him to finish him off. It would have been an act of mercy. Instead, she pressed her hand upon his chest, and he felt himself chill, freezing from the inside rather than having the cold drain the heat from him. He briefly thought she was freezing him as Rasputina had his arm, but it brought no pain. In fact, it equalized his temperature so that the pain of the external cold was tolerable, though he knew it was cold enough to freeze a man in minutes. Concentrating, she closed her eyes, focusing her power. As she meditated he felt his veins flowing with ice, so cold it felt like razors coursing within him. Rather than hurting, however, it brought him some comfort and his shoulder, he saw, cauterized, and he breathed more comfortably. She continued concentrating, running his blood cold, healing him.

He heard Rasputina's voice echo on the wind from above them. She howled, "Take him, Mara! Take him down! Take him to Ramos! See that he gets the message!"

She took him off the mountain, although he would never know how she could have. He fell unconscious, lulled comfortably by her life-giving ministrations.

Tangling the Threads of Fate

December 2

Sebastian demonstrated no fatigue nor uttered a breath of complaint as he trudged through a stagnant channel of the sewers, several paces behind his master, Doctor McMourning. The channel was narrow and fairly shallow. Intended as one of the thousand such drainage channels that fed excess water and the filth of the denizens of the vast city above them out of sight (and smell, of course), to be taken away to some unknown place beyond Malifaux's boundaries. In many places within the intricate waste removal system, those tributary channels all met, forming one great river of waste that coursed with the flow of any above ground river, sometimes even dropping in successive steps of elevation creating raging rapids.

Here, though, the width was no greater than several long strides for a man such as McMourning, and a few more for the short-legged shuffling of Sebastian. The muck, here, did not move, locked, no doubt, by some blockage of filth further down its course.

Although Sebastian uttered no complaint of the heavy burden McMourning had strapped to his back, the quickly packaged remains of the abomination and Death Marshal, in addition to numerous tools and scientific apparatus strapped randomly about his portly body, they did slow him down. As McMourning stepped around the vertical pipe that marked the last turn in the subterranean trek to their hidden lab, Sebastian was plunged into darkness. The illumination of McMourning's dented old brakeman's lantern cast a ruddy glow upon the oxidized patina around the thick bolts and joints of the pipe but could not bend around the corner to help Sebastian see his way. He tripped and nearly fell, creating quite a commotion as he struck the wall and his various tools clattered about his belly and waist.

McMourning's head emerged from around the drainage pipe, and he lifted the lantern to examine what had befallen his assistant. Sebastian merely smiled, the soft rosy cheeks like apples on either side of his bulbous nose. McMourning chastised him saying, "Do be careful with my equipment!" Sebastian continued to smile rather vacantly, wiping the sweat from his brow and fleshy upper lip with the back of his sleeve. "And keep up. We haven't all day to linger in the sewers!"

Soon, McMourning was at the top of the iron ladder cursing at Sebastian, twelve feet below, for not shining the lantern so that he could see the trick lock properly. To his credit, Sebastian did move the lantern as instructed, but McMourning seemed to always follow with a shift of his own torso, blocking the light shining from below. Finally, with a metal upon metal clang, the round portal swung open, and McMourning scampered out of the sewers and into the relative comfort of his apartments above.

Sebastian licked his lips and began the arduous labor of climbing the iron rungs, one hand still holding the antique brakeman's lantern, two corpse remains strapped to his back, and the various equipment lashed about his robust form, catching against each bar as he climbed. Eventually, panting and sweating rather profusely, he emerged to see McMourning playing with the three large dogs he had reanimated to guard the building in his lengthy absences. A mastiff, a Doberman, and a bulldog, each scampered about his feet, now bootless as he had discarded them beside the open portal leading to the labyrinthine sewers below, showing all the playful loyalty a living dog might have demonstrated toward a master returning home. Save a heightened passion for killing, and patches of missing flesh (either through the natural process of fleshly decay or the necessary removal for McMourning's work), they could, indeed, pass for living companions. It was part of McMourning's greatest discoveries: while higher sentients were most often risen with a distinct lack of their passions in life, lower life forms retained much of it. Nicodem adamantly refused to wage war with an army of canine remains, however. McMourning, kicking away the zombie Chihuahua that had finally come into the old room, yipping and nipping at the big toe protruding from a hole in McMourning's sock, had to agree that not all of his dogs were equally gifted.

"Sebastian!" he barked. "Break's over. Clean up our footwear and meet me in the primary lab. We have much to prepare and little time. No dawdling now." Sebastian had already begun those preparatory steps before commanded but nodded toward McMourning nevertheless.

Minutes later (though McMourning would chastise him for taking his time), Sebastian was quickly shuffling down the main hall in the upper level of what might have long ago been a mansion for a forgotten Neverborn aristocrat. Neither he nor the doctor saw what the building may have once been, for their dark arts, practiced deep within the Quarantine Zone, needed the open chambers that the ornate and well-crafted building provided. Thick dust had accumulated along the sides of the hall, but the center was well-worn by their regular footsteps, the stain upon the wood blackened over the ages. Sebastian rarely perceived the small eyes glowing at him from the shadows along the ceiling or behind the ribbed vaults and protruding buttresses due to the building's inherent menagerie of McMourning's creatures and original statues both standing alone or carved in relief on the wood and marble structure. "Clean out the vermin" was, to date, the only command he had not been able to fulfill. When he had gotten close enough to grab whatever small creature might be hiding in the shadows, his thick fingers would fall upon open air, perplexing him. He dutifully kept at it, throughout the mansion for days before McMourning chastised him for dallying. Of course, when Sebastian reminded him of the assigned task McMourning's response was, "What little eyes in the shadows?" and his own eyes darted back and forth in genuine paranoia. They came to ignore whatever mysterious creatures might inhabit the building with him.

He arrived at the reinforced iron door of McMourning's experimental lab. It was secured, and the frame had been equally reinforced with wrought iron. He pulled the large lever that released the long bolts within that frame, and it swung open with a groan on thick hinges. Getting *into* the lab was easy. Once the great door closed, however, those iron bolts would clang into place and it would take several moments to navigate the strange locking mechanism to open it again to leave. Like so much of McMourning's attitude toward life, the appearance of security was a reversal of common expectation. He gave no concern in keeping anyone out of his research lab. It was designed to keep his experiments in and withstand their assault to the contrary.

Sebastian nodded politely at one of McMourning's nurses that sauntered toward him as he entered the

small chamber adjoining the larger lab beyond. In the dim lighting of the ante-chamber she might have seemed young and beautiful. Her outfit, a small dress designed more for a schoolgirl, was grimy, a stained mockery of the uniform of a proper hospital nurse. Her legs and arms were bare and struck him, as always, with temptation. He fought against it, turning from her and hurrying into the main chamber where he, unfortunately, collided bodily with another of McMourning's beautiful nurses, standing just within the final entry to the lab.

Before she could turn to face him, he was struck by the sickly cloud of perfume she wore, mixed with the sweet scent of alchemical mixtures and formaldehyde. Her hair, long and thick, was cocked too far to her left; a wig, shifting upon the wrinkled flesh beneath. Her smile was as much an illusion as the rest of her beauty. The skin was pulled taut from either side of her mouth and pulled up toward her ears. Her forehead and eyes, too, were pulled by the flesh toward her skull. Her eyes, in fact, most quickly dispelled the illusion of youthful beauty. The flesh of her face was merely a mask, the skin of another woman, young and beautiful, removed and placed upon this venerable woman, desperate to retain a youthful beauty that was now denied to her. The flesh around the eye sockets was drying quicker than the rest, treated perpetually with various concoctions designed to preserve the flesh and stave off the inevitable decay and rot of death. Her own dark skin beneath the mask was visible along the edges of her eyes, wrinkled in age.

Not many beyond Sebastian had seen McMourning's nurses. One might suspect that he, like his counterpart, Seamus, surrounded himself by women he made beautiful. McMourning, however, took little notice of the women charged with the task of maintaining his creations. It was the nurses, themselves, desperate to preserve a beauty that had long since faded, that filled their own veins with the diluted formulas they used to preserve the flesh of McMourning's monsters.

She stared at him, rather vacantly. Her grasp of reality was tenuous at best. Sebastian nodded at her and squeezed past.

A large wheel window far above them offered the only light into the room and cast illumination upon the series of four tables bolted to the floor in the center of the room. Dim light fell upon animated creatures confined in cages within recesses along the periphery of the chamber. Great bottles and beakers contained brains, hearts, and other organs collected from various animals, people, and Neverborn. They decorated the room and were found on every shelf and cabinet. Salted limbs from numerous creatures hung in rows as might be seen in a horrible meat cellar. The scene might disturb any man, even a seasoned Death Marshal like the corpse on the table before McMourning. But not Sebastian – he had prepared most of the macabre spare parts about the room.

"Sebastian!" McMourning exclaimed, startled when his assistant cleared his throat beside him. "Well, it's about time." He pointed at the Death Marshal killed earlier at the morgue. "Do you think his brain will fare better than the one we have installed in Big Frank?" He hitched his thumb over his shoulder at the great flesh construct chained to the wall behind them.

"I wouldn't know, suh," Sebastian admitted. Although eager to begin his quest for his old professor, McMourning's facial twitch indicated his mind was exploring several full thoughts at once. McMourning had the singular brilliance that enabled him to carry on those unique thoughts a normal man could only handle individually. The doctor could juggle several at once, each with precise detail. His awareness of the tangible world, however, became unfortunately suppressed during these odd meditative visions, leaving it to Sebastian to look after him and protect him from any evidence that might *implicate him in the narrow-minded view of others too enslaved by antiquated notions of morality that forever impeded the progress of science.* At least that's what McMourning said with fair regularity.

"Hmm. We don't have time anyway." He turned from the corpse and faced the abomination remains on the next table, then hesitated and turned back to stare at the Death Marshal once more. "Good point," he said in response to nothing Sebastian said and looked quickly over his shoulder to be sure no one else was there. "Hate to waste it. Only hours old. Surely superior to the criminal's brain we've got in there now. Very well, Sebastian. You've convinced me!" He clapped his assistant on the back, violent enough to briefly imbalance him before he could step back and stand upright again. "Preserve the brain for later. Get the stem this time, too. You always cut too close to the base of the skull. Oh, just get the whole column right to the pelvis." He turned to face the abomination then spun back to the Marshal. "Hate to preserve it, too, huh?"

Sebastian spoke for only the second time since entering the lab. "I don't mind, suh."

McMourning continued with a conversation Sebastian was only vaguely privy to. "Exactly! The preservation might actually impede the recall functions. Good point. You'll help me install it into Big Frank while I journey into the wilds!" He smiled broadly, wringing his hands, though his plan had him doing two things at once. Sebastian understood. Although absent-minded and often unaware of events occurring around him, McMourning's thoughts were perpetually on his anatomical sciences, working out the most obscure mysteries of nature. Sebastian had come to understand that part of his addled confusion came from the feverish attempt he made to have his experiments catch the fleeting thoughts cascading through his brilliant mind.

"Will you be needin' assistance in the wild, too, suh," he hesitated, pondering the strange thought in his mind before continuing, "or is it sufficient I should stay b'hind to assist … *you* in the op'ration?" McMourning thought of both necrotic operations and believed he was in both places at once. Sebastian played along rather than engage in an inevitable argument about their reality.

McMourning looked at him as if the shorter man were truly crazy. "Don't be so dim, Sebastian," he said. "Of course I need you to assist me here while I find the professor."

"I see," Sebastian said, but he didn't. "Very good then. The wilds are fairly wild, suh. Canno' take Frank as you'll, well, *you'll* be workin' on 'im here. As it were. Should you be takin' another to help out there?"

McMourning got a gleam in his eye. "Oh, goodie, goodie. A field test of the chimera!"

"Yes, but one 'ed don't seem to be workin' quite right yet."

"One 'ed'? Oh, 'head'! Yes, well. So long as it doesn't fall off it'll suffice. It's just the ram's head. Not good for much."

Sebastian nodded and spun the crank on his circular saw until it sputtered to life, black smoke pouring from the engine on his back, the gears spinning loudly in a roar that filled the room. He slid the quickly twirling blade into the back of the Marshal, severing the torso in a clean line. Blood, not yet congealed, sprayed upon

Sebastian and across the lab. It was a clean cut but not exactly surgically precise. McMourning took no further notice of the operation, however, preparing the abomination for travel once more, and he carried it to the three-headed necromantic creation confined in the bowels of the lab, sure that he was also recreating Big Frank all the while.

The wilderness north of the Bayou now cracked with a jagged scar that stretched far beyond the surveyor's expeditions, teemed with dangers both natural and strange. Those unexplainable dangers that sought to play upon his fears and anxiety were met with the strange and twisted mind of McMourning, lost, partially, in a strange dementia already, for he had done heinous deeds and had contemplated far more, enough that his grasp of reality was already stretched thin. In dealing with natural threats, McMourning and the great chimera, a necromantic monstrosity never imagined before, handled with relative ease.

The creature's massive body was once a Sabertooth Cerberus, created by arcane magics unfathomable to McMourning, but the massive body had been further enhanced, augmented by his own perverse experimentation. Seeking to outdo its original design, McMourning had replaced the three heads of the beast, offering it new abilities to make it superior to the stock beast upon which it was based. One head, for example, now demonstrated his greatest mastery of anatomical science and necromantic art, for a towering Razorspine Rattler's head rose at its center; a perfect merging of reptilian and mammalian biology. To its left was the head of a rare Northern Ram, a beast found only at the highest point of the Northern Mountains. The rams stood as tall as a man at the shoulder and have been seen to pounce from at least a hundred feet to strike its prey with their colossal rack, breaking the skull or spine before the victim knew it was even being stalked. Like many species native to Malifaux, the Northern Rams were voracious carnivores. Unfortunately, despite the grand effort and expense McMourning put into the capture of the creature, the bounty hunters managed to bring him only a hornless runt, seemingly abandoned by its pack, and not quite as clever as they were rumored to be. McMourning had still made use of it though it had a tendency to look at the surrounding landscape while the other two heads fought with the bestial ferocity they were known for in life. It also had

the strange urge to bleat incessantly, but only when McMourning tried to sleep or ordered it silent to avoid detection. Its third head was the original Sabertooth's that had been removed so that a different creature's head could be mounted in its place. Naturally, no more ferocious creature could be found, so he put the original back on. He didn't realize it, and wouldn't have likely thought it an important detail, but he used the Sabertooth's original *left* head and mounted it on the right spinal branch so the entire beast had a habit of jerking the wrong way at the last second of a charge, forcing the Razorspine head to snap over the other until it could turn appropriately. The ram head would simply look on confused. Despite these oddities and setbacks, it was still formidable, and most predators gave them a wide berth, no doubt perceiving something supernaturally strange about the great beast.

So he walked, unimpeded and without fear, through the woodland whose canopy far above blocked out almost all light. Other than the gray darkness making his steps uncertain, there was sparse undergrowth to slow them. Although frigid, the previous day's snow was soft and light and did not penetrate the wooded canopy to accumulate more than an inch.

Like most of Marcus' prey, McMourning had no idea the muscular man traversed the thick branches above with the ease and quiet of a squirrel, despite the bulk and various hunting trophies of bone or tooth that decorated his body on necklaces and lashed to armbands or woven into the knotted dreadlocks of his hair. He maintained the pace of the grotesque monstrosity below him, stinking up his woodland territory for many miles around, and its Resurrectionist creator was far worse, smelling of sweat, sewage, and acrid chemicals that had stained his skin too deeply to wash away. Marcus could smell them easily, even from his perch dozens of feet above.

McMourning spoke to the zombified creature, complaining about its bleating though it was he who could not remain silent, his voice carrying over the still air of the forest floor.

Marcus focused upon the power of the bear, his thick muscles swelling into dense knots, and he channeled the fast firing muscles of the serpent, twisting each fiber in his body. The process took but a second, although it was painful as his own anatomy bent into a new configuration of reshaped muscle and bone. He gnashed his teeth, suppressing the pain although he couldn't help but growl gutturally with the unpleasant sensations and the rising anticipation of the hunt that was about to come to an end. He leapt from the branch, extending his body as he moved to the next tree some twenty feet away. His hands found the branch easily, and with a jerk he propelled his body forward toward the trunk. If McMourning had looked straight up he would have seen the predator stalking him and darting directly overhead. The Sabertooth's ears twitched and the head did look up, but too late, and caught only the trailing blur of Marcus legs as he disappeared again in the foliage. It ignored it.

Marcus ran lithely and with the surefooted movement of a hare upon the twisted and knotty branch. He focused again upon the power of the serpent as he dove from the branch, striking like an eagle from above. The hooked wooden staff upon his back was pulled from the leather strap that held it in place, and he felt the familiar twisting of the wood, dense and solid from his own arcane experimental perversion of the natural fibers so that it was all but indestructible although as light as a twig. It twirled at his side until he had the balance of it correct, and he held it firm as he dove. His body hit the ground in front of McMourning, and he grunted audibly as the violence of his fall drove the wind from his lungs. One leg was bent below him, ready to propel him forward in attack.

McMourning squealed, much akin to a young girl, Marcus thought, and jumped back. His repulsive chimera crouched quickly and prepared to spring, but Marcus' own Sabertooth Cerberus burst from behind a thick copse growing upon the forest floor beside McMourning's path. It was a perfect place for ambush, and McMourning walked right into the trap. The living Cerberus batted the head of its dead counterpart with a heavy paw, claws raking deeply into its dry flesh. The Razorspine head reared back, hissing and prepared to strike, but the living Sabertooth's three heads howled ferociously, reverberating in a Doppler echo as each sounded identical to the other. The necromantic beast hesitated, which gave Marcus the chance to end it, or its master, Doctor McMourning.

Instead, crouched in a striking position before him, Marcus laughed, deep and throaty. He rose before McMourning and said, "Did you wet yourself or is that the stink you bore into my woods?"

"Marcus, damn you!" McMourning growled. "You scared the hell out of me."

"You weren't being careful enough. Not out here. I thought I taught you better than that."

"Yes, well, it's been a long time since I've sat through one of your lectures and the 'how to survive an attack by a crazy man in the woods' was likely as boring as any other lecture you gave, so I wouldn't remember it."

Marcus snorted. "Boring? I remember you had found my lectures somewhat different than that."

McMourning ignored him. "Look what your tri-rostal machairodont did to my masterpiece!" McMourning said sarcastically. "Tore the skin right off its cheek. That'll leave a mark, you know!" He shook his head. "Well, what's done is done. You're looking well. Beefing up, I see." He looked upon Marcus with unbidden jealously. Although decades older than him, Marcus looked robust and young; more vibrant and virile than should be possible for a man of his advanced age. "Eating well, or something," he said with a sneer.

"You have no idea."

"I suppose not. How's my niece?" McMourning asked. "You still using her as one of your infernal lab rats?"

Marcus was about to answer but an odd voice behind McMourning that sounded both familiar and foreign, interrupted him. The words sounded as if they were made by the brushing of sticks and branches. It said, "I am no lab experiment!" McMourning turned just in time to see a dense tree and shrub change before his eyes as it *moved*, charging him, shifting into a wolf-like creature but made entirely of flora. He had no time to move, but his mind had just enough time to understand it to be a legendary Waldgeist, a woodland spirit beast. As it pounced, its form shifted again, and in the moment its hind legs left the ground she became the beautiful Myranda.

McMourning smiled briefly, recognizing his niece, but saw at once she was not happy to see him. Her arm, human once more, twisted from her forearm to the end of each finger so that it became a sinister claw bearing thick and sharp talons. She clearly meant to kill her uncle.

Marcus caught McMourning beneath the ribs with the curved hook of his shillelagh and pulled him aside. He leapt forward in a flash and caught Myranda's wrist and held it firm. She struggled to get free, but Marcus held her fast.

"Not doing any experiments on her?" McMourning asked sarcastically, rubbing his side.

Marcus said, "None my mate doesn't want, herself."

"Did you call her your 'mate'? What's next, a litter? Oh, Myranda, the family will not be happy with you. You know how they feel about our former professor, now living in exile. And he's old enough to be your grandfather."

Marcus was unperturbed by his taunting, and even grinned wolfishly at his masculine conquest, but Myranda spat, "Go to hell, you freak! Like they'd welcome *you* back after what you did to me?" McMourning could see that the scar on her exposed midriff had disappeared, likely a result of their work on reshaping the physical form. *He* had apologized and was only trying to help her anatomical studies after all. He thought she should be over all of that by now anyway. He had forgotten it. "Look at this thing," she jerked free of Marcus' grip and motioned to his necromantic beast. She stomped away, between McMourning and the creature, glaring at her uncle all the while. "It's deplorable," she said in a growl. "*You're* deplorable." The ram's head stretched out its dark gray tongue to lick her as she passed, and it bleated loudly when she jerked away.

"Ugh!" she protested, and, not to be stopped this time, her powerful claw ripped down through its neck at the point where it was affixed to the body, nearly severing it completely before she turned into a black jungle cat and bound away. The ram's head dangled from the body by several thick cords of flesh and muscle. It bleated again but sounded choked as it dangled upside down.

"She seems more difficult than ever," McMourning said, knowing that her anger was directed solely at him and not the beast he had animated.

"I've noticed. A byproduct of the bestial changes her body's going through. I'm working on it."

"I should never have introduced you two."

"She's as devout a scientist as you ever were," Marcus said. "Perhaps more so."

McMourning rolled his eyes. "Do you not question the ethics of your experimentation?" Marcus arched an eyebrow, silently accusing McMourning of hypocrisy. "You're right, you're right," McMourning admitted. "Fine. Look at this," he said, thrusting his open palms at the head dangling from his creation, turning in place, confused. "Do you have any idea how much work that took?"

Marcus bent to examine the exposed anatomy, rare to see its cross-section in movement even in a condition such as this. "Interesting choice to connect the vertebral synapses from the inside of the ram's eighth vertebrae to the Cerberus' third, along the outer perimeter of the tissues. Why did you do that?"

There was no accusation in his voice, merely scientific curiosity. McMourning had no answer and didn't really know whether he was supposed to answer the question regarding the number of vertebrae or the connective tissue. He hadn't, honestly, thought either of those issues bore any significance to the operation of the beast. "Oh, you know, just allows it to behave more normally this way." He had no idea. Still, Marcus nodded.

"I understand you must replace much of the living fluid with this foul necrotic substance, but wouldn't it be better to bypass the primary aorta, here, and pump it through the smaller vessels surrounding it? Seems that it would give it more longevity as well as more natural responses to external stimuli."

McMourning had never considered that, either.

"Still, the anatomy between the two creatures is so different that the head of the Razorspine should not function at all. I'd like to see your notes on the connectivity and functionality of the grafted union between species."

McMourning beamed beneath the scrutiny and praise of his former professor. "Yes. It's my finest accomplishment. It's the best of the three, too!" Of course, McMourning took no notes on any of his work. It would implicate him too severely should anyone discover them, and he had near full recall of every experiment he had ever conducted, down to the most minute detail.

"I wish I had the opportunity to study it in greater detail. Good work, Doctor."

With the rare praise offered by Marcus still ringing in his ears, McMourning gave a semi-mocking bow and gestured at his creature. With the flourish and bravado of a stage performer, he said proudly, "Just take it. It'd probably lose that head before I could make it back to my lab anyway."

Marcus nodded, inspecting the two halves, genuinely confused and impressed by some of the connections McMourning had made. He shook his hand with a snap and primal green flame erupted from within him to engulf it. He pressed the head against the base of the Cerberus' body and where the organs met, he pressed the flame. The beast shifted uncomfortably, but Marcus held it in place, his bare arms flexing against the powerful movement of the creature, remarkably unable to resist him. He shushed it with a warm and reassuring glance and continued to rub the flame in the severed wounds like a balm. Soon he was done and shook his hand again, and the flames grew brighter so that McMourning had to shield his eyes from the brilliance. The head was firmly mounted again, and it bleated happily at Marcus. He pressed the flames against its forehead, above the eyes, pushing hard against it so that it was pushed backward. Within moments two horns pressed from its skull, growing before McMourning's disbelieving eyes until they curved around its ears and along its jaws, thickening, too, even as its entire head and neck grew, the muscles more defined and thick.

"Why'd you use such a sickly specimen?" Marcus asked him as the fire dissipated. McMourning sighed, thinking of the months it took and the thousands of Guild script to bag this one. He just shrugged.

Marcus stared deeply into the eyes of the Cerberus head, and with a wave and deep throated growl, the beast understood his command and it bound off into the woods to await the will of its new master. It moved with the more natural gait of the feline it once was, which irritated McMourning further. Marcus took a deep breath and turned toward him. "Why are you out here?" he asked.

McMourning said, "Looking for you. For your lab."

"You found me. And you're in it."

McMourning looked around. Of course this was his lab. Gone were the days of the meek professor lost behind a mound of books for hours on end. He now lived and breathed those experiments that sought to stifle the processes of disease and aging, perhaps to abolish them altogether. Judging by his appearance, he may have unlocked those secrets. "You know I hate to ever have to admit it, but I have a problem that only you may be able to solve." He pointed toward the package containing the ancient abomination several yards away on the ground, where he had inadvertently hurled it when Marcus fell in front of him. Marcus crouched above the canvas bag where it was discarded and removed it to examine those remains the Ortegas had brought to McMourning months before. He explained his findings, that the strange humanoid was neither human nor Neverborn. Marcus needed none of the research apparatus McMourning had brought, not even the magnifying glass. He just squinted and stared at the smallest thing and seemed to understand it on a fundamental level.

"I agree," he said after a brief examination. "I cannot tell what this poor creature might once have been. It does share many of the attributes of both species, which should not be possible. But, then, look at you and me," he said, rubbing at the rough stubble on his face. "Defying natural law is our bread and butter." He sighed and stood in a smooth movement. "Go back to your lab. I'll send a messenger when I've discovered something."

"I can't." He explained how his crimes had caught up with him and how the Guild had more than a strong suspicion he was behind the missing bodies from the morgue.

"You play such a risky game hiding amongst the Guild. Doing their work for them so that you can do yours right beneath their noses. You need to shift the blame or cut your losses and run."

"I'm working on it. Of course, I could hide out in the woods and conduct my little experiments?"

McMourning didn't know she was there, but Myranda had perched in the tree above them in the form of a large raptor and quickly shifted back into her natural state, now much more in control than she had been minutes earlier. "The girl Kaeris asked us to examine," she said ambiguously.

"What girl?"

Marcus frowned. "I don't want to get involved," he said up to Myranda, lounging against the trunk of the tree.

"You already are. They came to us because of her ability. To heal in minutes rather than days."

McMourning nodded, impressed, and considered the changes to various glands and organs that might allow it, his mind working thrillingly to figure out the biological processes. "How does she do that?"

"We do not know. I haven't studied her."

Myranda said, "But you want to. And it might kill her. Or, if her ability's strong enough, she may live through the vivisection, and then you'll have to kill her or she'll rat you out to the Guild. Make her look like the Doctor's body thief and then have your way with her. Besides, you cannot ignore Ramos. He's given you this girl as a gift. It may provide answers to the last of your questions."

"But is it a gift? Or a test of my loyalty? It's been a long time since he and I taught together at Vienna. He needs me more than I need him."

Myranda didn't agree. "We need him more than you care to admit. Consider his funding. This girl he wants you to examine. You owe him more than you're admitting."

Marcus considered her words. "Yes. Always in his debt. How do you know he does not simply want her as another warrior in his crusade?"

Myranda laughed. "He wants *you* beside him much more than some girl with an over-active glandular problem."

Marcus nodded reluctantly. He sought escape from the people of civilization, and the further he went to escape, the harder they worked to bring him back in. He sighed. Turning back to McMourning, he said, "So you cannot go back to the City until we clear your name. You cannot survive out here for more than a day, and—"

McMourning cut him off. "I've been out here for two days already!"

"I've been following you since you entered the wood, at Rook's Trail. Otherwise you'd have been dead." McMourning nodded. That was where he entered the woods. Marcus continued, "And I doubt you'll be able to keep up with us."

"Where are you going?"

"Down into the pit. I need to see where these things are coming from."

"We're getting the girl, first," Myranda said matter-of-factly. Marcus scowled at her. "Field test."

The Writing on the Wall

December 18

Sonnia Criid bent her head against the cold pouring down from the mountains in the distance. She pulled the wide brim of her hat down to her shoulder to shelter her face from a biting wind she had never before experienced. It was severe, even for early December, and stung the back of her hand, pricking the flesh with sharp jabs. Small flakes flew sideways, but it was too dry in the badlands for any great accumulation. The snow came down from out of the Northern Mountains, and a single dark cloud swirled ominously over one tall peak in the distance, stretching out far overhead in a sky lit occasionally with lightning.

She walked from the town, her duster fastened tight around her torso, but the ends snapped sharply behind her. The heels of her boots dug into the hard soil, gray and cracked from endless years of abuse by the cold dry wind that beat constantly against it. Sparse vegetation managed to eke out a meager existence, stretching up feebly between wide cracks in the hard soil.

Samael Hopkins approached her, his head bowed with one gloved hand holding his hat upon his head. His own duster was heavy with the oil that weatherproofed it, but it snapped toward her as the wind raged at his back. A bandana hid his features, leaving only his eyes exposed to the elements. Even the horse he led, Cinder, looked dejected and miserable and kept its head low while its mane and tail whipped in the wind.

"Any luck?" she called, voice rising above the moaning wind.

"Yeah," he shouted back, leaning toward her. "But you're not going to like it!"

She drew close to him, and they returned to Redemption City, a mere six buildings and another dozen or so makeshift homes situated beyond the small town's perimeter. Samael looked ahead at the thick black smoke rising above one of the poorly constructed houses. "Is that Old Man Milner's place burnin'?"

She shouted back, "Yeah. But I didn't do it!" Samael had a habit of accusing her of starting every fire he saw, so she beat him to the punch. The look on his face conveyed the somber attitude that typically showed only during the hunt or apprehension of a criminal.

"Volcanic activity spread out here? That's a bigger circle'n you predicted."

"It's moving all through this area. Beneath us. The surface gave way out there beyond the Weiland home. You can see the lava flowing below. Like a river rapids."

He moved nearer to her as they walked, for the hope of warmth and to hear one another better. "Maybe I can warm my hands and toes by it!" he called, feigning a smile.

After Hopkins sheltered Cinder in the livery, he joined Sonnia in the abandoned General Store she had converted to her private study. The walls were more solidly constructed than other buildings around them, allowing only a bit of the wind to whistle through gaps between the planks. She had a large mug of hot coffee ready for them both. "Milner's place just collapsed," he said, taking the dented metal cup from her and sipping at it thankfully. Although she made it too bitter, too strong, he wasn't going to complain. "They make it out okay?" he asked.

"Yesterday. Took off before sun up. Before their place caught fire."

"Anyone left? Wadsworths? Cunninghams?"

"Nope. The Schadles left just after you and the Milners convinced the Wadsworths to go with them."

Samael nodded, slapping and rubbing his upper arms to get some life moving in them again. "So we're all that's left? The Hopkins and the Criids? So much for Redemption City. How long has it been here?"

"Just under two years. When that soulstone vein was discovered."

"Two years and now abandoned." He shook his head.

"Not exactly their decision," she said as the ground rumbled, shaking up through the shoddily constructed building. Bottles and cans on the store's shelves wobbled and slipped from their perch with a clatter. The ground growled a long, deep rumble from the heart of the small abandoned town. It subsided as the two waited it out, looking at one another, expecting the worst.

"Tell me what you found out there," she said as the goods along the wall stopped tinkling against one another.

"Nothing you didn't tell me I'd find."

"You said, 'I'm not going to like it.' You find the entrance to the pit?"

"Oh, yep. Found the cave entrance. Goes down into a pretty elaborate labyrinth of twisting caves. Can't figure it out by walking randomly, either. Didn't go too far as you instructed, though I'm sure I could have found my way out."

"You'd be surprised. I don't think it's a natural labyrinth and natural confusion I'm worried about. Otherwise, you'd have no trouble, I'm sure. There should be markings on the entrance walls. A code or some part of the key."

"It's there. How I knew it was your cave. Marks are old, but don't look entirely Neverborn, neither, though I'm sure they had to be."

"Go on. I can tell there's more. The part I'm not going to like. What are you holding back?"

He smiled and shook his head. "Well, like I said, you ain't gonna like it. Some of those ancient symbols and glyphs and such weren't the only things written on the walls. In fact, parts of those old symbols were scratched off and new writing was there."

"Damn it." She sighed and rolled her eyes. "Did you write it down?"

"Much as I could. Got some written down here," he said, pulling the narrow journal from within his long coat. He unfolded it and opened the book to his drawings of the cave. "Mostly matches the drawings in one of the books you had me retrieve from your office. You still owe me for that one, by the way. Matheson nearly caught me snooping about."

"Owe you? You didn't get half the books I sent you for and not the *one* book I really needed."

"'Cause he followed me right into the Investigator's offices. Dropped your damned book right on Hoffman's lap! I swear that Secretary looked right at me as he walked over to that monster, Ryle. Looked right at me. Froze my damned blood. You know how tough it'd be if they caught me. You're not exactly in their good graces, you know."

"Sorry you're in it with me. Can't trust any of them anymore."

"Not Lucius Matheson, that's for sure. Guy gives me the creeps."

"Not our beloved Governor, either, I fear," she said, and emotion seemed to drain from her face as her eyes focused on something far away. Her countenance took on that strange introspective look every time the Governor's name came up, but she wouldn't reveal what she knew or suspected. She was holding something in, that was certain.

"Anyway," Samael said, "I didn't write down all of them," as he tapped his drawing there in the book. She looked at him quizzically. "They're not appropriate for ladies' eyes." He winked at her.

"Me? Not appropriate for me? As if I've not heard it all from the number of felons we've apprehended. Especially those we've purged."

"True. Burning a man's spirit out does seem to encourage a most foul discourse."

She read the first graffiti image Hopkins had copied, realizing it was a limerick verse,

I knew a woman on Malifaux's streets
Who swallowed a handful of seeds
Within half an hour
Her breasts were aflower
And her knickers were covered in weeds.

Finishing it she said, "Rude, crass, and not terribly clever." She read another:

Per'aps you're wishing to die, Ma'am?
Down your throat my cane I could cram.
Your question's quite rude
Asked of my streetwalker brood-
"Are they any real threat?"   Well I am!

Following that she said, "Limericks about a 'Streetwalker brood' leads me to believe it's that lunatic —"

"Seamus," Hopkins said, interjecting. "He actually signed the wall with his name in one limerick which I hesitate to even bring up. It says something about 'Me and my girl Molly / befouled this cave with —', well, I needn't go on with more of his rude verse. Suffice it to say that he was happy enough to let us know he was there and what he and Molly did while there. Made me anxious to get out, even into the blistering cold.

She didn't hear him. She was staring beyond him as she often did, eyes darting as her mind raced. He knew what would likely come next. Well, one of several possibilities. She'd either get so obsessed by some obscure detail, calling it a "symbol of providence" and pour through book after ancient book day and night without eating or sleeping. Or she was about to go off on some fool adventure, nearly get them both killed, all to track down yet another lost book in some Neverborn ruins. Or, what he hated most but suspected was most likely, she'd send him off on some dangerous mission while she re-read or translated an arcane text.

He sipped his coffee and pushed his hat further back on his head, peering at her from the depth of the shadows it cast upon his countenance. Her eyes came to rest on his. "I have a mission for you," she said.

So, the third option. It's what he guessed. "Of course you do, darlin'. Back to the cave?"

"No. Back to the City." Something was different about her demeanor, he thought. She masked it well. But he was too experienced in finding the most minute detail and using it to make bold understandings about his prey. She looked at him almost regretfully, like they were saying goodbye. To her credit, she was fairly convincing. He was better at seeing through obscurity. "That book Lucius dropped on Hoffman's lap. It's important enough. About grafting, of all things. Hooking up mechanika to the body. Something I'm overlooking. Get me that book, Sam." There was more to her story that she wasn't sharing. He was certain.

"Meet back here?"

She hesitated, which added to his unease. The ground rumbled again, and they heard a spout of lava erupt from just north of the town. It seemed to spark an idea, and she said, "I don't think Redemption City will last that long. I'll meet you back at the secret apartment I keep in the Quarantine Zone. Day after tomorrow."

"Fine," he said. "What about you, though? Volcanic activity's gettin' stronger. From here all the way to the cave."

She smiled. "Sam," she said. "I'm not worried about the *heat*. It's the cold that worries me." She winked and waved him off, seeming too anxious to get back to deciphering the Neverborn text they had recovered from some Arcanist patsy months earlier. So it was, late in the evening, that he set out to return to Malifaux on her bidding. He rode late, anxious to get free from the howling wind but also to put the pieces together to explain her odd behavior there before he left. She relied upon him for his tracking, but he was shrewd and didn't need much to go on in order to figure out a mystery. It was hours into his trek that he spun Cinder and dug his spurs into the stallion's flanks, hightailing it back to their makeshift camp in Redemption. It had been nearly five hours since he had left and, bursting into the dark space of the general store, found it abandoned, as he feared. A glance at the dwindling embers confirmed to him that the fire had not been tended for exactly the length of time he had been gone. He spun in place, taking in the missing goods from the store, comparing discrepancies of what he now beheld against the nearly perfect image of the place from when he last stood there. The small changes were clear in the mental snapshot that so perfectly remembered every minute detail. Basic rations, rope, lantern, survival knife. Her stack of books was missing only two, including the journal he gave her with the writings on the cave wall scribbled within. Most of her own notes were there as well.

An envelope rested upon one of the books she had kept of the translations of many of the arcane symbols and glyphs regarding the coming return of the Tyrant Entities. It was what consumed her and drove her. The Tyrants. The envelope was not addressed but the back bore Sonnia's wax seal symbol of the flaming serpent. It was dry and cool, but still soft as he cracked it. The letter therein read:

You never could follow orders. My guess is that you didn't get more than an hour before returning here, suspicious of something I said or did that 'didn't sit right'. Your instincts are strong. But, unless you catch me writing this letter, then you'll be too late.

You'll still need to get that book to corroborate some of my findings in my journal. Turn yourself in to Matheson, too. Explain what I've done and how you didn't have anything to do with it. Offer my work as proof of your loyalty to the Guild.

You'll need to take control of the Witch Hunters.

If I'm right I'll soon either be dead (as I now fear and suspect) or I will have seriously pissed off one of the greatest Tyrants known to us. Either way, I plan to buy you time, at least, to figure out how to stop them.

You must search for an answer, Samael, and I trust no man to find anything more than I trust you.

Godspeed,

-S

PS: Be wary of Lucius Matheson. He's more than he seems.

He opened the gate in the front of the potbelly stove, cooling as the embers within diminished. The parchment of her letter flared up briefly as the embers consumed it.

Within moments he was back atop Cinder, riding the unhappy animal hard. He rode throughout the night, stopping only as he must to give Cinder water and a brief moment to catch his breath. He hated to push him right to the very edge of death, but such was his need for haste.

"Hold in there, boy," he said as the City drew into sight beneath the uncanny orange glow of the twin moons overhead. The sun was about to break in the east as he slowed to a canter. He'd have to avoid the checkpoint into the City. He would retrieve that book from Hoffman, however it was not a book he was urgent to find, but a man. A man that was all too good at not being found. A man that just might have the answer Sonnia had been looking for. He was after Seamus.

Shortly thereafter and in a different part of the city, Seamus stood before the great plague pit, a mound of bodies piled high in the Quarantine Zone, smiling a sinister smile as he surveyed the hundreds of victims that had succumbed to the Plague these past months. Molly stood apart from him, in the distance, watching him from between crumbling buildings in the dark shadows. He was not without escort, however, as three of his favorite Belles stood nearby, mouths agape, eyes and heads lolling this way and that as they entertained whatever meager thoughts might still be possible in their addled brains. They were not dressed for the evening; however, as Seamus was on a very important mission, and one that might change his destiny forever, perhaps even the fate of all of those in Malifaux. Flung unceremoniously upon the mound of bodies were the Guild Guardsmen stationed at the Plague Pit. Other than slit throats or deep lacerations from a Belle's dirty fingernails, they wore only their red thermal drawers, relieved of their attire to dress his girls appropriately for their most serious mission. One girl wore the pants, boots (though one kept managing to fall off for it was several times too large for the slight Belle), and long gray coat of a Guild Guardsman while another wore the more austere business attire of an investigator. More Guards lay nearby, and Seamus didn't care to have them brought to the pit nor even stripped to hide their identity. Molly urged greater discretion, but he was agitated with that particular group of Guardsmen. In their midst rested a full-fledged Death Marshal, now face down upon his mysterious coffin, a supernatural gateway to the aether-world. Seamus could hardly go near the thing even though one of his favorites, Juliana Myrtlebeck, was still trapped within the coffin. Seamus glanced to the third of his companions whom he now pretended was his own Death Marshal consort. He could not bring himself to fully disrobe the real Guild Marshal, wanting instead to keep his distance even though he fired more than half a dozen rounds into his body before quickly pulling his duster, dripping with blood from the merciless assault, and put it over the girl's soiled evening gown. He decided that a hat stuck on her head and a pistol strapped tightly around her waist fulfilled the illusion well enough. He pulled the withered daisy from his lapel and stuffed the dry stem through a wet bullet-hole in the front of the coat. It was stiff and freezing quickly. He called her "sir" and saluted whenever she passed him, ambling about with the air of importance, or so he pretended.

He had Molly dressed as a librarian, despite her persistent reluctance to join him and the other Belles. She was supposed to record the event, and he spent hours showing her how to use the lead pencil he wedged between her gray fingers. "You lick the pencil like this," he showed her, licking the lead, "and then start scribbling." She didn't respond, but she looked right at him. It was an odd thing for his girls to focus their eyes upon him, and he didn't really like it. "You were a reporter, right?" he asked of her, time and again. "That's why ye're the one that's reporting this momentous event. Aye!" he exclaimed. "Ye daft garl," he muttered under his breath. "I swear ye are being difficult on purpose."

"Kelly," he called to his Death Marshal Belle. She shuffled quickly to him as he bent forward, eyes darting back and forth conspiratorially. He motioned for her to remain silent even though she had never uttered a sound since her resurrection. "I have a mission for ye, bonny lass!" he whispered loudly. "That cowboy, Samael be nearby. Scroungin' and looking for one such as me. See to it he finds his way here in short order. I'm in need of him. There's a good lass!" He turned toward Molly, still standing aloof, curious about her behavior toward him. She was a strange one, even by his eccentric standards. He shouted to her, "He sure took the bait, Molly-girl! Just like I told ye he would!" His smile was broad. "Be in for a big surprise when 'e comes round the corner,

though, aye?" She didn't answer. He shrugged. He went back to examining the great pile of bodies, inhaling deeply the sickly sweet smell of decaying flesh that made most men wretch.

Molly knew what he was doing, what he intended. She wasn't sure it was the right thing to do. Still, Seamus had better intentions than Nicodem might, with the masses of decaying bodies piled right there in the open. Of course, the plague had ravaged much of their bodies, continuing to devour flesh and tissue even after the victim had fallen. Some of the bodies almost fully liquefied on the inside as the plague left only a black tar-like substance in its vile wake. Some of the handlers of the victims would grab hold of the arms or legs to fling the body upon the pile only to have it burst like a balloon and splatter its dark contents upon them. They would find themselves on the pile within days, sometimes hours. So, if Nicodem had considered building an army of the damned from the plague victims, perhaps he had thought it not worth the time to pick and choose viable corpses from the rotting masses. Or perhaps he did not want to risk the proximity of a plague that could devour flesh with such potency and impunity. Seamus either hadn't considered the danger or didn't care. Maybe both.

"This is the spot," he said as he finished the fifth pass around the mound. "Riiiiight here." The sky above grew very dark. The wind howled and their coats and dresses snapped in the gale. Then it went suddenly still. The cold that had descended upon Malifaux these last months seemed at first to draw toward that mound of corpses, localizing upon them. The girls didn't seem to mind, and Seamus was too preoccupied to care, though his fingers were red and numb and his boots did little to stave off the cold. Then, as the wind died, the temperature jumped, bathing the entire area in a throbbing beat of increasing warmth. The thick frost upon the cobblestones and corpses evaporated in one of those pulses, the heat coming in those steady waves as if carried upon a strange heartbeat that enveloped them all. "You better be writing this down, Molly!" he called to her. Snow that lingered in along the drainage culverts adjacent the dilapidated sidewalks and forgotten buildings turned to a foggy steam that snaked its way up and around them and the corpses. At their feet where the steam began, it first thickened with that strange throbbing heartbeat and then became opaque, enveloping their legs from the knees downward. As the sky above grew as dark as night, the light gray steam about their feet coalesced, writhing around them as if monstrous snakes, and it, too, darkened to black.

Seamus concentrated upon that pulsing rhythm, knowing that to any other normal man walking about it would feel as though only some strange heat wave had descended upon that one lone spot within the otherwise blistering cold that blanketed all of Malifaux. Seamus could feel far more. He could feel the infinite masses of spiritual energy that called to him, not from the bodies of the recently dead, but from beyond the thin boundary that separated this world from the aether. These spirits lingered, lost in the void and unsure where to go, for they were not from this world and their spirits did not know in death what they might have known in life. They were a beacon for the other, older spirits. And they came to this spot, fueling Seamus. It was the Event, just months ago, that unlocked the great gate that kept the worlds separate. The Breach was the first unnatural tear between worlds, and the Fiery Cage was a stab through the ethereal barrier, not to Earth, but directly into the realm of shadow and twilight. The unleashed power of that spiritual energy remained in Malifaux, and Seamus reached out with his will, collecting it to him, feeling the gossamer edges of that surreal power with the outstretched arms of his mind. The tingling energy was both very familiar, akin to the breaking of a soulstone, but also foreign because it was constant and much stronger. Where the rush of a soulstone was fleeting, this power was dizzying and assaulted his every sense, filling him with power so that he felt as though his flesh might not sustain it.

Seamus was filled with the dark energy and approached rapture, finding it more and more difficult to perceive the reality in which his body stood, seeing only into that purple world beyond with thrilling flashes of multi-colored stabs through the shifting void. He hardly cared about his old reality, longing to enter the world beyond where sensation of that rapturous absorption of a Soulstone might be his, eternally, at every moment.

His arms thrust out to his sides, palms and face lifted to the heavens, the inky tendrils lifted him from the rough paving stones, stained by the spilled contents of the plague victims. The darkness became substantial, squeezing him, embracing him, filling him with energy beyond his comprehension. "Yes!" he howled, and his eyes popped open, now black, mirroring the black tendrils that embraced his lower body. "Come, Death! Come!"

It was the fearsome Grave Spirit, an ancient Tyrant Entity thought to have the least influence or desire to walk upon Malifaux again. Only at places rich in death, with a tenuous gateway to the aether-world, such as the shrine at Kythera, could he even be communicated with. Or so it was assumed. Seamus had researched the issue well, driven more and more insane with each dark passage he read. But the Event had awakened in him a greater understanding of the power unleashed upon them all. He gathered it, and in such a place where innumerable spirits lingered and were drawn from the other side, the mighty Spirit could be called.

It was at that moment that Kelly, the Belle that Seamus had sent to lure Samael to him, bound around the corner of a building with a loping gate, the warm steam rising quickly around her bare feet. Samael Hopkins, following quickly behind, slid to a halt beside a partially toppled wall perpendicular to the alley in which Molly stood. His eyes darted from one image to another, and he understood at once what was occurring before him. Samael had witnessed nearly the same event not half a year earlier at the Kythera remains. He remembered with distinct clarity the sensation of fear and awe that had consumed him then and felt it again now. Others, weaker of will than him and Sonnia, though still strong, succumbed to the madness that lashed into their spirits with the inevitable sensation of eternal death and damnation. He struggled against it again, feeling only the need to flee, to escape that which gathered before him and could not be escaped. It was Death. The great Tyrant Entity, the Grave Spirit, gathered and as It grew in strength, focusing Its will to this reality once more, Samael's will wavered as the great spirit sought dominion.

Barely able to concentrate, it was a feat nothing short of miraculous that Hopkins focused the fear down deep in the center of his chest and channeled it out through his arm. His Colt barked before him, and a bullet trailed fire as it struck the first Belle in the center of her back, exploding on impact and punching a hole through her the size of a cannon ball. The bullet continued on, striking a second Belle in the shoulder, which set her aflame. The first fell in smoldering remains, and the second looked upon Samael emotionlessly though her clothing and dry flesh burned.

Still held aloft by the manifestation of the Grave Spirit more and more imminent, Seamus turned his head toward Samael and muttered, "Right on time, boyo," though no one could hear him.

The dark mist enveloping the entire area drew quickly toward Seamus, circling his legs in increasingly rapid swirling arcs. It pulled away from Hopkins and began to take on a hulking form as screams from beyond the grave filled the air.

Hopkins knew his sanity was teetering on collapse. He had seen those other men at Kythera break, their minds shattered by the mere presence of the Grave Spirit as It only *began* to take presence in this world. It brought with It the stain of damnation, showing an unholy and eternal realm of unbridled suffering and anguish. That stain washed over him now, the vapor writhing at his feet. He would soon be lost to the great macabre imagery, he realized, his body, instinctively trying to overrule his will, took several steps away, back into the alley that brought him here. The momentum of that movement was nearly enough. He would flee, he realized, and they would be lost, but he could not leave with the prophetic imagery of his own tortured existence beneath the Tyrant that would enslave them all and feed upon their lost spirits invading his confused mind.

Hardly able to discern his own reality, he withdrew a set of shackles from his belt with trembling hands. He quickly clamped one to his wrist and the other end to a dark iron gate still anchored to a brick wall with a thin chain and lock he would use on the arrest of a criminal. He needed to flee and could not control the urge. He jerked and tugged at the chains he trapped himself with until blood flowed at his wrist, irrationally crying in fear as a schoolchild might. Samael lifted his Colt but could not aim, could barely focus his will into the weapon but knew as the bullet flew that it carried the full weight of his arcane will and trailed white fire as it sought Seamus' chest. Its trajectory was true, but as it entered his flesh, the energy enveloping his bullet changed from yellowish-white to bright green and hit Seamus full in the chest and passed through him. The energy rippled out his back like a pebble dropped into a still pool, in growing circles to dissipate far above and beyond him.

"YES," Seamus growled, his voice a strange echoing mixture of his natural voice commingled with the Grave Spirit. "AMOST DONE, BOYO," he said from across the distance to Samael. "NOW GIVE US A WEE MINUTE. I'M IN THE MIDDLE OF SOMETHING." He struck his head violently. As the ripple of energy finally dissipated fully, Seamus grasped his head, his fingernails growing into thick claws that tore into the flesh, his large top hat knocked from the thick red curls of his head, now turning raven black. "NOW, NOW. SETTLE DOWN, YE BASTARD. NONE O' THAT." Samael understood he was

speaking not to him, but to the entity consuming him and his mind.

The black tendrils holding him aloft had jerked away from where his bullet's energy had penetrated Seamus and finally pulled from him entirely, joining into one great black arm that stretched up and above him. His body twisted as he fell to the ground, and he bellowed in pain and laughed hysterically, maniacally. He rose to his knees and his back bulged and split the green wool coat in several long lacerations. Where the dark mist of the Grave Spirit touched, color drained away, leaving his clothing dark gray and his skin lost its warmth, turning ashen and strange as his arms and legs bulged and thickened in incredible muscular growth and the bones beneath them clearly snapped, broken by his transformation. "NO, NO!" he shouted. "WON'T BE ENOUGH," he roared. His head shook, sending blood flying in wide arcs as he flailed his head repeatedly against the ground "WON'T BE ENOUGH TO BEAT US!" He shook and pounded his meaty fists upon the ground which split the stones. "LET US THINK, YE DAMNED SPIRIT." He turned to face Samael, growling incoherently. He spat and snarled, reduced to more of a mindless brute than a man. The dark tendril that was the Grave Spirit reared high above and prepared to strike like a viper. Abruptly, the massive head snapped to the side, facing Samael. His eyes were consumed by the blackness of the stain of damnation, reflecting no light. He laughed maniacally. "SHOOT ME! SHOOT ME IF YE'RE GONNA!" he bellowed. "RIGHT IN THE HEAD IF YOU'RE GOING TO AT ALL!" Seamus laughed maniacally, his voice echoing strangely even within his own throat.

Samael, barely conscious as his mind reeled with unreasoning fear, assaulted by endless imagery of what could only be described as hell, had his weapon leveled as well as he could upon the brute that was Seamus, his clothing hanging upon his muscular back in tatters, the gun shaking. Samael swallowed hard and with eyes closed, let another bullet fly.

Seamus, now a towering monstrosity, growled in unison with the roar of the gun, and the bullet struck him in the head just as the black tendril lashed downward to burrow into Seamus. Both struck Seamus' head, the bullet a fraction of a second ahead of the dark tendril, and the black grave vapors blew out in a puff, denied the mind of Seamus as Hopkins ended him.

The blackness lightened to gray as the mist froze over, and the dark cloud above slowly broke to reveal the cool blue beyond as Seamus fell to the ground, his body twisting and writhing back to its normal humanity even as his life expired. A great pool of blood radiated from the gaping hole at the back of his head. His dead eyes returned to normal, save the color. They were no longer the deep green that so many women found irresistible. Now, stained by the Grave Spirit that withered away, they were pale gray.

Final Journal Entry of Constable Brian T. Hamm

Why the hell did I take this job? The Guild sends its Elite Divisions in pursuit of creatures that would drive the sane mad and maybe the mad, sane. We Constables are left investigating whatever the Elites decide is beneath their concern. It never ceases to amaze me that humanity is all but besieged in this damn City, yet we are still eager to turn on one another, just as we do Earthside. This last string of murders though. Maybe it's time to turn what I've learned over to the Elites and let them handle this.

At first it appeared to be the standard murder/suicide. O'Hare family: husband, wife, and children dead in their beds. Doors and windows secured. It happens. Some things here push a man to madness; some things he sees can't be forgotten. But then, Marcia Partridge, butchered in her rooms, doors and windows locked from the inside. Then another, and another, the sealed rooms linking them all together. Now we're at a dozen, and the lunatic is leaving calling cards, written in the blood of its victims. "Sweep, Sweep, Sweep away. With their blood I'll make them pay", and "Catch me, catch me if you can, don't look up, I'm the rooftop man". Little rhymes to taunt us. Or perhaps to draw our attention. The witchhunters ruled out sorcery and necromantic magic, chastising me for wasting <u>their valuable time</u>. Damned Elite Divisions! People are dying, and we are no closer to finding this butcher, and I get a lecture from a self-important school marm?

I may be on to a lead. Chimney soot has been found mingled in the bloody notes. Each of the homes had a fireplace, could it be the killer is coming down that way? A killer strong enough to overpower entire families yet able to shimmy down a space too small for a Malifaux Rat to traverse   ? Gives me chills.

Lately it seems as if somebody is watching me. I feel eyes on my back when I turn away from my own hearth. It's as if the killer knows I am piecing this puzzle together. I must be getting jumpy in my old age, but writing this, I swear I can hear someone on my rooftop. Silly old man

CATCH ME CATCH ME IF YOU CAN...I'M THE ROOFTOP MAN...IN YOUR HOUSE I'LL COME TO PLAY...AND SWEEP, SWEEP, SWEEP YOU ALL AWAY

Constable Hamm Murdered
Found in his home, all the doors and windows locked from the inside, Constable Hamm's body was found lying across his journal. Murdered in the same manner as the victims of the crimes he was investigating, Hamm...

PUZZLE BOX

TO: Matheson, Lucius; Governor's Secretary

Following the disappearance of Stalker 263, I attach the papers that were discovered. There is still no trace of Thorpe.

Day One

I write what I see. I see a cell. It has stone walls and a door. The door is locked. I see a plate and fork. The plate is empty. I see this parchment, and a hand holding charcoal. I see these words. That is all I see.

I write what I know. I will endure to hunt and kill with the sword and gun, until I am dust. I will obey the words of my Master, and the righteous ordinances of the Guild. I will destroy the witches who seek to oppose them. This oath I swear on the lives I have wrongly taken. I will endure. I will obey. I will destroy. That is all I know.

I write what I feel. I feel nothing.

Day Two

I write of what has just occurred.

My Master brought me out of my cell. I walked behind her up a flight of stairs to a yard. She struck me in the face and bid me wait alone in the yard. A gate opened in a tall wall, and I saw a street with carriages going by.

The rain fell, and my hood and cape became wet. A raven flew over the yard. The rain stopped.

When the sun went down, the gate was closed. My Master appeared, and returned me to my cell. She told me I had done well. I sat down and wrote these words. When I finish I will hide the paper and charcoal in the hole behind the third brick on the seventh row.

Day Three

My broken sword is hanging outside my cell. My Master told me she can find me through it. I must remember this, although I do not know what it means.

I was taken to my sword this morning. My sword is very important. I know well that guns have their place, but it is the sword that smites the witch. The Instructor brought me from my cell and down a different set of stairs. The Instructor is smaller and older than my Master and requires a stick to walk as I do. He does not like me, and knows that I am murdering scum. He tells me so that I know it well.

My Master was waiting. The room where she waited was long and low and full of torches and swords. The swords were broken. As my Master spoke, they shone brighter than the torches. My Master placed her sword next to many of these broken swords, until she found one that would be my sword. It had words written along its blade. The words are different to the words I write here, but I was able to read them. In this writing, the words say, "Die Thou, Unsung." My Master asked if I was reading them. I said I was. My Master asked if I knew what they meant. I said I did not.

I have seen words written like those before. It hurts to think of them.

Day Four

I have received my second branding. Spells were written on my back. It took most of the day. I felt pain.

My Master told me that words have power. They can be spoken, or they can be written, or they can be read. Sometimes, words can be all three at the same time. Then they have a great power. That is why the words are placed on my skin. Placed there, they become words of great power. They will give me the strength I need to smite the witch, and protect me from his magics.

Day Five

I am not the only one.

Day Six

Yesterday I was late back to my cell from training. The Instructor trains me in sword and gun. He tells me I have never held a gun before. I do not know how he knows this. He is old and wise, so it must be true. He tells me I have held a sword before. I must ask my Master when this was. I do not remember it. After training ended, the Instructor told me I would join the other scum for training from now on. I did not know there were others like me. I did not want to forget this, but I am not allowed to write after the midnight gong has sounded, so could only write one line.

Today there was more training with gun and blade. There was also training with words. The Instructor spoke and we listened. I learned of the Guild, and the Witchling Masters and the Witchling Stalkers. My Master is one of the Witchling Masters known as Handlers. Before she was a Handler she was an Apprentice.

I am a Witchling Stalker. I do not know what I was before I was a Stalker.

I know well that all Witchling Stalkers are witches who have taken the lives of innocents with their magics and been caught by the Guild. For their crimes they are remade into Witchling Stalkers. Witchling Stalkers do not remember anything from before. I know well that the past is a slate the Guild burns clean. I do not remember my crimes, but know well they were hateful and wrong. I must atone.

I will stop writing now. I feel tired.

Day Seven

Many things happened today. I will write of them in the order in which they occurred.

But first I will write about what has just happened. The Instructor entered my cell and found these papers and charcoal. He was angry and struck me many times. He wanted to know where I had got them from. He did not believe me when I told him.

Then my Master appeared. My Master and the Instructor went away to speak. I have been ordered to stay in my cell until I am needed, but they left my cell door open. I went to the doorway and listened. I heard them talking in loud voices. I kept my feet in my cell, but leaned my head out. In this way I was not disobedient. I saw my Master poking the Instructor in his chest with her finger. She spoke quietly to him. I did not hear her words, but they were few and hard. The Instructor's face reminded me of the witch I will write of later, and he walked away. My Master read these papers. She told me I had done well.

But I must write of the morning. This morning I was taken back down the flight of stairs by my Master. Instead of going to the hall with the swords she took me another way. I went down three more flights of stairs, and passed through three doors. My Master unlocked them and then locked them again when we had passed.

My Master brought me to a room where there were others like me. There were four of them. They wore hoods and capes like mine. They had guns and broken swords. The swords had writing on them, but my Master has told me not to read that kind of writing again. Their skin was black and burnt. Mine is, too. I had not noticed until that time. I must ask my Master how we all came to be burnt.

I joined the four in a circle around two witches. I know well that witches are a pestilence, and that their subversion arouses hatred against the learned men and women of zeal who tirelessly serve the offices of the Guild in the name of the Governor. One witch was a man. He did not look at us. He was young and dark-skinned, with chains on his hands and feet. The other witch was a woman. She was also young, with golden eyes and wore chains. She looked at us. We looked back.

My Master asked if I knew her name. I said her name was witch. The woman did not look at us again.

My Master was joined by the Instructor and by other Masters, men and women. The Master's Master arrived.

She had short red hair, and was dressed all in black like a raven. My Master has long, black hair, tied back. She wears faded, brown leathers lined with fur, like a dirigible pilot, and she has knives in her boots.

The Masters spoke many words I will not write down. The man was sentenced to service, and taken to receive the first branding. Fear came into him, and he struggled. He was taken through a large, yellow door made of stone that was locked and barred with many bolts and seals. I believe I have seen that door before, but I do not remember when. It gave me a strange feeling in my skull when I looked at it, and an image of a maze came into my mind. The red-haired Master of Masters went with him.

The Instructor told me the golden-eyed woman was not suitable for branding. I killed her with my broken sword.

Day Eight
Today I served the Guild for the first time. I will write of that.

Me and the four like me gathered in the yard. The night had been cold, and there was a white frost. We received the last branding, which is an iron collar. It is heated over a brazier of coals and then clasped in place. The spells written on the inside are burned into the flesh. I ignored the pain, as did the others like me. I have been burnt before, I know. I will endure.

Then I went with my Master into the city, through underground tunnels. My Master carried a torch, and I realized I did not need light to see in the dark places. It was then I realized I do not have any light in my cell, either, and that I have written all these words in darkness. Are there other things about me I do not know? How can I ask, if I do not know the questions?

My Master talked of her work. She hunts rogue spell-casters, witches and those known as the Arcanists. My Instructor says they are all the same, but my Master rolled her eyes when I told her this. Her eyes are blue, like river ice. She wears hunter's kohl around them, to make them fierce. I will help her in this work. This is how I will atone.

My Master talked of hunting. Most hunts are short affairs, and most prey are feckless and stupid. Such hunts are not sport, as only one side knows they are in a game. Some hunts go on longer. Such hunts can last for months, or even years, and the target is as much predator as prey. Such a hunt brings out the tiger in all who take part, and there is peril on both sides. She said that those who have hunted dangerous men and women long enough never care for anything else thereafter. She also said there is nothing so bittersweet as after the final chase, when the hunter stands victorious. I wanted to ask what these things meant, but my Master signalled for silence.

We ascended to the city, where we walked the streets. Even in the busiest lanes, none came close to us.

I asked who we were hunting. My Master laughed, which I had never seen her do, and said we hunted the past. She did not explain how that was possible. She said that sometimes prey would go to ground, and the hunter would need to wait them out, but that today we would not hunt anyone. Today was simply about getting my boiler running and making sure I did not blow a gasket. These are her exact words. I remember working with engines, and how boilers should be tested before they are connected to a drive-shaft. I am pleased that I understand this.

My Master took me to several different places, and at some of these there were people she spoke to, and at others there were none. In certain empty places I felt the words written on my back squirm and read themselves through me. This happened in a cellar, and again at the top of a tower on a bridge, amid the scattered ruins of some machine. I told my Master of this, and she said it was normal. I was sensing the residue of past magics or the taint of long-gone witches.

We went to a tall, thin house in a street of tall, thin houses where a woman lived alone. She was not a witch, and my Master spoke to her kindly, although the woman seemed anxious. They talked for a while, she short and round and my Master tall and thin like the house. I noticed that although it did not seem like it, everything she said to the woman was a question.

When we left, I asked about the woman. My Master told me that the woman was decent. She made a living any way she could, hand to mouth, sometimes crossing the line, but not enough to rouse the Guild. It had all been to raise enough scrip to send her son back through the Breach, and away from this life. But her son had been killed by a wolf my Master had once hunted, a wolf who had turned mankiller without warning.

My Master said that the woman had not wanted to see me, not even to spit in my eye. She seemed disappointed at this.

Later she returned me to the cells beneath the Guild Academy.

I do not think my Master was talking about a real wolf.

In the old woman's house, I saw myself in a mirror for the first time. I was curious to see what I look like. As my Master and the woman talked, I removed my hood and face cloth. My head is bare and burned all over, and the skin scarred and pale. I do not recognize my face. It is possible no one would. I have a deep wound on my head, which is well healed. It runs all the way around my head, from back to front, in a circle. I do not remember how I was cut there, or when.

The woman with the golden eyes frightens me. She is in my cell, and will not go away.

Day Nine

During the night my Master came for me. I took *Die Thou, Unsung* from its hook outside my cell and received my handgun and ammunition from the Instructor. When we assembled in the yard, I could smell smoke on the air. It was cold and the stars were sore to look at.

We went through the city to the river where a fire burned. A building had fallen, its façade turned to rubble. A crater outside suggested explosives. I wanted to examine the crater, but my Master led me into the ruined building. It had been a teahouse, which in this part of town, my Master said, means a whorehouse. Behind it, a connected warehouse burned. The fire was too fierce to approach, although other Guild agents were present and their mechanical forms enabled them to enter the fire. I told my

Master that witches were here. The writing on my back told me so. My Master waved my words away and spoke with two men, both of them also Masters. She returned and told me this was a waste of time, and our business lay elsewhere. I asked what that business was. She did not answer. I asked who the witches were, and why we did not hunt them. She told me they were Three Kingdoms, and that other Masters hunted their kind. I asked if the Three Kingdoms had different witches and different magics. She shook her head, and told me I asked too many questions.

Everything I see is a question waiting to be asked. A question unasked is like a puzzle unsolved.

We travelled on foot to Dockmast Four, and from there by tethered aircar out over the Quarantine Zone, along the newly-repaired Sourbreak line. We did not go all the way to Sourbreak Station, and my Master called a halt at an unmanned Dockmast deep inside the Quarantine Zone. The Guild Guard who crewed the aircar's guns asked my Master how long we would be stopped there, and when we would be leaving. She ordered them to await our return. I saw fear come into them. They fetched more ammunition for their guns, and strung heavier netting around the portholes.

We descended the dockmast stairs. At the bottom my Master opened a heavy, iron door and we passed through into an unlit street. My Master locked the door. The keys sounded loud in the silence. There were many deep claw marks in the metal around the lock.

"No lights, not here," my Master told me. "You must be eyes for both of us."

She spoke quickly, her voice low, and gave me directions. I followed them carefully, past buildings of many different ages and styles. All lay in ruins. My Master made no sound as she walked, but I could not move as she did, and the scrape of my boots echoed. The writing spoke its warnings. Small things stirred as we passed, or large things that stirred slowly. *Die Thou, Unsung* felt eager in my hand. At one corner, the writings spoke of the ruined pillars down a street to our left. My Master put a hand on my shoulder and we waited. We waited a long time, for what I do not know, and then at her whispered word hurried past the ruined pillars.

We reached the destination without further incident. My Master was breathing hard as she opened a hidden doorway in a timber and plaster wall. Steps led down. She closed the door behind us. Warning me to step where she did, my Master took every second step and then, near the bottom, every third. We stopped before another door, and my Master told me to open it. Having no key I pushed at the door. My hand tingled briefly, and then I heard a click and it swung open.

A suite of rooms lay beyond. The ceilings were low, the walls tiled in brown brick glaze and broad arches led from room to room. Yellow anbaric lights on the walls sparked into life as my Master flicked a switch. The furnishings were rich, but without prettiness or female embellishment, as one would expect in a bachelor's apartments. The rooms held no clear purpose, and as we walked through them I saw many tables spread with papers and contraptions of glass and silver whose functions were not obvious. I saw writing desks stained with ink, and many boxes of nibs and rolls of spare paper. I saw one table entirely covered with drawings of mazes and labyrinths, and another empty but for a small, wooden puzzle box. Mixing jars and bottled compounds filled a nested set of boxes on a side table. I saw machines and devices, wired together in elaborate arrays not unlike the cable network we had made use of. A stand held a glass helmet studded with inwardly pointing rods and what looked like chisels. I saw one device with heavy rollers that smelled of printer's ink. In a back room, the component parts of a Stirling engine lay disassembled in neat rows. Most of all, I saw books and journals of all kinds, most arranged in bookshelves but many piled on tables and on the rugs, some closed and some pinned open, some printed and some handwritten. I saw intricate illustrations and rough etchings, brilliant color plates and crude hand printed pamphlets.

"This was the den of a rogue known as Damian Ravencroft," my Master told me, stopping to examine the titles of a stack of journals piled on a tall stool. She waved one of the books at the rooms surrounding us. "What do you make of him?"

I understood she meant me to deduce facts about the man from the way he lived. I told my Master I saw many books.

"Which tells you what?"

I replied that Mr. Ravencroft liked to learn.

"He was a magpie. He hoarded. This was his nest." She waved the book again. "What else?"

I spoke of the device with rollers. It printed words. He wished to share what he learned with others.

"He loved being the center of attention. He loved spreading rumors and raising awkward questions. Questions tempt lies. Lies tempt unrest. What else?"

I thought of the chess board, the drawings of labyrinths and the puzzle box. I said that he liked games.

My Master nodded. "In that we agree. He liked games. He liked winning them most of all." She swept some papers off a high-backed armchair and sat down. "Damian Ravencroft was an oddity, even among the witches we hunt. He did not live among others of his kind, but they sought him out, even here, among the perils of the Quarantine Zone. If I heard his name from one witch I caught I must have heard it from a hundred. Damian Ravencroft had told them what an arcane device was for, and how it worked. Damian Ravencroft had translated some ancient runes for them. Damian Ravencroft can get them passage through the Breach. The good Doctor Ramos himself had occasional need to consult with none other than Damian Ravencroft. Damian Ravencroft had travelled everywhere, seen everything and could probably dance on the head of a pin while he did it."

She stood, with a snort, and began turning out papers from a series of pigeon holes. "There are two sides to every story, and one must be careful who one trusts in times like these. Some in the Guild said he was just a rogue like any other. Others thought there was something different about this one. Some said he was the head of a great underground network working against the Guild, a cunning, dangerous man who posed a potent threat. A master criminal with connections in all the wrong places. Others thought he was cunning and dangerous, yes, but in a different way. He was a seeker of knowledge. An inquiring mind. His greatest desire was to see his knowledge of magic and arcana spread as far and as wide as possible, shared out so that a pauper could know as much as a king. A true democracy of the learned. Some thought that was even worse. Others," she paused, "were not so sure."

She paced over to a marble-topped chess table and moved the pieces around on the board without purpose. "Most so-called Arcanists care nothing about other people. They are in it for themselves. Their powers flare up, they go on a spree and we knock them down." She toppled a row of pawns over one by one as she spoke. "Feckless and stupid. But Ravencroft seemed like something new, something I hadn't seen before. A man who imagined something bigger than himself." She picked the king up and put it back beside the queen on the first row. "And so the name of Damian Ravencroft continued to be heard, but the man himself, despite years of searching by the Guild, remained hidden."

"And then it all changed. The wolf bared his fangs." My Master's face became hard when she spoke these words. "In the space of a month he killed three people. Murdered them. Witnesses saw it. He had never killed anyone before, but those three lives put him on my list. I hunted him. So did many others, but I knew him better. Or thought I did. He ran, which told me all I needed to know. It was the most dangerous hunt of my life, but finally I ran him to ground. Here, in his lair. I don't know why I'm telling you this. It doesn't mean anything to you." She shook her head, and picked the queen up from the chess board. She placed a finger on the king, leaning it over. "He confessed, readily. He was unrepentant. He wanted me to know what he had done, the power he commanded. He left me with no choice, and I gave him no mercy."

She toppled the king over, and turned slowly, staring at the room. "And so we are left with questions, which lead only to lies." She tossed the queen away into a corner, and left to examine the other rooms.

I did not understand all of this, and that irks me, but I recount it here as best I can recall.

I returned to the wooden puzzle box I had seen earlier. It sat alone on a table, on a white cloth. It was made of a dark wood I cannot name, and inlaid with a lighter wood in intricate curling patterns. As I look at it now, here in my cell, I think those patterns form a labyrinth. I try and trace a route through it, but it shifts and changes, and I lose my place.

I have tried to open the puzzle box many times, but have failed so far. I will continue. My Master has not said anything about the puzzle box, and I assume she does not mind that I took it. In any event, the golden-eyed woman said I should.

I was going to finish writing there, but I remember one other thing that happened before we returned to the aircar network. My Master was looking at a collection of old bones set in a glass case. There was writing carved on the bones, writing that gave me a strange feeling when I looked at it. I asked what the bones were. My Master replied that they looked like memory charms, powerful ones, but could serve no purpose she could tell. Some of the head bones had been carved with what looked like more labyrinths. She said she would return here, until every one of Damian Ravencroft's puzzles were solved, and then burn everything, as he had been burned.

I asked if the bones were the remains of Mr. Ravencroft's three victims. My Master looked distant for a moment, lost in thought, and then told me that they were not, and that the bones were much older and probably bought from a supplier of such things, but that I had finally asked a good question.

My Master told me her name while we rode back in the aircar. She is called Bellaventine Thorpe.

Day Ten

I know well that Witchling Stalkers do not sleep, but last night I dreamt. I will write about the dream.

I was looking down on myself, at the scar that circles my head, and it became a stone circle in the floor of my cell. I have seen this circle before, and it had writing around it. I recalled some of what was written around the circle. In the dream, writing appeared, growing like snakes across the floor. I could not remember any more, and the writing remained incomplete.

The woman with golden eyes was in my cell. The blood from where I killed her dripped onto the floor. She told me I had to complete the writing around the circle.

I told her I was sorry I had killed her. She walked into the circle and disappeared.

I did not awake, but I was aware the dream had ended. I spent the rest of the night trying to open the puzzle box. I failed. The wooden patterns on the puzzle box are definitely a labyrinth, but try as I might I cannot make progress and solve the maze. It changes and I lose my place every time.

The Instructor came by shortly before the morning gong. I asked if he could assist with the puzzle box. He looked around my cell, but did not look at the box, which I was holding up to him. He spat through the hatch in the door, and told me there was something wrong with me.

I do not believe this is so. I feel well.

I will endure.

Day Eleven

Today was spent training with gun and sword.

My Master told me to write about whatever I want, so I will write about her.

My Master is like the puzzle box. I look at her and think I understand, but every time I look closer I get lost.

She came to me during training and ordered me away from the others. She was unsteady on her feet, and slurring her words. She smelled of brandy. I was glad to go, as the Instructor was being very hard on me.

To begin with she was angry with me, and shouted at me. She delivered many insults. Then she quietened and stopped talking for a while. Finally, she told me she was right about me. She told me the other Masters were starting to question her judgement, but that she knew she was right. She repeated it several times, and I did not reply. I did not know how to. Her final comment, before returning me to the training, was that the only things she did not understand were how, and why.

I think I am a puzzle box to my Master. I do not think she enjoys puzzles as much as I do.

I had the dream-that-was-not-a-dream again. I remembered more of the words around the circle on the floor. What will it mean when I remember them all?

Day Twelve

Today I failed the Guild and, more importantly, my Master. I am ashamed, and know well that I must always obey my Master in all things.

So why can I not? Is there something wrong with me?

We were running a rogue witch to ground, in an area of the New Construction near the Penitence Viaduct. His name was Marco Bonatti. I later learned that he had been visited by the Guild seeking information about a murder at a guesthouse in Arble Street. Thinking he was going to be accused of the crime (he was not) Bonatti killed the Guard officers and fled. His use of arcane witchery in doing so was what set my Master on the hunt.

We picked up his trail without difficulty. The writing on my back found him as a needle finds a lodestone, but he had been reckless in his use of his powers, and had left more than just magical traces. Anyone who had got in his way was dead. Each of them had been torn apart, either by claws or teeth. I later learned that Bonatti's witchcraft enabled him to send forth the tribal drawings and other tattoos on his body in physical form.

The trail led to the viaduct. It has not been used since Hollow Marsh Pumping Station was commissioned, and has fallen into ruin in many places. Much of the New Construction area has stone from the viaduct in its foundations.

The trail led like a glowing path through the ruins, but my Master could not follow it as clearly as I could, and she fell behind. Her sword and *Die Thou, Unsung* were still connected, of course, and she could follow me anywhere.

I was able to surprise Marco Bonatti and get close to him, but before I could strike he tried to use his witchcraft. I felt a surge of energy like a great wave, and saw the macabre creatures inked on his arms writhe and coil.

Then there was a sound in my head like the tide going out a long way over a pebbled beach. His power drained away into nothing, and the writing on my back read and wrote and spoke itself all at once. He tried again, but the sea was vast and empty and nothing he had could fill it up. His energies poured into the void. I stood before him on the dry beach and felt his despair. I raised *Die Thou, Unsung,* speaking its name to the witch Bonatti so that he would know his fate.

I could not strike.

The woman with the golden eyes knelt before me, not Marco Bonatti.

"Die Thou," I said. I was still frightened of her. "Unsung."

She spoke. "No. You alone will sing of me."

Marco Bonatti writhed in anguish, pinned like a fly in amber as he awaited my strike. I lowered my sword. The woman was gone.

My Master arrived and I helped her restrain the witch Bonatti so that he could be taken for questioning. My Master did not speak to me of what had happened until after he had been placed in an iron Witch Cage to nullify his poison, and the Guild Guard had taken him away.

She asked if it had been my intention to capture or kill him. I replied he had been a danger to others, and I had intended to kill him.

"But you did not."

"No," I replied. I offered no explanation. I was concerned that if I mentioned the woman with the golden eyes, my Master would agree with the Instructor that there was something wrong with me. Why did I not strike the witch Bonatti? I cannot say. I just could not.

My Master did not ask for an explanation. She just nodded, as if she agreed with something I had not said. Then she told me that we would pay a visit the next day to the Guild morgue.

I asked what would happen to the witch Bonatti. My Master told me that he was an ideal candidate for being made into a Witchling Stalker. I asked if this would be done.

"Not in all cases, but we are short on numbers. The Sourbreak disaster didn't help, of course. We lost quite a few there. I expect Mr. Bonatti will be joining you for training soon enough, once we have put him to the question. He won't be Mr. Bonatti any more, of course."

"How is it done?" I asked.

My Master sighed, with a half-smile. "You never could stop asking questions." We walked a while before she spoke again. "The magic involved is some of the oldest and most potent the Guild possesses, and I do not know it myself. Sonnia Criid, the Master of the Handlers, takes the witch alone into the Yellow Crypt. I have never been in there. Once inside, Lady Criid uses that place to burn out whatever magic is within the witch. How it is done exactly, I do not know. All the witch's power is lost, along with their memories and personalities, leaving behind a bottomless pit inside the witch. The new Stalker now acts as a lightning rod, attracting and exhausting all magic near it, and it is what makes you such an effective tool against your former comrades. While you last."

Day Thirteen

I have seen my Master look at me many ways. Sometimes I see anger or disappointment, sometimes hatred. Tonight, when she returned me to my cell after the visit to the morgue, there was something new.

She looked at me like a tiger.

In the morning she had come for me as usual. She had an unusual sense of energy about her, as if nothing could happen quickly enough.

My Master asked me to recall the short, round woman she had taken me to see a few days ago. She asked if the woman had looked poor to me. I recalled that the house was clean and the woman had food and drink to offer my Master. Her clothes were well-mended. I replied she did not look poor.

We went to the Guild morgue, beneath the monolithic Guild headquarters. There, she spoke to the head of the morgue briefly, a Dr. McMourning, and he passed us to one of his assistants.

She led my Master and I into a long hallway lined with rough wooden cabinets. My Master gave the assistant a list of three names, two male, one female. My Master tapped her fingers on a cabinet until the assistant returned with three brown folders, secured with string. Each bore an "Autopsy" stamp on the front, as well as a warning that the subject's remains were magically contaminated.

On the way to the morgue, my Master had explained that the bodies and effects of those killed with magic were often retained by the Guild School of Surgeons, in case the Witch Hunters had need of them.

My Master demanded to be taken to the remains. The assistant, a girl who seemed tired and bored, led us to a sub-basement level, and through a series of metal doors. The air grew colder with each door, until our breath fogged. The assistant took a heavy coat from a hook and put it on. My Master had to unlock the last door, which had the Witch Hunter's sigil upon it. Beyond, a series of connected halls held row after row of locked caskets of varying sizes. Frost covered them, and crunched underfoot.

The assistant consulted books of records. This took a while, due to the heavy gloves she wore. I could see my Master was having trouble remaining patient.

"There are no remains for any of those three names," the girl said when she had finished.

"Then what was collected at the scene?" my Master asked.

"Ashes. We discard those." The girl was sniffling with the cold.

"How were the bodies identified?" my Master demanded. The assistant turned to her books, but my Master pushed her aside and did it herself. "Personal effects", she said when she was done. She swore. "I should have seen this sooner."

She did not speak to me for the rest of the day.

...

I am not supposed to be writing this now, as the midnight gong has sounded, but I believe I should.

I had the dream-that-was-not-a-dream again, and I have nearly remembered all the writing on the circle. It is almost complete.

The woman with the golden eyes was here. She told me that the only key to a labyrinth is a map of the labyrinth itself. She told me I already have it.

I asked the woman what her name was. She told me she did not know. I asked what it was like to be dead. She said the woman she looked like was dead, but that she was not that woman, and that I should think of her as an *aide memoire*. I asked why she looked like the dead woman. She replied that that was up to me. I told her I was sorry, anyway.

Day Fourteen
Much has happened. I think much more is about to happen. I am about to open the box. If this does not work, if it all goes wrong, then whomever is reading this – whoever you are – you will read this, and mock whatever is left of me, but I risk it all for what I believe in. Remember that.

The morning gong sounded, but it was midday before Bel came. She was fully dressed in her faded aviator leathers with the fur trim, and she was armed. A tiger's heart, wrapped in a woman's hide. She stood in my cell door, staring at me for some time. One half of her face was chalked pure white. Over the top, she had drawn a skull's stark lines in black hunter's kohl. She looked fearsome.

"Is there something you require of me?" I asked.

"The game is drawing to a close. I think I know the how, just not the why. So this is last time I will come for you," she said.

"Am I going somewhere?"

"If you're leaving, it won't be with me. But I will be waiting for you."

"Why would I leave?"

"Because you'll have done what you came for. Whatever it was. I hope it was worth it."

"I did not come here. I was caught."

She smiled. It lent her eyes a terrible aspect. "Were you now?"

She left. I have not seen her since.

I spent the rest of the day in my cell.

I returned to the puzzle box. I still could not understand what the golden-eyed woman had meant when she said I already had the key to open it.

Then the dreams returned. That is, I thought they were dreams. They are memories.

I saw a man with dark glasses standing on a platform at Malifaux Station. He met with a young man and his mother, a short, round woman. He gave them both money, and the young man got on a train. This happened twice more, with another man, and a woman. I hope they are well.

I saw a crypt with yellow walls. Inside a circle on the floor knelt a man, bruised but defiant. I was that man, once. Outside the circle stood a woman with hair like fire. Around the circle was the oldest of magics, the Guild's most jealously-guarded secret, written in the stone floor. I heard a sound like the tide going out a long way on a pebbled beach, and realized I was the tide. Everything I was drained away into a void. The oldest of magics burned brightly all around me, and I burned with them. The first branding.

I saw myself, only a few days ago, a golden-eyed woman lying dead before me. She will not have died unsung. I will make the Guild pay for her death at my hands.

Back further into memory. I saw myself, unburned. I was in a room with dark furnishings, and anbaric lights glimmered on the walls. I placed my head in a glass device of my own invention and it cut me, like a surgeon would, a single, clean cut all the way around. While aetheric fields shielded me from pain, I directed the machine with thought and gesture. Chisels with soulstone tips wrote words in the living bones of my skull.

Some words have power. They can be spoken, or they can be written, or they can be read. Sometimes, words can be all three at the same time. Then they have a great power. That is why the words were carved on my skull. Placed there, they become words of great power. They gave me the protection I needed from the stone circle to come.

I saw myself in the same room, fashioning a puzzle box from thought alone. I knew what was inside that box now.

I was.

All my knowledge, all my memory, all my power. Once I open the box, it will return to me.

The chisels carved a witch-maze in my head with their soulstone fingers.

In my cell, I touched my burned scalp. Words beneath the skin. In the bone. Words much more powerful than anything written on my back, or on the collar around my neck.

The fingers of my left hand followed the lines of the witch-maze etched beneath the flesh, while the fingers of my right followed the lines of the labyrinth on the puzzle box. I had my key, and it had been with me all along.

The puzzle box unlocked.

I dived back into memory one last time.

I saw a crypt with yellow walls. Inside a circle on the floor knelt a man, bruised but defiant. I am that man. I looked upon the oldest of magics written on the stone around me, that which no man has ever seen and lived to remember. The Guild's most powerful, most secret magics.

I remember them all.

Tigress Bel was right about me. I have what I came for.

It is time to go.

EXORCIST - MINION

Remarkably, Earthside beliefs have provided the Guild with some of its most efficient weapons against the Resurrectionist threat. Centuries of histories, practices, legends, and myths point to several methods for eliminating evil spirits and the walking dead. Death Marshal Exorcists are tasked with learning to use these weapons effectively in the Guild's ongoing efforts to eradicate the growing number of undead in Malifaux.

An Exorcist's talents are honed not only by numerous encounters with the undead but also by countless hours spent researching occult texts on the subject of banishing evil spirits and bringing peace to the restless dead. They are students of a specialized type of military history, applying their learning daily to their duties protecting the citizenry of Malifaux; practitioners of lost arts, not holy men and women.

When facing one of the walking dead, the Exorcist's blessed symbol of office and crossbow cut through the aetheric ties binding the undead to this world. Their litanies of exorcism disrupt spirits and other unliving beings, allowing them to be dispatched with mundane weapons as easily as a creature of flesh and blood. Most impressive is their ability to drive back scores of undead with an invocation, often demonstrating even greater control over their foes than those who raised them from the grave.

30MM BASE **SOULSTONE COST: 6**

DEATH MARSHAL, RARE 2

WK/CG	HT	WP	CA	DF	WD
3/-	2	6	5🟣	4	7

SYMBOL OF OFFICE	
RG	⚔ 2
CB	6🟣
DG	1/2/3

SANCTIFIED CROSSBOW	
RG	🏹10
CB	5🟣
DG	2/3/4

TALENTS:

Abilities

Fear Not Death: This model receives +2 **Wp** in Duels with the Undead when it is the defender.

Hard To Wound 1

Intractable: This model cannot be sacrificed or buried.

Slow to Die

Stubborn

Weapons

Sanctified Crossbow: Magical.

Symbol of Office: Magical. This Weapon's Damage Flips receive 🔼 when damaging non-living models. Attacks with this Weapon ignore the **Armor** and **Hard to Wound** Abilities.

Actions

(+1) Driven by Purpose: This model suffers 1 **Wd**. Push this model up to 3".

(0) Blessing of Banishment: ⚫6. The basic melee Weapons of other friendly models gain Magical.

(1) Last Rites: (X)6. Sacrifice all Corpse and Scrap Counters not carried by models.

Triggers

Ca/Cb (🟣✗) Banish to Oblivion [Exorcise/Symbol of Office]: Instead of flipping for damage with this attack against a defender with the Undead, Soulless, Spirit, or Nightmare Characteristic, sacrifice the defender unless its Controller discards two Control Cards or one Soulstone. Only models with the **Use Soulstone** Ability may discard Soulstones.

Cb (🟣) Critical Strike [Sanctified Crossbow]

Cb (🟣) Final Repose: After killing defender with a melee attack, defender does not generate Corpse or Scrap counters.

SPELLS:

(0) Turn Undead
(CC: 12💀 / Rst: Wp / Rg: (X)8) Push models with the Undead, Spirit, or Soulless Characteristic 4" directly away from this model.

(1) Damning Oratory
(CC: 13🟣 / Rst: - / Rg: ⚫6) Enemy models with the Undead, Spirit, Soulless, or Nightmare Characteristic cannot declare Triggers.

(1) Exorcise
(CC: 12✗ / Rst: Df / Rg: 🏹10) Target model with the Undead, Spirit, Soulless, or Nightmare Characteristic suffers **Dg** 2/3/4.

LATIGO PISTOLERO - MINION

Despite several off-color rumors to the contrary, not every resident of the Ortega family's compound at Latigo is related. Many of Latigo's supporting staff have been recruited by the Ortegas for their particular talents and specialties, including the fighters the Ortegas select as mercenaries.

Hired from some of the lowest of dregs found in the City's bars, these pistoleros are selected for their hardened demeanors just as much as for their skill with a pistol. It takes a cold heart and bold spirit to survive for long in the Ortegas' employ. The Nephilim keep the compound in a quasi-state of siege, testing the mettle of anyone who would attempt to reach it or reside there for long.

Ironically, this crucible of danger ties the pistoleros through bonds of interdependence with one another and with the Ortegas. A lifetime of anger slowly gives way to pride as each pistolero is called upon to believe in himself or herself, and those he works with. Trust in one another, given begrudgingly at first, becomes the norm as the very survival of Latigo's residents depends on their ability to work together as a cohesive group – as a family.

30MM BASE　　　　　　　　**SOULSTONE COST: 3**

FAMILY, INSIGNIFICANT, RARE 3

WK/CG	HT	WP	CA	DF	WD
4/6	2	5	4	5	5

HUNTING KNIFE		PISTOL	
RG	///1	RG	⌐10
CB	5	CB	4
DG	1/3/4	DG	2/3/4

TALENTS:

Abilities

Ornery: This model cannot be activated by another friendly model's Talents. This model cannot activate simultaneously with other friendly models.

Stubborn

Actions

(All) "Look out!": (Γ)4. Friendly Family models that have not yet activated this turn receive +2 **Df** until they activate.

(0) Follow Their Lead: This model gains +1 **Cb** when targeting a model that was targeted by a friendly Unique Family model this turn.

Triggers

Cb (🗡) Critical Strike [Hunting Knife]

SPELLS:

(0) Shrug Off
(CC: 10 / Rst: - / Rg: C) Discard one Token or end one effect on this model plus one effect or Token per 🗡 in the casting total.

PALE RIDER - MINION

A tireless and soulless tracker, the Rider doggedly chases its quarry. Unmoved by actions of the living it encounters, it rides hell-bent for leather, in single-mindedly pursuit. Witnesses have dubbed it "the Pale Rider" because it appears as a masked Guild Death Marshal riding a pale, almost phantom-like steed, yet no record of such a Death Marshal or his mount exists.

Its motivations are a mystery. One theory, supported by the sworn statements of several witnesses, suggests the Pale Rider is called to sites of impending death. It has been sighted along a ridgeline, a ghostly statue watching as an encounter between Neverborn and Guild was fought below, every combatant dead by the end. Another sighting of the Pale Rider put it alongside the River, watching silently as a ferry boat sank, all hands and passengers lost to the River's icy currents. Yet several others mention the Pale Rider taking an active hand in death-dealing, deadly accurate with the hunting rifle always at its side.

Whatever the Pale Rider's ultimate purpose, its presence in Malifaux is seen by residents as a harbinger of death. Individuals witnessing the Pale Rider's arrival at its destination soon experience their own deaths, either at its hands or by some unexpected catastrophe.

50MM BASE

SOULSTONE COST: 9

CONSTRUCT, SOULLESS, UNIQUE

WK/CG	HT	WP	CA	DF	WD
6/10	3	6	5	5	9

FINAL MOMENTS

RG	⟋12
CB	6 🌀
DG	2/3/4

TALENTS:

Abilities
Bulletproof 1

Chasing Death: At the start of this model's activation, it gains the benefits of one of the three **Stages** below. The **Stage** this model is in depends on how many models have been killed or sacrificed during this turn before the start of this model's activation. This model benefits from only one of the three **Stages** at any time.

Stage 1: Hungry for Death (0 models killed or sacrificed this turn):
- Cb (🌀) Critical Strike [Final Moments]
- Final Moments: This Weapon's Damage Flips receive ♣.

Stage 2: Reveling In Death (1-2 models killed or sacrificed this turn):
- Armor +1
- (2) Rapid Fire

Stage 3: Glutted on Death (3+ models killed or sacrificed this turn):
- (+1) Fast
- Hard to Wound 2

Gunfighter [Final Moments]

Immune to Influence

Weapon
Final Moments: This model heals 2 **Wd** each time it kills a model with this Weapon.

Actions
(2) Mounted Fusillade: Push this model up to its **Cg**. This model may interrupt the Push to make one Final Moments **Strike**. Continue the Push after resolving the **Strike**.

Triggers
Cb(🌀🐎) Ricochet: After damaging defender with a Final Moments **Strike**, another model within 3" of the defender suffers **Dg** 1/2/4.

SPELLS:

(0) Visions of Death
(CC: 9 / Rst: - / Rg: C) This Spell may only be cast if it is the first Action this model takes during its activation. This model increases or decreases its **Chasing Death Stage** number by one. This model gains the benefits for the new **Stage** under **Chasing Death**. This model loses any other **Stage** it had gained.

WARDEN - MINION

40MM BASE

SOULSTONE COST: 5

CONSTRUCT, GUARDSMAN

WK/CG	HT	WP	CA	DF	WD
5/7	2	5	4	5	6

MECHANICAL FIST	
RG	///2
CB	4🌀
DG	2/3/4

RESTRAINT CLAW	
RG	⌐8
CB	4🌀
DG	1/2/3

TALENTS:

Abilities

Armor +1

Immune to Influence

Mobile: This model ignores severe terrain and climbing penalties when taking the **Walk** or **Charge** Action.

Pursuit: This model's Attack and Damage Flips receive ♦ against models that have already activated this turn.

Actions

(+1) Relentless: Discard one Control Card. This model immediately **Walks**.

Triggers

Cb (🌀🌀) Pinning Blow [Restraint Claw]: A defender suffering 1 or more **Wd** from this Weapon receives **Paralyzed**.

Cb (🌀🐾) Toss [Mechanical Fist]: After damaging defender with a Mechanical Fist **Strike**, Push defender 1" directly away per wound inflicted, ignoring intervening models and terrain.

As the Guild discovers the benefits of using Constructs as ersatz Guardsmen, it continues to commission the design and implementation into service of new models. One of the newest models, dubbed the Warden, provides a very specific function, guarding the most hardened prisoners in the Malifaux Gaol.

Serving side-by-side with its human counterparts, the Warden makes an excellent prison guard. The Construct is a tireless, incorruptible machine with one edict: *guard*. Where its human counterparts can succumb to fatigue during long shifts, the Warden ceaselessly patrols the walls and cell blocks, the cadence of its heavy metal feet a disturbing lullaby for the Gaol's reluctant guests. Where graft is a fact of life with living Guardsmen, no prisoner has yet found a means by which to influence a Warden into turning a blind eye at roll call or to be away from its post when an escapee has crept by.

The Warden's armaments are designed for the containment and protection of prisoners as well as escape prevention and riot containment. Its fists are capable of smashing aside improvised barricades of debris, giving it easier access to its targets. The ingenious restraint claw mounted on the Warden's other arm allows it to bring down unruly prisoners in the yard as well as escapees who the Guild would rather be brought back alive than be gunned down by Guardsman sharpshooters.

The horrific Guild ritual used to create a Witchling has the adverse effect of nearly destroying the subject's mind in the process. Only through artfully delicate manipulation of the energies, which turn the subject's powers against herself, is a Witch Hunter able to preserve the subject's magic talents while at the same time wiping away the personality.

Once this process is complete, Witchlings return to Guild Headquarters as blank slates ready for whatever propaganda the Witch Hunters known as Witchling Handlers choose to encode on them. The Handlers are masters at their craft, feeding a Witchling just enough information to reinforce its connection to the roiling energies it possesses while at the same time keeping the reason for its punishment and plight a mystery.

Equipped with tools both mundane and magical, Witchling Handlers take Witchlings into the field as part of their indoctrination as well as to hone their magic-hunting talents. Handlers are capable magicians in their own right, directing their magical learning toward aetheric suppression rather than purely offensive spellcraft. They leave the true dirty work to the Witchlings under their command.

Over time, the bond between the pair grows, transforming into a sense of attachment the Witchling feels for its Handler. Many Witchlings obey and seek the favor of their Handlers much in the same way a loyal hound would its master. These 'hounds', however, are 'bred' to seek out a particular prize, and only the foolish Handler forgets just how dangerous his or her charges were and still can be if not kept on a short leash.

30MM BASE

SOULSTONE COST: 7

RARE 1

WK/CG	HT	WP	CA	DF	WD
4/6	2	6	6	4	8

RUNED GREATSWORD		PISTOL	
RG	2	RG	10
CB	6	CB	5
DG	2/3/5	DG	2/3/4

TALENTS:

Abilities

Magic Resistant 2

Teamwork [Witchling]: This model's Attack Flips receive 🃏 while engaged with an enemy model that is also engaged with one or more other friendly models with the indicated Characteristic.

Words Read: After this model successfully resists a Spell, draw one Control Card.

Words Spoken: Df and Wp flips made by friendly models with the Witchling Characteristic within 3" of this model receive 🃏. This model ignores damage inflicted by the **Immolating Demise** Ability.

Weapon

Runed Greatsword: Magical. Models damaged by this Weapon lose all suits associated with their **Ca** stat. Damage Flips with this Weapon receive 🃏.

Actions

(0) Distort Magic: 🃏4. Nominate one suit. Enemy model's casting totals containing that suit receive -2. Enemy models cannot declare Triggers involving that suit without first discarding one Control Card.

(1) Words Written: Push a friendly model with the Witchling Characteristic up to 4" toward the nearest enemy model.

Triggers

Cb (🔑) Critical Strike [Pistol]

Cb (📖) Magical Disruption [Runed Greatsword]: After hitting defender with this Weapon, defender's Casting Flips receive ⊟ during its next activation.

Df/Wp (🔑📖) Reflect Magic: After this model resists a Spell targeting it, the caster replaces this model as the target and suffers the Spell's effects. Use the difference in casting and resist totals if a difference is required. The reflected Spell has no effect if the caster could not be affected by it.

SPELLS:

(0) Goad Witchling
(CC: 14🔑 / Rst: - / Rg: 6) Inflict 1 **Wd** on target friendly model with the Witchling Characteristic. That model then receives +1/+2 **Wk/Cg** and its melee Weapon Damage Flips receive 🃏.

(1) Dispel Magic
(CC: 13 / Rst: Df / Rg: 12) Discard one Token or end one effect on target model. Wounds on the model or Tokens carried by the model cannot be discarded.

BRUTAL EFFIGY - MINION

Zoraida constructed the Effigies to fight fire with fire, turning the strengths of the various factions fighting in Malifaux upon themselves. Her scheme would have worked, had Fate not taken a hand. The Event breathed independent life into her creations, each pulled by invisible strings toward their own kind.

Resembling a Death Marshal with four equine legs, the Brutal Effigy's appearance links it to the Guild's iron-fisted aggressive will. Drawn to their manipulation of the most aggressive streams of aether, the Brutal Effigy has chosen to ally itself with the strongest forces of the Guild. Brutal's hand-sewn face remains hidden behind an outlaw's mask, aetheric power leaking from the mask's eye holes, as it provides martial support for whichever Master it feels has the most potential at any time.

Guild agents have begun to regard Brutal's presence during a fight with more gratitude than suspicion after its first sudden arrivals and departures during conflicts. Its weapons are a welcome addition when the tide of battle turns against the Guild.

30MM BASE

SOULSTONE COST: 4

OBJECT 1, SPECIAL FORCES (DOLL), UNIQUE

WK/CG	HT	WP	CA	DF	WD
4/6	1	6	4	5	5

TALENTS:

Abilities

Aetheric Connection: One friendly model with the **Aetheric Connection** Ability within 6" of this model may activate after this model's activation ends.

Aetheric Demands: Non-Neverborn Crews hiring this model must nominate one leader per model with this Ability they hire. Those leaders cannot attach Totems.

Other Allegiances [Neverborn]: This model may be hired by the indicated Faction's Crews at no additional cost.

Stubborn

Weapon
Chastiser Blade: Magical.

Actions
(+1) Melee Expert

Triggers
Cb (♥) A Pause for Thought [Chastiser]: If this Weapon inflicts Moderate or Severe damage on the defender, the defender receives **Slow.**

Cb (◉) Critical Strike [Chastiser Blade]

SPELLS:

(0) Invigorate
(CC: 13 / Rst: - / Rg: 6) Target friendly model performs a Healing Flip.

CHASTISER BLADE	
RG	🌙 1
CB	5 🐾
DG	2/3/4

CHASTISER	
RG	⌒8
CB	5
DG	2/2/3

RESURRECTIONISTS

DEADLINE

The side door of the old brewery swung open with a bang, and there stood Seamus. He wore a tweed suit as green as his eyes and held a leather satchel stained black as the night behind him. He threw Molly a smile, full of roguish charm and come-hither devilry. Fog swept about him as he entered, but either the fog or the smile was so cold Molly could feel the chill in her dead bones.

"Tell you what, Molly dearest," Seamus said, his eyes twinkling as he stalked across the flagstone floor. "The evening seems to have gotten away from me." He planted his leather case on the table next to Molly, with a thump that rattled the rows of bottles and distilling equipment, and flourished forth a set of bloody steel forceps. He frowned, waving the forceps to and fro. "I can't say as I remember using these."

He tossed them on the table and plucked a slender metal tube with scissored finger-grips from the bag. He chuckled. "Now, this! The Southey tube. When he sold me this, Sober George told me it was," he contorted his face and put on a posh accent, "*minimally invasive!*" He laughed again, tossing it back into his bag. Blood spluttered from the tip as it disappeared. "Then you're using it wrong, I told him! How we laughed! You've met Sober George, right?"

Molly realized Seamus wanted something complimentary. "He swears with great imagination," she offered, and that seemed to be enough.

Seamus paused for a moment, an odd blank look coming over his face. It passed, and he turned to Molly and grinned. "Wouldn't go near Mrs. Choke's Guesthouse on Arble Street for the next few days, Molly-me-love. Between you and me, the landlady's lost her charm." He shrugged his city-coat off and threw it at her. "Bit of claret spilled. Get some lye on, see if it'll come out. Now, how's me brew getting on?"

Molly handed off the coat to one of the Belles, who shuffled away behind the old sherry barrels, then she held out the papers she was carrying. Seamus, who was already toying around with the beakers on his table, took a few minutes to notice.

"Mail?" he exclaimed. "Oh, no! Not again! Not after the last time! I don't care if this one's my biggest admirer in all of Malifaux, unless she's included a portrait–"

"Mademoiselle Vestige delivered these," Molly interrupted, not wanting to stand through another re-telling of that sorry incident when Seamus had learned what it meant to have deluded ingenues falling in love with him by dark reputation, and wanting to meet. He'd been so disappointed when the lady in question, a Miss Abilene Shrivel of Number Twelve Clovequarter, had not quite lived up to her self-description – by several years and many, many more pounds – that he hadn't killed anyone for days. Molly placed the leaflets on the table, avoiding the spills that were already smoking gently.

"Mam'selle Vestige?" Seamus bounded over to Molly's side of the table and snapped them up. He rifled through them, discarding several with loud snorts of derision, and then fanned three out on the table with a cry of satisfaction. Each leaflet contained an address at the top, a lithographic image of a building beneath, and a description, written in the Mam'selle's flowing, artful script.

Molly had no idea what Seamus would want with a real estate agent, but something about one of the ones he'd discarded caught her attention. She picked it up while Seamus blathered on. Something was familiar about this building. She placed it on the table, on top of the other three.

"This one."

Seamus tried to brush the particulars away, but Molly's pale white finger pinned it to the oak.

"This one," she repeated.

Seamus straightened up, glanced at the Gorgon's Tear hanging around her neck then back up at Molly. He licked his lips. "You sure?"

Molly just stared back.

Another grin split Seamus' face. "Course you are, Molly dearest. What would I do without you? *Get me own way, like as not*," he answered himself in a stage-whisper before doubling up in laughter. "You meet with Mam'selle Vestige – be nice to her, she's got angles, that one – and she'll show you round that dump you've picked. Let me know what you find. And I've only just remembered what I used those forceps for." He fished around in the top pocket of his silk shirt and dug out an eyeball, dangling between finger and thumb by its own bloody optic nerve. The eye twitched and looked at Molly, the irising pupil somehow conveying a look of utter bewilderment and terror.

"Take Mrs. Choke with you. Show her round. Let her get a good eyeful, eh, Molly love?"

"Oh, I'm not just any real estate agent, Miss Squidpiddge, as you are not just any shuffling, mindless Undead, n'est pas? If it's not haunted, I don't touch it."

Mam'selle Vestige was a lot younger, and her French accent a lot less pronounced, than Molly had expected. She wore a lot more makeup, and in a much darker shade, than Molly would have been comfortable with – back when she'd been bothered about things like being comfortable. The woman's hair was as straight and black as an ebony waterfall, and she dressed in dark purple silks that had an Arabian air about them. Although they covered her from neck to toe, they seemed to be always promising to give a glimpse of scandalous flesh but, due to either remarkable dressmaking or impossible luck, the promise remained just that.

Molly was also fairly certain there was more than one weapon hidden in those eastern folds, but she had a good feeling about Mam'selle Vestige. She hadn't batted any of her heavily-blackened eyelashes when Molly had loomed out of the night fog pale as a sheet, her black hair piled atop her head like a thunderstorm, with dried blood crusted all down her chin and the front of her yellow, crinoline dress.

She had also only offered a courteous, "Mr. Tombers, I presume," when Molly had introduced the reanimated head in question to see what reaction it evoked. On her way to meet the not-just-any real estate agent, Molly had grown tired of Phillip Tombers' protestations at her carrying him by the hair like "a child swinging a damned sack of marbles by her side," and had decided to teach him a lesson. One terrified mother later, whom Molly had allowed to run away screaming with her infant safe in her arms, and Molly had arrived for her meeting with Phillip Tombers' apoplectic head being pushed in a wrought iron baby carriage. The pink woolen bonnet with the rabbit ears, Molly decided, had been the crowning touch.

As for the disembodied Phillip Tombers himself, he'd stopped sulking, and Molly could swear he was rather taken with the dark silk swishes and long black fingernails of Mam'selle Vestige.

"My clients are few and select, Miss Squidpiddge, as are the properties I handle. Seamus sent word that, as part of his new brewing endeavors – no, don't tell me," Mam'selle Vestige held up a hand, although Molly hadn't said a word. "I only ever drink whisky that's been shipped from Scotchland unopened, so whatever Seamus is up to is none of my business. And I always mind my own business. Which brings us here," she waved at the imposing brick edifice across the foggy street, "and although I have skipped the part where I tell you what Seamus wanted with this place, I have a feeling it is you that it wants to see, and not him."

Footsteps sounded, bare feet on cobbles, and an urchin dashed out of the cold, coiling mist, carrying a leather-wrapped parcel in her hand. Dressed in rags, she was nothing but skin and bone. A length of dirty sackcloth was tied over her lower face, but from above it burned black bitter eyes that looked at Molly without fear. The fingers that held the parcel were strangely long, and their tips seemed to disappear into the fog. Mam'selle Vestige unwrapped the parcel, read the letter within and with a wave of her hand the words on it vanished. She bent close to the girl, whispering words in a language Molly did not know, and when Mam'selle Vestige straightened up, the girl was gone. "One of my Crooligans. Well, I say mine... they keep an eye on things for me. They don't usually show themselves when I'm with others, but I think she quite liked you. It seems Malifaux is a busy place tonight," she added with a wink. "She tells me there's a former lodgings on Arble Street I might need to add to my books."

Molly felt Mrs. Choke squirm in her pocket, and she gave her an admonitory slap.

The fog cleared slightly and gave her a better look at the building. Near the edge of Downtown, this was not prime real estate, and the building was worn and tired looking. Clumps of gray vegetation sprouted from windows and cracks in the brickwork, and thick, dark stains flowed from leaks and gutters. Grime coated the broken glass in the many windows.

She knew this building, and started across the empty cobbles towards it, Phillip Tombers bouncing in the pram.

"You won't be going in alone, Miss Squidpiddge,"

The lone working gaslamp on the street guttered almost on command, and Molly saw two people standing beneath it, next to a shuttered and barred door. She aimed Phillip at them and applied the brakes just outside the cone of gaslight.

Mam'selle Vestige swept past in a tease of perfume and silk, a lit cigarette waving in her hand like a firefly on a wand as she made rapid-fire introductions. She had her business face on now, Molly saw.

"Miss Squidpiddge, this is Mr. Clarifester Drove, an independent mortuarial consultant and the creator of Drove's Spirit Cabinet, which can be seen weekly at the Star Theatre, and this is Ms. Divesta Honeychild, of the Mountbank Honeychilds. She is an authority on the Neverborn."

"The Manifestata," the diminuitive Divesta Honeychild corrected, with a frown. "The term Neverborn is not only incorrect, but offensive to these poor creatures. The writings of Dubious Peake on the subject in 1828 are–"

"–are no longer as widely read as they should not once have been," interrupted Mam'selle Vestige. "And this is Miss Squidpiddge, former reporter for the Malifaux Daily Record and now greatly skewing the average intelligence of the ranks of the Undead, and these are the earthly remains of Phillip Tombers, the hat is not his own."

Clarifester Drove was taciturn, fat and sweating in the cold air, with a humorless face that looked like a boiled potato. Strapped to his back in a whaling harness was a whining contraption of brass tubes, gleaming condensers, and naked electrical connections whose end product seemed to be a brass apparatus attached to a wide-bore pistol holstered on his left leg. He didn't even look at Molly, but kept staring up at the building through an assortment of lenses mounted on spidery brass rods.

With her tiny figure hidden under a full-length, black fog coat, her hands clasping a small, beaded bag, and her hair in a bun so tight it pulled the corners of her eyes up in a look of perpetual alarm, Divesta Honeychild looked like every stern choirmistress Molly had known growing up, although considerably smaller. She could actually see the moment where Ms. Honeychild dismissed Molly from her mind as being not worth thinking about, which only reinforced the memory.

"It's an open viewing tonight," Mam'selle Vestige carried on, "but I won't be accompanying you. Try not to get in each other's way, don't damage the fixtures, and send any offers to me, care of any Crooligan you can catch. The owner of this one would appreciate a quick sale, no strings." She flicked a finger at the door, and it swung inwards, the loud creaking swallowed by the fog. "Take as long as you like, and neither the vendor nor I are responsible for any injuries, mental or physical, you may sustain etc etc including death or Undeath etc etc. D'accord? Oui? C'est tout." And she walked out of the light, leaving only the tip of her cigarette beckoning through the fog before that, too, was gone.

Molly pushed the baby carriage through the open door, the wheels crunching over bits of rotted plasterwork and broken glass. The door was evidently a servant's entrance and led to a long, functional looking hall lined with doors and draped in shadows.

Clarifester Drove took up position in the middle of the hall, examining a softly glowing globe attached to the apparatus on his back. He stared up at the ceiling. "More than I expected. I'll be upstairs. You both stay down here for the next hour." He stumped off towards the stairs. "If you know what's good for you."

Divesta Honeychild *hurrumphed!*, placed her fingers on her temples and spun on the spot three times. One hand snapped away from her head as if burned and pointed away down the hall, away from Drove. "The confluence is strongest when diametric!" She sent a withering glance at Molly. "You may glimpse aetheric fire from my coronic discharge. Do not be alarmed, if your kind are even capable of such reactions. It is how I communicate with the Manifestata." She walked briskly away and vanished around a corner.

Molly looked down at Phillip and, with a twinge of remorse, tugged the bonnet off his head and tucked it away.

He looked up at her with a melancholy air. "Were people this mad before we died?"

She shrugged, blood trickling down her chin, and pushed him slowly down the hall.

"There are unquiet spirits here," said Phillip, keeping his voice low. "I reckon that's what Drove's looking for. More supplies for his Spirit Cabinet, perhaps. But it's you *they're* looking for. Be careful, Molly. This place has a lot of hidden faces, and they're all watching you."

She could sense the same presences Phillip could, but Molly had more immediate concerns. She was certain she knew this building, but her memory was more full of holes than any one of Seamus' victims. This building had been important, once. An idea occurred, and she headed for the public entrance.

It took a lot of raking around in the detritus of the main lobby, but she eventually found what she was looking for. The building's faded brass nameplate: Octavius Hall.

She stood for a moment, desperately trying to bridge the gaps in her memory.

Of course! *Octavius Hall.*

"Are you feeling all right, Molly?" Phillip asked, and she realized she'd been clutching her head and moaning.

Octavius Hall. She'd let them down. "Feel?" she asked, throwing the nameplate back into the pile of junk. "I'm feeling angry."

She wrestled the pram back through the pile of rubbish and headed for the basement, ignoring the sounds of something watching her from the lobby balcony.

7th May
Controversial Investor Seeks Stake In Octavius Hall Convalescent Home!
Manager Refuses To Answer Questions
By Molly Squidpiddge

The Malifaux Daily Record has unearthed a series of back room deals by the controversial businessman Mr. Elphinstone McTeague, that have caused the elderly residents of Octavius Hall to fear they may find themselves out on the street this winter.

Mr. McTeague, who is known for buying up lots and forcibly evicting tenants to make way for...

A white, wooden chair sat with its back to the main hall, and the pram knocked it on its side as Molly passed. Over the crash, a skittering sound could be heard from the floors above.

"Unless that was Drove, and I don't remember him having that many legs, we're being followed," whispered Phillip, and Molly nodded mutely. More and more of the story was coming back to her, and her sense of anger was growing by the minute. The door leading to the basement stairs was just ahead.

18th May
Octavius Hall Not For Sale!
"We'll Protect Those In Our Care!"
Declare Board of Governors
Public Outcry Forces Elphinstone McTeague To Withdraw
By Molly Squidpiddge

Had it not been for the intervention of this newspaper, and its crusading lady reporter Miss Molly Squidpiddge, the Malifaux Daily Record believes that dozens of impoverished, sick, and frail elderly men and women with no living relatives would have been evicted...

The pram bounced from step to step as Molly steered it down the wide stone stairs, Phillip holding on to the bedclothes with gritted teeth to stop himself flying out.

At the bottom of the stairs, huge stretches of brickwork and masonry had been removed and piled in the corners. Scaffolding and iron buttresses held up the walls and ceilings, and, where the tiled basement should have been, a dirt slope stretched away into darkness. The body of Divesta Honeychild lay like a collapsed doll at the top.

```
29th May
Octavius Hall Closes!
Blames Emanations From The Sewers
All Forty One Residents Taken To
Facilities Earthside
By Molly Squidpiddge

One of Malifaux's most well-
regarded public services has been
forced to close.

Overnight, the forty one elderly
residents of Octavius Hall have
been decanted from their beds and
rushed to Malifaux Station and
from there to convalescent homes
Earthside for their own well-being
and protection from "noxious
vapors arising from the sewers",
according to a statement issued by
the Board of Governors.
Suggestions of unauthorized
underground works were dismissed
as malicious speculation.

Expressions of regret were issued
by many of Malifaux's public
citizens on learning of the
closure, including...
```

Molly propped Phillip up to get a better look and bent to examine Ms. Honeychild's corpse. It looked like she had burned from within. Her fog coat was charred and smoking, and the smell of scorched flesh filled the air. Her face was frozen in a rictus of horror, and a small flame was slowly consuming the tightly-wound bun atop her head. There was no other sign of fire in the room. Molly blew on the flame and put it out.

"Make a wish?" suggested Phillip.

Molly closed the woman's eyes. Being careless and self-deluded in Malifaux was rarely a recipe for long life, and she had clearly encountered something that cared little for her coronic discharge.

Molly picked her way down the earthen ramp into the darkness. This wasn't the sewers - the air was old and dry as the dust in her mouth. What had they been doing here?

"You're just going to leave me?" Phillip shouted after her in an anguished voice. "I can't defend myself, I'm a head!" His last few words dropped almost to a whisper, presumably as he realized that, being all alone, shouting might not be such a good idea.

Molly's undead eyes could see fairly well in the almost total blackness, although the glow from the Gorgon's Tear around her neck helped pick out the steep passage and low ceilings. Tools and equipment lay everywhere, covered in dust and abandoned in a hurry.

Reaching into a pocket, she lifted out Mrs. Choke and tucked her behind her ear, making sure she got a good view. She hadn't known Mrs. Choke before she'd died, of course, but everyone liked exploring, didn't they?

The passage ended where a sunken stone wall had been broken through. Molly stepped through the breach. Inside was a chamber, the walls lined with rusted iron plate, and the floor covered in shattered glass and scraps of machinery, buried under rust and verdigris. Plinths of stone and brass stood at regular intervals and, from the jagged spears set into the rims of each one, it was clear these were the source of the broken glass. There was only one left intact, an enormous bell jar big enough to hold two men, lying on its side next to a large pile of filthy canvas sacks.

Molly knelt beside them, her hands feeling the contours within. Skulls, bony bodies, stick-thin limbs. Long dead. She counted forty one sacks.

30th May
Molly Squidpiddge Murdered!
Guild Blames So-Called Mad Hatter,
Seamus
Condolences From Civic Leaders -
pg 3
Obituary - pg 4
By Gideon Trump, Editor

This newspaper is aware how greatly saddened its readers will be to hear of the untimely and tragic death of one of our most fearless and crusading reporters, Miss Molly Squidpiddge…

No rest-home Earthside had any record of receiving forty one patients from Octavius Hall when it closed, and so she'd died while in the middle of one of her biggest stories.

In Malifaux, that was no longer the handicap for a reporter it had once been.

She had let them down, and she could feel the ghostly presences all around her. She had let them down, but now she'd come back.

A skittering sound made her turn, and she felt rather than heard Mrs. Choke scream and faint dead away.

The exit was blocked. For a moment she thought the scrap on the floor had assembled itself while her back had been turned, but it still lay amongst the broken glass. What she was looking at was the intact version of whatever the scrap had once been. Four legs gripped the broken masonry of the breach with steel claws, the stone fracturing under the pressure. Two segmented arms, held as if in prayer, aimed twin hypodermic needles the size of small harpoons at her. Between the many limbs, a head of ancient leather and brass rivets nestled amidst an array of hydraulic pipes, its softly glowing eyes matching the green venom dripping from the needles. It settled back on its haunches, ready to spring.

Molly froze, and then smiled. "Here, boy!" she said, holding out her hand.

The machine paused, its head moving in jerking motions as if searching the air, then it bounded forward, scattering the detritus on the floor and curled its antique, rusting body against Molly's legs and dress.

She reached down and stroked its head, feeling the dry leather brittle to the touch. She scratched behind its pipes where they met in brass couplings faded gray-green with age, and the machine's hydraulic systems flicked on and off in pleasure.

"Good boy!" she said. She bent down and rubbed its flaking metal body with both hands, and it rolled onto its back. "Good boy!"

She could feel an energy coursing through this machine that fizzed and sparked wherever she touched it, resonating with something deep within her. Molly closed her eyes, and the machine stilled. The energies within them flowed as one, and Molly looked through eyes that had seen a thousand years pass, and more. Centuries of service to the necrotic power that animated them both, ending in this very room, not abandoned but stored, waiting, preserved in the huge glass specimen jars with its pack-brothers. Brief images of momentary consciousness flickered past, a fractured Kinetoscope of the years that followed as, one by one, the ravages of time destroyed the other jars and their contents slowly rotted away. And then - men came, picks and axes breaching the walls, the last jar being tipped on its side. Escape, confusion, screaming, running and hiding in the far reaches of the building, slowly regaining its power from the spirits of the dead who roamed the dark passages of Octavius Hall. Molly's sight returned to the near-pitch of the sunken room, and the necrotic machine wriggled again at her caress.

She glanced at the bodies in sacks. Those were not this machine's doing, although this machine was surely the reason the building had been abandoned in such a hurry. Who, then, had killed the residents of the Hall?

She had a feeling she knew exactly who.

Molly stood and headed for the ramp, the machine settling in at her heel. Phillip was going to be thrilled.

Drove was waiting for her at the top.

Phillip could only moan a warning, his mouth stuffed with cloth, as Drove raised the wide-bore pistol and blasted searing lightning at the machine by her side. It was lifted off the dirt and slammed into the iron scaffolding. It lay curled and smoking, bits of its casing glowing red hot like embers in the dark.

"What in the world was that?" Drove demanded, turning his lightning gun towards Molly, but still staring at the twitching remains of the necrotic machine.

Molly didn't answer. She glanced back once, and continued walking slowly towards him.

Drove smiled cruelly and adjusted a dial on his pistol. The whine from his backpack increased a whole octave. "Your master has no idea what he did when he made you, does he? Or when he gave you that." The scorched barrel of the pistol jabbed at the Gorgon's Tear around her neck. "I couldn't let that stupid woman live, after she'd seen me here with you. Word might have got back to Seamus, and I really don't want that maniac knowing my name. The Mam'selle won't tell - as long as she gets her commission, she minds her own business, and she's not afraid of Seamus. So you and that remarkable Soulstone are going to come with me, and I'll show this world what Clarifester Drove and his Spirit Cabinet are really capable of." He aimed the pistol at her face. "That's far enough!"

Molly glanced a warning at Phillip and he screwed his eyes shut. With a smile, she lifted the Gorgon's Tear off her breast, and - with a whisper and a burst of green light from the Tear - let the unfortunate Clarifester Drove see what truly lay within.

He'd been on his knees, lips frothing and body shaking, for a whole minute before he was even able to start screaming, and Molly waited patiently for him to stop. She took the cloth out of Phillip's mouth, set him upright again, and brushed his hair flat, while Drove raved and howled and sobbed behind her.

When the screaming turned to whimpers and then to dry heaves of his chest, Molly went to him and clasped his tear-streaked face to her bosom. She retrieved Mrs. Choke from behind her ear, severed some of Drove's electrical cables and tied them to the former landlady's wriggling optic nerve.

"Well, Mrs. Choke," Phillip said, grinning ear to ear. "If you're feeling at all aggrieved at the way your life has recently turned out, you may feel the need to express some of that dissatisfaction in what I hope will be a cathartic experience for you. In short, I bet you could murder someone right about now, eh, Mrs. Choke?"

The eyeball twitched angrily in Molly's hand, stretching to get free of her grasp. Molly imagined her being similarly infuriated at a guest not using a coaster, or putting his feet up on the furniture.

"Attagirl, Mrs. Choke," Phillip crowed. "We've got a live one here, Molly!"

Molly let go, and the Undead eyeball dropped with a sickening plop into Drove's gaping mouth, trailing the wires. His hands flew to his throat as his face turned red and he gasped for air, then his eyes bulged as he made a very surprised-sounding swallowing noise. He grabbed at the electrical cables protruding from his mouth, but just a moment too late, as Molly flipped the power switch on his backpack and stepped back.

The whine of power was satisfyingly full-throttle, and Phillip whooped as flames shot from Drove's mouth and ears and his clothes caught fire. The sound of sizzling body fat filled the room as smoke roiled upwards in great clouds, and then the intestinal gases in Drove's voluminous belly ignited. His midriff exploded with a wet-ripping pop and Molly, in one deft move that raised a cheer from Phillip, caught a hurtling Mrs. Choke in one hand.

Drove's corpse collapsed in a reeking ruin, and Molly turned back to the necrotic machine.

"So what exactly is that thing?" Phillip asked.

It was a simple matter, now the connection had been made, for Molly to reach out with a fraction of the energy within her, and pour strength into the dying machine. Its limbs ceased twitching, and it sprang upright a moment later, before bounding over to Molly and racing round and round her.

Molly thought back to hazy memories of when she had been a child, and her father had produced a gleeful, scampering bundle of legs and soft hair with a very wet nose and bright, bright eyes from behind a glittering Christmas tree. "Ponto," she replied.

The little girl Crooligan came out the fog when she called, and led her by back alleys and zigzag lanes to the Mam'selle.

"I thought I might be seeing you again," the woman said as Molly approached, pushing Phillip in the baby carriage - which he was now growing rather fond of, and had requested Molly add certain personal touches such as lanterns and a supply of cigars once they returned to the old brewery - with the machine pacing at her heels.

Mam'selle Vestige was leaning with effortless ease against what appeared to be an upright but dead-drunk Guild Guard officer, watching an illegal bare-knuckle fighting contest in the cobbled yard below. Shouts, bets, oaths, and meaty thunks floated up from the pale ghosts exchanging blows and the gathered crowd.

"Who owns Octavius Hall?" Molly demanded, dark blood spilling from her mouth as she spoke.

"Perhaps you, mon cheri, if you meet the asking price." The Mam'selle turned back to the fight. "My money's on the red-head. Caledonians are so fiery-tempered, n'est pas? That, and I have poisoned his opponent." She gave a Gallic shrug of indifference.

"I will ask only once."

"Don't let us quarrel, Miss Squidpiddge." A ring of smoke disappeared into the fog. "Neither of us would profit. I seek to make only friends in this town, and what would my reputation be if I gave away the identity of a client?"

"Then I will pay the asking price..."

Mam'selle Vestige gave Molly her full attention.

"...but only in person."

Vestige regarded her for a few moments between draws on her cigarette. "And what would my business be if I lost a client?"

Molly produced a drawstring silk bag and placed it on the parapet between them. The presence of the Soulstone within was unmistakable.

"That should cover your commission," Phillip said. "And a little bit extra to make sure he comes alone."

A smile spread across the Mam'selle's face like ice across a winter pond, and Molly wondered if she really was as young as she looked. "A pleasure doing business with you, Miss Squidpiddge. I will arrange the rendezvous. Octavius Hall, I presume?"

Molly wheeled Phillip away, the voices of forty one ghosts whispering in her ears. "Tomorrow at midnight. I have a deadline."

He did not, of course, arrive alone. Unscrupulous, black-hearted businessmen were rarely so stupid.

Molly had known who it would be. She had suspected long before she died, and the memories had come flooding back since the previous night. And there he stood, tall and stooped with a silver cane, a slick of receding white hair, a black suit and the air of a miser whose only problem was that everyone else had too much money. The seller of Octavius Hall, Elphinstone McTeague. It could only have been him.

He had brought three bodyguards and a lawyer with him, all with weapons and lanterns. No matter.

McTeague never saw what hit him. He was standing in the echoing lobby of Octavius Hall, facing the wrong way, when Molly wound up her arm and hurled Phillip out of the darkness.

"Tally-hoooo!"

He struck McTeague in the back of the head with a sound like two barrels banging together, and the tall man crumpled without a word.

"Right in the coconut, Molly!" hooted Phillip as he bounced off, and then let out a string of curses when his cigar went the other way.

The lawyer took one look at Phillip's flying death-mask and ran screaming. As the bodyguards, thickset men on hire from the Miners' and Steamfitters' Union with faces like bruised meat, milled around in confusion, the necrotic machine dropped from the chandelier above. The hypodermic syringes flashed and stabbed, *snickety-snack*, and it was all over before Phillip had stopped rolling.

The whispering voices of the dead surged. Molly grasped McTeague's tongue in a vice-like grip and began to drag him towards the basement.

McTeague awoke in complete darkness. He was lying on something hard and lumpy, his head and mouth were in agony and he could feel rough cloth. It took only a moment to realize that the cloth was a hessian sack and that he was inside it, and then Elphinstone McTeague began to thrash and yell.

The sack was closed tight around him, and terror threatened to rob him of his wits, but after a moment he found the neck and forced a thin arm through with a hoarse cry. He heaved, and the rope slipped loose. McTeague tumbled out, kicking and cursing the darkness, until he lay breathless and exhausted, his head throbbing in pain.

"Thank you for joining us, Mr. McTeague," Phillip said, as Molly struck a match and lit one of the bodyguard's lanterns. She gave McTeague a moment to take in his surroundings.

Molly sat on a white chair before the breach in the wall of the underground chamber, Phillip on a plinth to one side, and Ponto squatting on the other. Mrs. Choke looked on stoically from a vantage point high in Molly's bouffant hair. Molly held a notebook in one hand and a pen in the other. She had no need for them, but it felt good to hold them again. Elphinstone McTeague himself lay on a pile of forty one hessian sacks.

It had taken Molly all the previous day, but she and the necrotic machine had made certain changes to the Soul Gin Seamus was working on. Empty bottles lay scattered around the iron-walled room, and the effects of their contents on the remains of the forty one inhabitants of Octavius Hall were just starting to be felt.

McTeague froze as the lumpen shapes beneath him shifted.

"Aaaaah!" he cried as he scrambled to his feet, but the sacks were now all in motion beneath him, and he fell, cursing.

"We're on the record, Mr. McTeague," said Phillip. "Mind your language, now."

McTeague rolled to the side, kicking legs and flapping arms, until he slid off the pile of sacks onto the debris strewn floor. He crawled away through the rusted metal and glass and cowered against the far wall, clutching his chest and wheezing.

"Just want to get the facts down, Mr. McTeague," said Phillip. "Won't take long. Now, would it be fair to say you purchased the Hall in secret, lied to the Malifaux Daily Record and, indeed, everyone else about it, and then killed the elderly paupers living here so you could dig around beneath the Hall for ancient relics and profit without anyone knowing?"

"Saints preserve us!" McTeague moaned, as the mass of filthy sacks thrashed like a hive of brown maggots and began to writhe and wriggle across the floor towards him.

"I would take that as a 'yes', Molly," Phillip said out the corner of his mouth. "And would it be fair to say that you broke into this chamber, awoke m'colleague's many-legged friend and abandoned the dig and the Hall in terror, making up some story about 'emanations from the sewers' and sealing Octavius Hall shut for the last year?"

"Help me!" McTeague gasped, his hand white-knuckled over his chest, all color gone from his pinched face. The sacks were like a tide of giant vermin now, lurching and twisting their way through the debris in silence, threatening to swarm him at any moment.

A grey hand made of bones covered in the most paper-thin of rotted skin burst from one of the sacks and gripped his ankle. He flattened himself against the wall and screamed.

"Another 'yes', I would say, Molly," advised Phillip. "Would you like us to rescue you, Mr. McTeague? Get you safe from these upset former customers of yours? The press is always willing to protect its sources."

McTeague's mouth worked open and shut a few times, but when he couldn't get any sound out, he started nodding as vigorously as he could.

At a silent comment from Molly, the necrotic machine sprang forward, reaching McTeague in a single bound. It carried a letter in one hand, and a pen in the other.

"Sign that, if you would," Phillip called.

More hands burst from the rotting sacks, grabbing McTeague's feet and legs, and he snatched the pen and scribbled his signature, a low moan of terror escaping his bloodless lips. The machine retrieved the letter and picked up McTeague effortlessly. The hands grasping him released their hold.

Molly rose, crossed the room and joined the machine next to the plinth at the far end. The necrotic machine sat the trembling McTeague on the plinth, then stabbed one of its needles into his chest. He screamed, as pale green liquid flowed out the reservoir and into his body.

"No! Wait! What-?" he cried, and then Molly lifted the last remaining intact bell jar, taking all her Undead strength to do so, and brought it down around him, cutting his pleas off. The rim sank into the groove running around the plinth with a grinding noise, and Molly twisted it to lock it in place. Inside, McTeague banged his fists feebly on the thick glass, but all Molly could hear was a faint drumming as if from far away.

She picked up Phillip and left the room, turning back for one last look. McTeague knelt awkwardly, hammering his fists against the confining glass walls of his prison. The concoction in his veins would not kill him. Instead, it had imbued him with some of the necrotic machine's Undead essence. It would keep him alive in that jar, even once the air had been exhausted, for centuries. She turned off the lantern, and utter darkness fell.

"Seal it up," Molly said to her faithful machine. "Bring the roof down behind us."

As she walked up the steep slope, Ponto tore the metal scaffolding and supports from the dirt walls. Planks of rough wood crashed down, followed by multitudes of black earth that chased their heels all the way back to the basement and up the steps.

When they reached the street outside, Molly realized she could no longer hear the voices in her head. Octavius Hall was finally silent.

"Back to Seamus?" Phillip asked, as Molly settled him once again in the now rather dirty bedding of the pram. The one working gaslamp in the street spluttered fitfully.

Molly folded the letter McTeague had signed and another sheet of paper into an envelope with the word, "Editor", on the outside. She would drop that into the night box of the Malifaux Daily Record on the way back to the old brewery.

"Won't Seamus be, to put it mildly, a little annoyed that you took so much of his precious Soul Gin?" Phillip wondered aloud.

Molly gave her own Gallic shrug of indifference, and found that it agreed with her. Seamus had probably gotten bored with his brewing anyway and set off on some other wild pursuit. She lit Phillip's cigar using one of the matches she'd taken from the bodyguard and placed it in his mouth. There was a sizzling sound.

"The other way around, Molly, if you please."

Molly flipped the cigar over and put it back in, patting Phillip in apology.

"Here, boy!" she called, and Ponto bounded out of the fog into the light of the gaslamp, pressing up against her. She rubbed the manifolds on the back of its head, and it quivered in pleasure.

"You know, Molly old dear," said Phillip around the cigar. "I don't reckon that one is a boy. Just a feeling."

Molly thought a moment, and realized Phillip was probably right. She tore a strip off the pram's hood, and bent to the machine. When she straightened up, with a pleased expression on her face, the leather and brass head of her faithful companion sported a pink ribbon with a bow on top. It bounded happily away.

She got the pram underway, the wooden wheels slipping on the wet cobbles, and with Phillip puffing contentedly, they walked off into the fog together.

```
3rd October
```
Exclusive!
Elphinstone McTeague Signs Murder
Confession!
But His Whereabouts Are Unknown!
```
By Gideon Trump, Editor, and Molly
Squidpiddge (Deceased)

In news that has shocked Malifaux
society, the Malifaux Daily Record
has uncovered a grisly tale of
deception and murder...
```

CROOLIGAN - MINION

30MM BASE　　　　**SOULSTONE COST: 4**

SPECIAL FORCES [HORROR], UNDEAD

WK/CG	HT	WP	CA	DF	WD
4/6	1	5	4🐾	5	5

INFECTED DAGGER

RG	⚔ 1
CB	4✖
DG	1/2/3

TALENTS:

Abilities

Creepy: Living models within 3" of this model receive -1 **Wp**.

From the Shadows: This model may be deployed after all other models, in or behind any terrain more than 12" away from an enemy or the objective of any Strategy or announced Scheme. This model may not be targeted by **Charges** or ranged attacks until it performs an Action other than **Pass** if deployed this way. If multiple models with this Ability are in play, players alternate deploying them using the deployment order for Crews.

Scout

Weapon

Infected Dagger: Poison 1

Actions

(+1) Always on the Move: After this model performs an **Interact** Action, it may immediately Push up to its **Wk**.

(1) Curiosity Calls: Place this model in base contact with a friendly Crooligan that is completely within the 🔵 of **The Mist**.

(2) Return to Sender: Place this model in base contact with a friendly Master or Henchman within 10". This Action may only be performed if this model is engaged with an enemy model.

Triggers

Cb (✖ 📖) Malignant Rot [Infected Dagger]: This Weapon inflicts +1 **Dg**.

Df (🐾) The Mist's Embrace: After this model is hit by a melee or ranged **Strike**, this model gains the Spirit Characteristic until the start of the Resolve Effects Step.

SPELLS:

(1) The Mist
(CC: 12🐾 / Rst: - / Rg: 🔵3) **Ht** 5 obscuring for all models, including this model. Friendly Crooligans receive +2 **Wk** and +2 **Df** while affected by this Spell.

The mist which creeps sinuously through the Quarantine Zones has a mind of its own. There is something sinister about its movements as it seeks the lost and forlorn who have strayed from the lights of the Slums. Runaways and orphans have naïvely fled the very real dangers of their former lives and the predations of the Slums for the welcoming claws of the Quarantine Zones.

Sympathy and aid elude these children in Malifaux. Although the rare exception exists, the abandoned child left on his or her own stands little chance against not only the residents of Malifaux, but the City itself. The cagiest ones survive, making a home for themselves among the rubble of the crumbling City.

Their time living as ghosts in the ruins teaches them how to use the almost ever present fog to mask their passage from eyes which may be seeking them out. Eventually the children's willingness to not be found merges with aetheric energy lingering in the mists, passing into their blood and turning them into beings not entirely alive yet not entirely of the fog and death either.

Now a part of the City, these Crooligans drift where their curiosities take them. They choose to aid the living when the whim strikes, serving only those who treat them with the kindness they were so sorely lacking as living children.

DEAD DOXY - MINION

She pauses for a moment, reading the small calling card a gentleman had left for her after the show.

S. BAKER
AGENT, PROMOTER
MEANDERS-BY-NORRIS, No. 19

The name steals the breath from her lungs. Sebastian Baker, dream maker! She had heard the famous agent was in Malifaux but assumed he would have had his eyes on Cassandra, or Chloe, or one of the other girls. She'd never had what she felt was her due from Ms. Du Bois. Despite her perfect voice, she was always relegated to the chorus line. But that will all change starting tonight! She will be remembered forever, damn them! Still stunned by this turn of events, she reads the handwritten note on the back of the card, absently scratching at the small reddish-brown stain in the card's upper corner:

My dear Cherie,
Your dancing enraptured me. When you are able, please visit me and we shall discuss immortalizing you upon the stage.
Yours, S. Baker

A clap of thunder signals the arrival of one of the City's frequent showers, and she rushes to the warmly-lit doorway of Number 19, knocking rapidly on the rich mahogany door.

A moment passes, and then another before the door opens. A man wearing a foppish top hat and frilled coat stands there, something glittering in one hand.

"Ah, yes. I see you got my note," he chuckles. Before Cherie can utter a scream, the glittering hand slashes out, cutting her throat and perfect vocal cords.

✗ ✗ ✗

She hears the dull rhythmic stomp of feet and the gentle swish of fabric as if from a great distance. She can see little, save a single light shining down a long tunnel and into her eyes. It takes her some time, but she realizes that the stomp and swish she hears are her own feet and dress moving in clumsy accompaniment to the tinny music coming from an old hand-cranked phonograph nearby. She stops dancing and tries to scream, but the only sound that escapes her ruined vocal chords is a ghastly howling rasp.

"Loved the dancin', poppet. Not so much the tweet-bird singing though. Thought ye'd make a fine addition to my little stage. Again, again," the man with the top hat shouts from the shadows, his manic clapping filling the empty hall.

Unable to control it, her body starts the performance again for the tenth, no hundredth time, and a sliver of what is left of her screaming mind realizes his promise of immortality has come true.

30MM BASE　　　**SOULSTONE COST: 5**

BELLE, UNDEAD, RARE 2

WK/CG	HT	WP	CA	DF	WD
5/-	2	5	5✗	4	6

FANCY CANE		CLOCKWORK DERRINGER	
RG	⚔ 2	RG	↗6
CB	5✗	CB	4
DG	1/2/4	DG	2/3/4

TALENTS:

Abilities

Flirtatious Wink: This model receives +2▨ Ca when **Casting** or **Channeling Inviting Approach.**

Hard to Wound 1

Part of the Harem: Models casting **Arise, My Sweet** may discard one Corpse Counter to Summon this model.

Shambling: This model ignores severe terrain movement penalties.

Slow to Die

Strangely Attractive: Enemy models more than 4" away must win a **Wp → 12** Duel when targeting this model with an attack or the Action fails. This may not be ignored by any Talent.

Actions

(1) Final Encore: This Action may only be used as a **Slow to Die** Action. Switch this model with a friendly model with the Belle Characteristic and at least 2 **Wd** remaining within 8". This model heals 1 **Wd**. Reduce the friendly Belle's remaining **Wd** by half to a minimum of 1.

Triggers

Ca (✗ ▨) Fatal Distraction [Seduction/Undress]: After applying the effects of this Spell to the defender, this model may perform a melee or ranged **Strike** against the defender.

Cb (✗ ✗) Rot [Fancy Cane]

Df (♥) Regret: After inflicting Moderate or Severe damage on this model, the attacker may not attack this model again for the remainder of the turn.

SPELLS:

(0) Inviting Approach
(CC: 13 ✗ ▨ / Rst: Wp / Rg: 12) If the target fails the Resist Duel, this model Pushes its **Wk** toward the target. If this model ends the Push within 4" of the target, this model casts **Seduction** on the target.

(1) Seduction
(CC: 12▨ / Rst: Wp / Rg: 4) Target model's Resist and Defense Flips receive ⊟ ⊟.

(1) Undress
(CC: 12 / Rst: Wp / Rg: 12) Target enemy model receives -2 **Df** until the Start Closing Phase.

Summoned from the foul waters to which they were consigned, the Drowned are brought forth to fight the Resurrectionists' battles. Disgustingly bloated by its time beneath the River's surface, a Drowned spirit drifts lazily, inches from the ground, eternally tethered to a spiritual version of whatever the victim was weighted down with when pitched into the River's black depths.

These horrible entities are victims of the power play between the Guild and Arcanists: spies, witnesses, and double-agents disposed of to make locating a body difficult for the Guild. This act of callous indifference left the Drowned's spirit trapped until released from its own prison of a rotten corpse. Once freed, the Drowned drifts in the direction of its murderers,

the black mark on their souls serving as a magnet for revenge. It calls on the final memories of its former life to fuel this vengeance, struggling against the crushing weight of the water, the explosive last gasp for air rewarded by the lungs filling with liquid, and that final fleeting moment of life spent alone in the darkness.

Once its desire for murder is fulfilled, the Drowned drifts lazily, content to be carried by the streams of spirit energy so prevalent in the City. This is when the Resurrectionist who summoned it can easily bind it to his will, confident in the knowledge that the Drowned no longer has a purpose other than to follow the commands of the person who rescued it from the deep.

SOULSTONE COST: 4

30MM BASE

SPIRIT, UNDEAD, RARE 3

WK/CG	HT	WP	CA	DF	WD
4/-	2	5	5✗	3	6

HEAVE BILE	
RG	⌐8
CB	4✗
DG	1/1/3

TALENTS:

Abilities

Bursting Spray: (✗)4, **Dg** 2 when this model is killed.

Float

Gunfighter [Heave Bile]

Slow to Die

Weighed Down: This model cannot be Pushed by other models. This model's **Wk/Cg** cannot be modified.

Actions

(+1) Driven by Purpose: This model suffers 1 **Wd**. Push this model up to 3".

(0) Drag Under: This model and target enemy model within 4" perform a **Wp → Df** Duel. If the target loses, this model's Controller Pushes it up to 3".

Triggers

Ca/Cb (✗✗) Fluid in the Lungs [Riptide/Heave Bile]: After resolving a successful attack, defender must win a **Df → 12** Duel or suffer 1 **Wd** and receive Slow.

SPELLS:

(1) Riptide
(CC: 14✗ / Rst: Df / Rg: 6) Target model suffers 2 **Wd**. Other models within 2" of the target must win a **Df →11** Duel or suffer 2 **Wd**.

JAAKUNA UBUME ~ MINION

One of the countless dangers waiting to lure pioneers and travelers to their doom is the wicked spirit known as the Jaakuna Ubume. This spirit appears only in bodies of water - shallow pools, slow running streams. Its appearance varies, but survivors of the attacks describe it as an older woman with wet bedraggled hair covering much of her face, standing alone, waist deep in the water, sobbing uncontrollably.

Three Kingdoms legends tell of a vile woman who, in a fit of insane rage, drowned her three small children in a stagnant pool while on a journey from their home to the provincial capital. The woman was so distraught at what she had done that she drowned herself in that very same pool. Soon after, she rose as the Jaakuna Ubume and began luring unsuspecting travelers to their doom, terrified of suffering the hell of her own creation alone. And this legend seems to have come alive in the wilds of Malifaux.

The Jaakuna Ubume pleads with passing travelers for help in saving her children. Only the hardest of hearts can ignore the plaintive wails of her children, which seem to surround the spirit's chosen victim. Those who come to the Ubume's aid can see the faint outlines of small bodies beneath the water's surface. Once a helpful soul steps into the pool, the Jaakuna Ubme strikes, using its connection to the water to grab hold and drag the victim down to a watery doom. Travelers are warned to harden their hearts to the less fortunate they encounter on the trail; otherwise they may come to share the Jaakuna Ubume's fate.

50MM BASE — SOULSTONE COST: 5

SPIRIT, UNIQUE

WK/CG	HT	WP	CA	DF	WD
4/-	2	5	5✗	4	5

TALENTS:

Abilities

Inviting Inflection: This model gains +▧▨ when **Casting** or **Channeling Siren Call**.

Pitiful: Until this model activates each turn, models targeting this model must win a **Wp → Wp** Duel or the Action immediately ends.

Spiritual Eagerness: Models casting the **Evolve Spirit** Spell may Summon this model by sacrificing a friendly Spirit within 6" and suffering 2 **Wd**.

Stay With Me: Enemy models within 1" of this model attempting to disengage from it must win a **Wp → Wp** Duel with this model or the Action immediately ends.

Weapon

Hideous Screech: This Weapon's Attack Duels are resolved using **Cb →Wp**.

Actions

(0) A Child's Cry: This model and a target model within 6" perform a **Wp → Wp** Duel. If the target loses the Duel, it receives a cumulative -1/-1 **Wk/Cg** at the start of each of its activations until it is in base contact with this model or its **Wk** is reduced to 1.

HIDEOUS SCREECH

RG	⌐10
CB	4✗
DG	2/3/4

(1) Drowning in Her Wake: Enemy models declaring an Action while in base contact with this model must win a **Df → 13** Duel or suffer 2 **Wd**.

Triggers

Cb (✗ ▨) Cower [Hideous Screech]: A defender damaged by this Weapon may not perform **Charge** Actions.

SPELLS:

(0) Denial of Sanzu
(CC: 13✗ / Rst: Wp / Rg: 8) Target model may not take movement Actions.

(1) Siren Call
(CC: 12▧▨ /Rst: Wp /Rg: ⌐15) Move target enemy model its **Wk** toward this model. If the target moves within this model's melee range, it receives **Paralyzed**.

RAFKIN, THE EMBALMER - MINION

Thomas Rafkin was always a little "off". His fascination with the body's progression from a living organism to a decaying husk began young. While the other boys were outside playing in the warm summer air, young Thomas was at the library, poring over a well-thumbed copy of *Gray's Anatomy*. Stray cats and dogs met early demises at his hands, buried in his family's back yard, then dug up to record the progression of decomposition, all in the name of science. His driving passion: restoring life after it had fled the body.

The years passed, and his desires deepened. Medical school bored him, focusing as it did on the preservation rather than restoration of life. He took it upon himself to create his own lesson plan, absconding with medical tools and cadavers to experiment upon, but without even a spark of magic, his efforts were doomed to failure. His true calling, it seemed, lay in embalming. He perfected techniques taught to him by bored instructors, developing a unique blend of fluids which kept decay from a body indefinitely. Eventually his "work" was uncovered, and Rafkin was expelled. It was then that Fate stepped in.

When the Breach reopened, Rafkin gathered his meager collection of medical implements, including his worn copy of *Anatomy*, and arranged a contract with the City's undertaker, Nicodem. Rafkin reasoned he could explore the arts of necromancy at the mortuary, this time with access to magic. Late one night, Rafkin stumbled upon his employer performing experiments he had only dreamed of.

"Teach me," Thomas Rafkin breathlessly pleaded. Nicodem nodded as a reply.

Since that time, Rafkin has exchanged his services for lessons in necromancy. Because of the mortuary's close ties to the Guild's morgue, Rafkin is often sent to McMourning on official Guild business, carrying messages between the two master Resurrectionists. His necromantic talents, he fears, will never equal those of either men, but his skills as an embalmer have earned him a place at Nicodem's side.

30MM BASE

SOULSTONE COST: 7

GRAVEROBBER, UNIQUE

WK/CG	HT	WP	CA	DF	WD
4/6	2	5	5✗	5	9

LISTON KNIFE		FLASK OF FORMALDEHYDE	
RG	〃 2	RG	⌒6
CB	5✗	CB	5
DG	2/3/5	DG	1/1☣/1☣☣

TALENTS:

Abilities

Body Parts: When you determine your starting Soulstone Pool, you may exchange any number of your Crew's Soulstones for an equal number of Body Part Counters carried by this model. This model may exchange one of its Corpse Counters for two Body Part Counters at any time during its activation.

Mithridatization: This model is immune to **Wd** inflicted by **Poison** Tokens, and does not discard them at the start of its activation as normal. During this model's activation, it can discard any number of its **Poison** Tokens to heal that many **Wd**.

Weapon

Flask of Formaldehyde: Poison 2

Liston Knife: This model gains one Body Part Counter each time this Weapon damages an enemy model.

Actions

(+1) Passion for his Work: This model may discard a Body Part Counter to gain **Fast**.

(0) Embalm: Target a friendly Undead model within 2". That model performs a Healing Flip. This model may then discard any number of Body Part Counters it carries. The target discards one token on it per Counter this model discarded.

(0) Quaff Concoction: This model performs a Healing Flip. If this model heals more than 2 **Wd**, its activation ends.

(1) Preserve Bodies: Each time a Corpse Counter within 6" of this model is sacrificed or discarded, this model gains one Body Part Counter.

Triggers

Cb (✗ 📖) Amputate [Liston Knife]: After damaging defender with this Weapon, defender must discard one Control Card or suffer a 1/2/3 Damage Flip which cannot be Cheated.

SPELLS:

(all) Hasty Disposal
(CC: 14✗ ✗ / Rst: - / Rg: C) This model Summons any number of Mindless Zombies and Guild Autopsies by discarding two Body Parts Counters it carries per Mindless Zombie, or four Body Part Counters it carries per Guild Autopsy.

(1) Forestall Decomposition
(CC: 13✗ / Rst: - / Rg: ⚫4) Friendly Undead models gain the **Hard to Kill** Ability.

CARRION EFFIGY - MINION

Wafting into Malifaux on the fetid winds of decay, the Carrion Effigy has been drawn to the powerful energies of the Resurrectionist Masters, their necromantic activities calling to it as a man struggling through the desert seems to summon the vultures.

Carrion's cause is a difficult one: keep the cycles of life and death continuing uninterrupted across Malifaux. Where life and death magic have warred eternally with one another, the Red Cage's descent has thrown off the natural balance between those two basic forces. The fulcrum, which ensured their balance remained in perpetual flux, is no longer situated where it should be, perfectly stationed between the two forces. Instead, the eruption of the rift and the waves of energy thrown into the aether have the fulcrum's center point shifting dramatically between growth and entropy allowing the creatures created by the Cage's descent to exist both in life and in death simultaneously.

Carrion is able to accelerate the natural progression of decay and prevent any magical means of forestalling decomposition thanks to the powers granted it by the aether. Its alliance with the Resurrectionists is a tenuous one, however, as they willingly seek to unlock the secrets of the rift and interrupt the never-ending cycle of life forever.

30MM BASE   **SOULSTONE COST: 4**

GRAVEROBBER, OBJECT 1, SPECIAL FORCES (DOLL), UNIQUE

WK/CG	HT	WP	CA	DF	WD
5/9	1	5	6✗	4	4

DISEASED BEAK		ROTTING BREATH	
RG	1	RG	8
CB	5✗	CB	4✗
DG	1/2/2+Slow	DG	1/2🟣/4🟣

TALENTS:

Abilities

Aetheric Connection: One friendly model with the **Aetheric Connection** Ability within 6" of this model may activate after this model's activation ends.

Aetheric Demands: Non-Neverborn Crews hiring this model must nominate one leader per model with this Ability they hire. Those leaders cannot attach Totems.

Other Allegiances [Neverborn]: This model may be hired by the indicated Faction's Crews at no additional cost.

Flight

Hard to Kill

Weapon
Diseased Beak: Magical. **Poison 1**

Actions
(0) Horrific Feasting: ⚫4. Friendly models, including this model, may discard a Corpse Counter within 4" at the end of their activations to make a Healing Flip.

Triggers
Cb (✗ ✗) Rot

SPELLS:

(1) Diminished Resistance
(CC: 12 ✗ / Rst: - / Rg: ⚫4) Enemy models cannot ignore effects and lose all immunities.

ARCANISTS

"But will it work?" the lawyer asked.

Haim Clements, chief civil engineer of the Guild's Transport Department, folded the blueprints. He did not enjoy being where he was, speaking to who he was, but that question had put him on safe ground. "Yes," he replied. "Absolutely! It's ingenious! It will improve throughput in the network by a factor of three or four, without re-cabling or erecting new towers. It's all down to the routing systems at the main branch stations. These gyroscopic hubs are admirable work. Where did we get it?"

The lawyer held out a gloved hand with an oily grace, and Clements returned the blueprints with some reluctance. "Thank you, Mr. Clements," the lawyer said. "That will be all."

Clements looked from the lawyer to the masked man sitting behind the desk and back again. Color rising in his whiskered cheeks, he left through the side door. The lawyer closed it behind him and handed the blueprints to the man at the desk.

Lucius Matheson, Secretary to the Governor, put the folded blueprints on his table, then placed a brass paperweight on top. He saw his own silver mask reflected in the polished metal. "I want these put into operation immediately. Top priority."

"As you wish," replied the lawyer, Olginous Flinch. Like all Lucius' lawyers, his deathly-pale face was fixed with a permanent, knowing sneer, and he wore an elaborate eye-mask. Today Flinch favored a courtly design, in the shape of two glittering, golden swans. His long fingers curled tight as he spoke, as if he captured secrets in his gloved palms. "Our man would like to return. He frets on his safety."

Lucius stood and walked over to the window, his tall boots silent on the thick rug, his steps weighted and precise, like a hunting cat. He looked out over the City, following the line of the railway through its buildings, past the New Construction on its way towards the mines in the mountains. "There is one more task I require of him, Mr. Flinch. And when you do speak to him, tell him we all fret on his safety." He turned his head, and although the silver mask covered all, it was clear to Flinch that Lucius was wearing the devil's own smile. "Tell him I never cease contemplating the harm that might befall him."

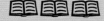

Four Months Later
Earthside; Breachworks Station

"You wanna see something?" Edward Estlin asked, his bony face sly and pale under the greasy Guild cap. "I mean, really something?"

His young apprentice, John Cole, nodded mutely, eyes wide.

Edward knelt and opened the iron hatch in the roof of the railcar, easing it back silently on oiled hinges. Impenetrable shadow hid what lay within, until the clouds parted and the moonlight fell.

John Cole jumped back with a gasp, nearly slipping. He crept back to the hatch and peered over the edge. A shiver ran down his spine.

"Never seen one up close?" Edward asked, glancing around. The enormous, fortified railhead was never silent, not even in the depths of night, but no one was looking their way.

John Cole shook his head, blonde curls swinging.

"This car is full of 'em, and the next," said Edward. "And the one after that."

John Cole swallowed. "They all could start a war with that."

Edward eased the hatch closed. "Good thing it's headed through the Breach then, eh?"

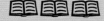

Sourbreak Supply Depot, Malifaux

"Message here for Master Waugh," sang out the runner.

Guild Quartermaster Leon Stubbs looked her up and down. Small, like a wren, with tiny, grey eyes behind huge goggles and a thick pencil tucked in her hair. She was dwarfed by Stubbs' unruly bulk and more so by the vast munitions warehouse. Not a pick on her, Stubbs thought, nor a curve to grab. She was naught but a child, really. He turned back to his shipping list. "Never 'eard of no Waugh. Beat it."

He thought he was imagining things, then he realized he really was hearing crying from the gangway behind him. He turned, angry. "That's enough of that! Girls your age should be down the mines, not getting lost in munitions yards and bursting into tears. A spell down the mines'd dry your eyes out for good." The sobbing continued. "For good and plenty! Try over at the Mast. They'll know him."

She sniffed, flipped up her goggles and wiped her eyes with her sleeve. "Beady Simmons'll skelp me if I'm late." She held out her message pad. "Could you? So he knows I was here?" As Stubbs hesitated, she added, "I dun't want to get skelped again, sir. *Please!*"

"Fine." It was probably quicker than giving her the back of his hand, and less chance of getting covered in snot and tears. "Give it here."

The girl handed the pad over with another sniffle but got the pencil tangled up in her goggles strap. It spun out of her hand and fell, end over end, disappearing into the tightly packed crates below the gangway.

The tears started again, and Stubbs hastily made his mark on the pad with his own pencil and pushed it back into her hands. "Off with you, you little wretch, and don't bother me again."

The girl turned and ran, and Stubbs got back to planning the loading arrangements for the *Munificent*.

When the girl was out of sight, she stopped crying, threw the pad and goggles away, and quickly made her way to the rendezvous point.

Far below, the discarded pencil hissed so quietly that none could hear.

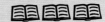

Malifaux City

"Not that I am offering any resistance," Leroy Billings said, his trembling hands still raised in the customary position, "but are you sure you know what you're taking?"

The masked man holding the gun said nothing, but that did not make Leroy feel any better. What if they realized what they'd actually stolen and in a fit of rage came back to his shop and shot him. And his assistant, too, but principally him.

"Look," he tried again, "you know what's in those bottles? It's not valuable. It's just—"

He stopped as the masked man pointed the gun. His compatriot picked up the two large brown glass jars and left through the back of the shop. The gunman followed, and Leroy and his assistant were left alone and, surprisingly, alive.

"—animal medicine," he finished in a whisper, as his young assistant fainted dead away.

The Next Day
Hollow Marsh Minehead

English Ivan looked so aggressively out of place in the industrial chaos of a working mine that new recruits had been known to stop working and simply stare. Their more experienced comrades quickly fixed that with a belt 'round the ear, and the lesson was soon learned – one does not stare at English Ivan.

Quite how he kept his black bowler and double-breasted frock coat so free of the dust and smoke that swirled around the great minehead complex remained a mystery among the members of the Miners and Steamfitters Union. No matter where he went, surrounded on all sides by laborers blackened by oil or made ghosts by ash, his pale, flared trousers and low, white boots seemed impervious to insult, and even in the dullest light his blue cravat shone like the summer sky. Outshining even that was the crystal clear soulstone on the top of his ivory walking cane.

Pretty much all the workers and overseers at the mine knew about English Ivan was his name, and even in that they were doubly wrong. He was not English. As anyone who had been greeted by him with a rousing, "Hullo!" could tell, his accent was as Russian as a steppe wolf. And his name was not Ivan.

There were rumors, of course, that he worked for the Washhouse. There were rumors that practically every stranger or oddfellow to pass through the mines worked for the Washhouse, and most of the old mine hands liked to hint that they had done work for the Washhouse at some point in the past, *word-to-the-wise, say-no-more*. As for the rumors about what the Washhouse did, well they ventured into the realms of myth and legend.

The rumors about English Ivan happened to be true.

He stopped on the sloped path leading up from Pithead Four, taking a moment to straighten his waxed moustache. Heavy steamborgs pistoned past, their iron-shod feet kicking up clouds of dust as miners stepped aside in front of them. Ivan ignored them, and the steamborgs walked around him. The building ahead was long, low, and tile-roofed, and a steady stream of workers coming off shift were going in and out. It was, in truth, a normal washhouse, one of many around the mineheads. This one, however, had been built in front of the Rising Machine.

Ivan stepped past the slow-moving queues. The chatter and splash of the washhouse quieted noticeably as he entered, and he walked quickly to a door in the rear. White Eye McGee, who sat on a stool by the door, nodded blindly to him and stopped playing his mouth organ long enough to flip the latch. Ivan walked out, onto the bare rock at the back of the washhouse. The door locked behind him. The rock trembled with the movements of the Rising Machine.

It was like the inner workings of a giant's watch had fallen from the sky and embedded in the earth. Jutting from huge notches blasted in the mountainside, dozens of iron cogs the size of Ferris wheels rotated on deep-hidden hubs and axles. All of them, from the point of view of the outside observer, rotated upwards, hence the name. Look at it for long enough, and you would be convinced the whole assembly was climbing back up into the sky.

The machine played a key role in the operations of the Hollow Marsh Pumping Station on the other side of the mountain, but the Washhouse had gotten involved at the planning stage, and the Rising Machine played an altogether more clandestine, secondary role.

English Ivan drew his gold pocket watch from the breast pocket of his waistcoat and tapped time with his cane. At the right moment, he stepped forward onto one of the massive cogs. Standing comfortably in the man-sized gap between the iron teeth, he rose quickly. The teeth meshed with another great cog, but Ivan simply hummed a symphony to himself as they approached. He passed through unscathed; a missing tooth in the next, horizontal, cog ensuring that he remained unharmed. It was all about timing, as he stepped off the first cog onto a hidden platform within the rock and straight onto another cog on the opposite side.

So it went, from cog to cog, higher and higher, each step timed to perfection. If a man did not know precisely where and when to step during the ascent, he would be brutally crushed by teeth that weighed more than rolling stock.

The last cog brought him to a door in a rock wall deep within the mountain. The sign on the door read, "Department of Ungentlemanly Affairs". He went in and waited for the others to arrive.

The first was Gibson DeWalt. Very short, black, bearded and wiry, he wore oil-stained dungarees and a leather belt slung with tools. "English," he said in a slow drawl, before settling on a stool in the small room. He glanced around, attention resting briefly on the cream envelope sitting on the small round table, then leaned back against the wall and closed his eyes. "At least there'll be crumpets."

Next to arrive was Hannibal Vholes. The door slammed open, and Vholes filled the iron frame. Even without his lifter's gear he would have been strong as an ox, but the powered harness that sat like a cage around his chest and shoulders enabled him to put a box car back on the rails all by himself. At his hip was a rifle with a barrel like a stove-pipe.

DeWalt cracked an eye. "Look, English. We're saved. All we need now is a mission that involves lifting heavy objects from down there to up here."

Hannibal walked in, the power-plant on his back hissing softly. "I don't know you, little man. Maybe you should sit this out. The Union needs men for this one."

"That'll be our little secret." Eva Havenhand shut the door behind her. She wore a welder's smock with a length of electrical cord at her hip coiled exactly like a whip.

"What the hell is she doing here?" Hannibal demanded.

"Bringing a little glamor to our happy family," she said. "Hi, English. Long time, and all that." She turned to DeWalt, stuck a gloved hand out and then pulled it back. "Eva Havenhand. We won't shake, no offense. You did come through a washhouse, though. Just a hint. Have we met?"

"No," said DeWalt. "But a man's luck can't last forever."

"Who the hell is she, English?" Hannibal said.

"Eva Havenhand," she said. "I would write it down, but that would just embarrass you further. I like your gun. I assume that was the biggest they had. Might want to sling it a bit more in front, if you know what I mean."

"Eva," warned Ivan. "Play nice with your new friends."

"Sometimes it takes a stranger to tell home-truths, English. That's all. You've put on weight. See? No one else would tell you but me."

"And there'll be no coarse language, Hannibal," Ivan said. "That's my number one rule. I told you last time."

"Dammit, English, get shot of these two and–"

There was a loud crack, and Hannibal stood in open-mouthed surprise. Ivan had slapped him.

"No coarse language, Mr. Vholes. Of *any* kind."

Hannibal flexed his jaw. "What the hell?"

Crack.

"English! Stop slapping me, dammit!"

Crack.

Hannibal's face darkened, and the pneumatics on his harness whined as his great shoulders flexed, but Ivan raised a school-masterly finger. "My number one rule."

Hannibal's shoulders slumped, and he sat on a stool. "By all that's – gosh and…golly."

Ivan walked to the small table in the middle of the room and picked up the envelope. He read the letter inside, and then passed it to DeWalt.

"Our benefactor is upset. The Guild has taken something they shouldn't have," he said. "So, we're going to return the favor."

📖 📖 📖

Later That Evening
Guild Headquarters

"They'll be arriving at Dockmast One around midnight. I have already signalled for additional Guardsmen to report here in an hour, so you'll have plenty of men. And no mistakes."

The Captain of the Watch nodded. "Sir, can I ask where this information came from?"

The Governor's Secretary tilted his head. "It came from far above your pay grade, Captain. Our enemies think they have a little surprise in store for us tonight, but I have eyes in places that would mortify them."

📖 📖 📖

11 Of The Clock

It was night, and the stars were crisp and brilliant. English Ivan and the three members of his Washhouse team waited quietly in the shadow of a brick wall thirty feet high. Above, gas-powered floodlamps illuminated the underbelly of a Guild aircar.

The aircar was an armored leviathan, with a cargo compartment of brass and wood slung beneath a bullet-shaped dirigible eighty feet long. Guns bristled from one-man pods all around the rigid, gas-filled balloon. The gondola underneath was dwarfed by the brass-ribbed envelope above, but Ivan knew it was nonetheless larger than most boxcars that pulled into Malifaux Station. It too, bristled with guns and defensive netting – the inhuman denizens of Malifaux could fly, and these aircars took personnel and valuable cargo great distances for the Guild over some of the most dangerous parts of the City.

The aircar did not float free, however. It was secured to a massive steel cable thicker than a man. The cable ran from the top of a dockmast two hundred feet tall and disappeared off into the darkness. Other cables led off in different directions, connecting dockmasts all over the City in a network controlled by the Guild. The cables shifted in the wind, and the scaffolding tower amplified the noises and groaned them into the night like the calls of some subterranean monster.

"Hard to believe something that big and heavy could just float," muttered Hannibal.

"That's because it's not heavy, you oaf," whispered Eva. "Or maybe it is. Maybe they call it lighter-than-air just to confuse deep-thinkers like you."

A door in the brick wall opened, and a head emerged. Owlish eyes blinked.

Ivan stepped forward briskly, tipping his hat with his cane. "A grand evening to you, Mr. Pell. I hope you are well?"

Mr. Pell stepped into the lane, looking nonplussed. His drooping mouth, hook nose, and bulging eyes made him look remarkably like a startled and ugly bird. "Ah, I am fine, thank you. Fine." He glanced around. "Er. How are you?"

Ivan nodded soberly. "It is a cold night, and sometimes my ankles get sore, but I wore warm socks. Otherwise, I can't complain."

"Good for you, English," said Eva. "Never ask Russians how they are – they take it literally," she whispered to Mr. Pell before pushing past him and darting through the doorway. DeWalt and Hannibal followed.

"Come along, sir!" Ivan called to Mr. Pell, heading after the others. "No time to dilly-dally."

Pell closed and locked the door and chased after Ivan, who found his team gathered at the foot of the enormous dockmast.

"Stairs?" said Hannibal, looking from the steps to the iron framework towering above.

"I knew he was the clever one," said DeWalt.

"Tell me, Hannibal, did you ever let a graverobber spend time alone with your head?" asked Eva.

"I meant," hissed Hannibal, "can't we take the cargo hoist? It must be twenty five stories."

"Mr. Pell says any use of the hoist will get noticed in the control tower," said Ivan. "We climb. Good for the blood."

It took them a long time to reach the top, where the wind howled and the bare metal was like ice. From there, Mr. Pell led them away from the main docking tower and to an unlit rope ladder that hung from the rear of the gondola. They climbed one by one, Ivan going last. As he climbed, the main docking steps retracted into the dockmast, and the departure sirens sounded. He climbed faster. Once aboard the aircar, he hauled up the ladder and spun the hatch closed.

He found himself in a cramped ballast storage room. The whole room shuddered briefly, and the superstructure grumbled.

"I believe we're underway," said Ivan, rubbing his hands together. "Comrades, welcome to Guild Aerostat *Impertinence*. This is Mr. Solomon Pell, a friend of our Movement."

"Hold it," whispered Pell hoarsely, "I'm no traitor. This is just about the money. You and yours can go hang for all I care."

"Beg pardon. Money is, of course, a noble motive. Why don't you tell us about the money?"

Pell's eyes lit up. "A million in mint Guild Scrip for the Treasury, coming in tonight. The Governor's office ordered all Treasury shipments of scrip onto the aircar network a while back. It's a damn sight–"

Ivan held up a warning finger.

"I mean, it's a clear sight more secure than trains, armored crawlers or, heaven forbid, wagons."

"Unless you have an inside man," said DeWalt, staring at Pell.

"Now for your part," said Pell to Ivan. "Which aircar is it coming in on?"

"Aerostat *Irascible*."

Pell's eyes widened. "But – but she's already docked at Guild Headquarters! An hour ago! They'll have offloaded the money!"

Ivan tapped the side of his nose. "Never fear, Mr Pell. You just get us to Dockmast One at Guild Headquarters, and we'll take it from there."

Midnight

Dockmast One, towering above Guild Headquarters, was where all cables led.

Halfway up the tower, Haim Clements was quietly pacing about the control room, from station to station, monitoring the aircar traffic. On a large glass display that dominated one wall, motorised rods and levers moved brass symbols along etched paths. Some symbols were small, denoting aircar taxis that ferried small groups or VIPs around. Larger symbols showed Guild patrol aircars, and the largest of all showed the mighty cargo aircars.

If Clements had been looking at this board only four months ago, before the Governor's Secretary had ordered the cable hubs and switching systems upgraded with the stolen designs, there would have been a fraction of the traffic he observed. But now –

"It is quite something, Chief Engineer," the shift supervisor offered, her voice warmly appreciative.

Clements nodded. The brass symbols reflected in his gold-rimmed glasses. "The operators don't need to do much, I see."

The supervisor shook her head. "Only now and then. The hub gyros sense the loads automatically and distribute according to scientific ratios and principles. It can be beautiful to watch. Mesmerizing, on a busy night like tonight."

"Security has been doubled, at least," said Clements. "No one is saying why, but it explains the activity. Look – there, you can see the effects of a new departure ripple through the whole system. Astonishing."

The supervisor stepped forward, putting her own glasses on to peer intently at the glass display board. "Sometimes it feels like it's alive. Like it's thinking." She turned away. "Apologies, Chief Engineer. That is foolishness."

But Clements was not so sure.

Dockmast One bristled with secondary berthing masts, like a crown of thorns atop an iron tree. From below, powerful arc-lamps sent harpoons of light into the night sky. The great whale-body of the *Impertinence* was pinned by several as it floated above its berth.

Pell came back from the hatch, his face ashen. "The berth is crawling with Guardsmen."

Ivan nodded. "They suspect something is afoot. Or they are taking the security of this consignment very seriously indeed. It was always a possibility. But do not fear, we are not discovered."

"But how are we to get down? We'll be seen!" Pell gnawed on an ink-stained knuckle. "We're lost. We're doomed."

Ivan slapped him on the back and handed him a tightly wrapped bundle. "Put this on, old chap. And keep your chin up."

Ivan had already put his on, and his team were nearly done with theirs. He checked his pocket watch. Timing was everything tonight.

"Think of it, DeWalt," Eva was saying as she donned her gleaming suit in elegant fashion. "This is almost certainly the cleanest thing you've ever worn."

DeWalt's reply was lost in the folds of cloth, but Ivan was sure it would have broken his number one rule.

"English," said Hannibal. "What the – er, good and golly are these things?"

The clothing was a single piece of woven metal fiber that covered them from foot to head. It should have been heavy, but was as thin and supple as silk. Ivan felt his skin tingle where it touched the metal cloth, as if micro-currents of electricity raced through it. "DeWalt? This is your brainchild."

DeWalt's voice was muffled as he donned the outfit. "They're Faraday suits."

After an extended pause, Ivan realised DeWalt considered that a full and complete explanation. He elaborated. "They are immensely sensitive to even the faintest corpuscles of light, and display a quite extraordinary property when fully illuminated."

DeWalt's head grimaced out the top of his suit. "Yeah, yeah, English. Do the thing with the match."

Ivan struck a match. It flared brightly in the dark hold, but as it did so, every Faraday suit lit up like a firefly. "Approach the light, if you please."

They took a step towards him, and he could see the surprise on their faces. They walked as if in a stiff gale.

"These suits amplify the pressure of light, like a sail amplifies the effects of the gentlest breeze. With a strong enough light, these suits could turn a walk into a sprint, or," he gestured to the hatch, "a death-plunge into a gentle descent." Their expressions changed from bafflement to ghastly shock as they realized how he intended for them to reach the ground. "If you would all move over to the hatch, we shall wait for one of the great spotlights below to play across our location. When it does so, jump. The suits will do the rest."

"But – but – won't we be seen?"

"You saw how the suits lit up, Mr Pell. You will be a candle hiding in a fire. Hoods up, and let's go."

Eva was the first to the hatch. The darkness flared electric white as a spotlight passed. "If I don't see you again, English," she said as she jumped, "I just wanted to tell you to go to–"

And she was gone, her words lost to a howl on the wind. DeWalt was next, but he was pushed aside by Hannibal ("No midget is gonna jump before I do!"). DeWalt followed right after him ("Then you can be a midget's landing pad!"). Solomon Pell was already backing away, but Ivan had expected that, grabbed him by the collar, and jumped into the light.

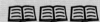

The Malifaux Sanitarium

The door opened, and Matron Cynthia Goodchilde entered. Before she shut the door behind her, Doctor Pendergast heard the wailing and banging from the East Wing that had been building since morning.

Matron Goodchilde bustled to the medicine cabinet, unlocked it, and started filling a box with tablets before she even gave the doctor good evening. "Phlebotomy and sweating have not improved their condition, Doctor," she explained. "If anything, they grow more and more agitated. They need more sedatives. I have never seen anything like it, upon my word."

"A noxious miasma from the river could be to blame, Matron."

She continued filling the box, exhaustion and impatience giving edge to her voice. "The windows have been closed all day and all night. Three of the patients have had such excitations of their spirits that I have had to bind them hand and foot, but their strength is unnatural. More sedatives are the only option left before commotion becomes riot."

Doctor Pendergast stood from his desk and walked over to help her. Then he saw the pills she was stuffing into the box. "Good lord, Matron! Tell me you haven't given those to any of the patients!"

She froze. "All day, doctor. The jars are marked, 'Sedatives.'"

Doctor Pendergast grabbed the box off her and closely examined one of the white pills. They were stimulants, given to greyhounds and horses prior to races. He started sweating. The worst of Malifaux's criminally insane patients had been receiving massive doses of these since morning.

He heard a distant crash, and the sound of a warden's whistle. He and Matron Goodchilde ran from the room, leaving behind the pills, and two large, brown glass jars.

📖 📖 📖

It was a timeless, otherworldly descent.

Ivan's skin tingled as if electric eels swam there, while all around him was a blinding whiteness that the buffeting wind could not displace. He was aware of a downwards motion, but gentle, like a falling leaf, and before long, even that sensation became distant and unsure. He held his grip steady on Pell's collar, and waited to touch down.

His feet bumped hard into something unyielding. He tried to stand, but lost his footing and rolled. The surface underfoot was smooth as glass and unpleasantly hot to the touch. The lens of the arc-lamp, he realised. Dragging an almost weightless Pell behind him, he bounced and scrambled to the rim.

The moment he was out of the pillar of light, his Faraday suit dimmed, and his mass returned in an instant. This time he was surer on his feet, although Pell landed beside him in a twisted bundle that grabbed at its bruised parts and moaned.

Two dockmast workers who had manned the light were slumped unconscious by a railing. Eva stood over them, unwinding her length of electrical whip-cord from around their necks. Hannibal and DeWalt were crouched at the top of a flight of steps.

Below lay a goods yard, speckled with yellow pools around gas lamps that revealed shipping crates and anonymous low brick buildings. On the left of the yard were the massive feet of the dockmasts, on the right larger warehouses that separated the yard from the Guild Headquarters, and past the high wall on the other side of the yard flowed the river.

"Just like old times, English," Eva whispered, securing the men's arms and legs. "Remember von Neumann?"

Ivan smiled. "The Brassheart! Yes, he had that aeronautical, robotic squid. Quite a contraption."

"Till you blew it up. Things do have a habit of going up in smoke around you."

"I couldn't possibly comment."

Ivan gathered his team quietly. "The money is in eight wooden crates marked 'Billing Records', and the crates are currently in that hut." Ivan's cane picked out a red door with a gas-lamp above it.

Pell frowned. "So what's in the Treasury boxes?"

Ivan shrugged. "I do not know. Billing records, most likely." His eyes twinkled. "Washhouse agents had them swapped before they came through the Breach, and now all we must do is gather them up, and then it is back to here, up to the *Impertinence* again using reverse-Faraday suits, and we'll be back in time for crumpets before they know what happened."

"I said there'd be crumpets," said DeWalt.

"The devil take your crumpets, Mr. Ivan," said Pell. "My breakfast is a one-quarter share. Do I have your word?"

"You have the word of a gentleman, sir. The Empire was built on nothing less."

Ivan led the way down the stairs and through the goods yard, keeping to the shadows. When they reached the brick hut with the red door, he waved Hannibal forward. "I have no key, Mr. Vholes. If you would be so kind?"

As Hannibal stepped forward, Eva's electrical cord lashed out and hit the gas-lamp. The light winked out. Hannibal placed both hands flat on the steel door, braced his feet and pushed. The power-plant on his back hissed violently, a ruddy light glowing behind the cowling. There was a series of popping noises like champagne corks. Bolts of brick-dust shot out, and the sheared ends of metal pins rifled off into the darkness. The power-plant gave an ominous rumble just as the door squealed in protest, then with an oddly satisfying *snap!* Hannibal staggered forward, the buckled door held firmly before him.

Ivan's comrades filed swiftly past into the hut, and then, once he was sure the noise had not drawn attention, he followed suit.

"Hannibal, the door, if you please."

The big dock worker leaned the door back in place. Ivan raised his cane, and a soft, creamy light grew from the soulstone atop it.

The hut was empty.

Pell turned, aghast, as the others looked to Ivan in surprise.

"What in the name of—" was all Solomon Pell managed to say before Ivan rapped him smartly on the temple with his cane. He collapsed in a bundle for the second time that night.

"Secure him, please, Eva. Gently. He has done us good service. Good, good, just place him over by the wall, there. He is not a sack of potatoes, Eva. He will bruise. Thank you." Ivan twirled his cane and then leaned both hands on it. "Gentlemen. Lady. The surprise has caused you great unease, so allow me to soothe your spirits with a dose of the unalloyed truth. There is no money."

There was a stunned silence.

Eventually DeWalt hawked and spat. "Figures. I knew something was up when you started talking about reverse-Faraday suits. Makes no sense at all. How you thought anyone would believe that bunkum is beyond me."

📖 📖 📖

Chief Engineer Haim Clements knew something was wrong. He had always had a gift for looking at a piece of new engineering and knowing whether it would work or not. Once he had started considering the ornate glass display panel in the dockmast control tower as a mechanical operation, a hideous feeling started to grow in his gut. If the panel had been a train, he would have said it was about to derail.

He called the shift supervisor over, waving at her urgently across the room. "Look at it! Tell me what you see."

She perused the display for a few moments and shook her head. "A great deal of traffic around Dockmast One, probably the most there's ever been, but—"

"Ignore the loads for once, forget the direction they're going in for the moment and just look at the destination tags!"

"But what does..." Her face went white. "Oh, my."

She started yelling orders to the operators, but Clements knew it was too late. Three quarters of the aircars on the network, hundreds of tonnes of steel and brass, were about to converge on Dockmast One at precisely the same time.

📖 📖 📖

Eva's face was unreadable. "Care to explain that to us, English? I don't like being played for a fool."

Ivan raised his cane. "Explanations? No. Instead, I will do this." Bolts of white lightning shot from the soulstone on the tip of his cane. One speared Eva in the chest, knocking her backwards with a thunderclap. Another did the same to DeWalt. They both lay where they fell, smoke rising in thin wisps.

"English?" Hannibal said, edging towards the door. His fists came up as his shoulder harness whined.

"Put them away, Mr. Vholes. You have no idea how much trouble you're in, but the Governor's Secretary will explain it all to you when he arrives. And by explain, I mean feed you to his lawyers."

"What?"

Ivan twirled his cane, then kicked DeWalt's body. There was no reaction. "Those plans you handed over, the ones for the autonomous hubs for the aircar network. They were a plant by our friends in the Movement. They wanted you to deliver them to the Guild, and like a stupid oaf, you did exactly that."

Hannibal said nothing, his expression close and wary.

"Unfortunately, once I learned what you'd done, it was months after the fact. All the usual communication channels out of Hollow Marsh were shut down by the Movement. I contrived this mission so that I would be sent here and I could warn Lucius in person, but it's too damned late. Yes, Mr. Vholes, I work for Lucius as well. "

"Lucius didn't—"

"Didn't tell you about me? Why would he? You didn't think he would have only one spy in the Union, did you? Our contact in the Movement doctored those plans so that at a preset time on a preset date, the logic engines at the heart of it all would contrive a disaster big enough to bring the entire network down. He used you. And it is about to happen, right above our heads. Tell me, Mr. Vholes, when he arrives, whom do you think Lucius is going to blame for this?"

Hannibal's face was sweating, and he had turned pale. He stammered several times, before saying, "It's not...that's not...I can..."

"You can explain? I will certainly enjoy watching you try, as pieces of aircar rain down upon us. At best, you'll die painfully. At worst, Lucius will decide you are actually a double-agent. If he thinks that, there is no telling what he might do to you. Who knows, he might even take off his mask and let you see what's underneath."

Hannibal's eyes were wide. He stepped forward, reaching out to Ivan, his power-plant whining softly. "You have to help me, English!"

Ivan spread his hands wide, with a 'what can I do?' expression.

"You have to help me! Wait! I have this. I have it here, hold on." Hannibal dismantled the ammunition drum of his rifle. Inside he pulled out a tightly folded bundle of papers and brandished them at Ivan. "This is the proof, English! If you tell him I'm not a double-agent, and he sees these, it'll all be fine! I know it!"

Ivan frowned. "What on earth is that?"

"Plans! For a prototype Leviathan! I swear it, English, on my mother's grave, I swear it. You have to tell him it wasn't my fault! I was going to break away from you all, first chance I got, and give Lucius these. I've been trying to get him to let me quit for months, and then you picked me for this mission, and I thought if I gave these to him he would let me get out. You have to tell him!"

"Yes, Hannibal. I picked you." Before the huge dock worker could react, Ivan snatched the Leviathan plans from his outstretched hand. "You two listening to all this? Sorry, DeWalt. Apologies, Eva. Temporary paralysis only. I couldn't count on you not interfering. I picked you, Hannibal, because we knew you had these plans somewhere, and our benefactor really, really wants them back, but we knew we would never see them again if we just asked you. But if we gave you an opportunity to deliver them in person, for example, if I picked you for a mission that just happened to take you to Guild Headquarters, why there was a pretty good chance you would bring them along." Ivan slipped them into his waistcoat pocket. "Thank you, Mr. Vholes."

DeWalt groaned and sat up. "Could you two repeat all that from the beginning?"

Eva stood, groggily, her electrical cable-whip in her hand. "Vholes, you traitorous piece of—"

Ivan raised a warning finger, just as Hannibal raised his rifle and clicked the trigger. Nothing happened. "You dismantled the ammo drum, sir. And I do believe that forcing open that door has depleted your power-plant considerably for now. However," Ivan leaned his cane against the wall and raised his fists, "if it's trouble you want, I have two good friends of the Marquess of Queensbury right here."

Hannibal ran. He toppled the door and sprinted off into the night. DeWalt and Eva rushed to the open doorway, but Ivan called them back. "Let him go. We have bigger fish to fry tonight."

Eva turned. "Okay, English. You got me. What is there possibly left to do tonight? And don't think I've forgiven you for shooting me with that thing."

"Just so we're clear," said DeWalt, rubbing his head. "There's no money, right?"

From across the river, a distant siren sounded, along with growing numbers of Guild whistles.

"If I'm not mistaken, and I rarely am," said Ivan, "that sounds a lot like it's coming from the Sanitarium. I wonder what could be transpiring there at this hour."

Those sounds were almost immediately drowned out as emergency klaxons blared into life across the goods yard, from the direction of the illuminated dockmasts.

"That's a collision warning," said DeWalt. "Did you mean what you said about those plans Vholes stole being doctored?"

Ivan smiled. "Come, we have one last job to do, and I am going to need your expertise, Mr. DeWalt."

The Aerostat *Munificent* was the largest class of military aircar the Guild possessed. Fully one hundred feet from nose to stern, it carried huge cargos. At present, it was proceeding under full automation along the Sourbreak line, heading towards the Guild Headquarters and Dockmast One. Its captain was frantically signalling the control tower as the *Munificent* and four other aircars approached the same hub at the same time. Tethered to the cables that were pulling them along, there was nothing the captains of any of the vessels could do.

In the underslung belly of the *Munificent*, crates of ammunition were piled high. Nestled between two of the crates, lodged deep where no one could see it, was what looked like a pencil.

Inside, the pencil was hollow, and a very precisely engineered plate of tin separated an acid from a liquid accelerator. The acid had been eating through the tin for just over a day, now, and as the *Munificent's* collision warning sirens blared, the tin gave way, and the liquids met.

The initial flare was small, but intensely hot, and the dry tarpaulins over the surrounding crates quickly caught fire.

The goods yard was in chaos. Dock workers and Guild Guardsmen were running back and forth as the huge searchlights played over the swollen bodies of the aircars massing above. Already, two had collided and burst into flames, causing burning debris to rain down over the river. The top of Dockmast One was ablaze, and the gyroscopic hub of one of the secondary masts had failed in spectacular fashion, wrenching the connecting cable so violently that the mast was slowly, inexorably, falling over. The scream of tortured iron was ear-splitting.

Ivan had led his remaining team members to one of the larger warehouses. If there had been guards present, they had deserted their posts, and Ivan and Eva were hauling open the main doors. Loud though it was, it went unnoticed in the panic and confusion.

Then, from the direction of the Quarantine Zone, along the Sourbreak line, there was a flash that lit the night like a new sun. Ivan had to look away, and then a few moments later, as the afterimages still danced in his eyes, the thunderclap of the exploding *Munificent* nearly knocked him off his feet.

Eva whistled. "Sweet Bayou Rose! I just know you had something to do with that, English."

The burning wreckage plummeted over the Quarantine Zone, ordnance and ammunition still cooking off as it fell. The sight would linger in the minds of every Malifaux citizen for a long time.

"I couldn't possibly comment."

They entered the warehouse. It was dark, and Ivan's eyes still tricked him with white ghosts of the explosion, so it was Eva and DeWalt who saw the inhabitants of the warehouse first.

Eva gave a yelp of alarm.

"Don't worry — they're not activated," DeWalt said, and then Ivan's eyes finally adjusted, and he gazed upon row after row of brand new Guild Peacekeepers. Each machine stood twice as tall as a man, with a heavy, squat armored body, two legs and four arms ending in claws that could crush a railcar. Their heads were all looking straight ahead, but there were no signs of power in any of them, despite the thick cables running from iron cranium to iron cranium.

"How many are there?" Eva asked, her voice soft with wonder.

Ivan grabbed DeWalt and hurried him over to a control panel positioned in front of a large logic engine. The cables buried in the skulls of the Peacekeepers all led back to this engine. "There should be thirty-six. They came through the Breach only a few hours ago, and they haven't been activated yet. Security measure. Eva, watch the door. DeWalt, I need you to reprogram these." Ivan checked his pocket watch, grimaced, and handed a sheet of punched card to DeWalt. "This. Use this. Be very, very quick."

Ivan ran over to Eva, and peeked through the doorway into the yard. The secondary mast had completely collapsed into the river, and fires and debris from the still-colliding aircars were everywhere. It was pandemonium.

"All this just to get some plans back?" asked Eva. "You should keep copies."

Ivan shook his head, as still more ammunition exploded in the distance, sending up fresh fireballs. "Yes and no. The plans were vital, but tonight is about Vholes. Lucius had him in our midst for a long time before we realized what he was up to. He was a member of the Washhouse. He had access to just about everything. Tonight is the Movement's way of warning the Governor. Once this is over, the Guild will blame it in public on pilot error or an engineering failure, but the point will not be lost on the Governor. 'Do not cause a mess in our own backyard.'"

"This is some warning."

"This? No, this is just the distraction."

DeWalt joined them. "The engine has accepted the instructions, but what's the point, English? Those things cannot be activated from here. It needs Guild hardware to make them initialize, and I can't fake that."

A new set of sirens sounded, these ones coming from the Guild barracks further down the river.

"You know what that sound is, sir, madam?" said Ivan. "The skies themselves are falling right on top of Guild Headquarters. The hundreds of inmates of the Sanitarium have broken out and are wreaking havoc across the river. Taken all together, it might, to a panicked captain of the Guard, be mistaken for an outright attack by hostile forces. Right on their doorstep. It is time for emergency measures. They call out the troops. They barricade every road. They fortify positions and–"

Behind them, the lights came on in the warehouse. Power hummed as a generator in the back coughed into life. Thirty six metal pairs of legs hissed as their pneumatics warmed up.

"–and they issue the emergency activation codes to all mothballed Guild assets," finished DeWalt.

Ivan turned and spread his arms, welcoming the thirty-six armoured heads that turned to look at him. "One must hand it to the Guild. They are sticklers for procedure. It might not be a million in Guild Scrip, Ms. Havenhand. These are worth a lot more than that. Not bad for a night's work. Viktor Ramos does so love new toys!"

Ivan walked over to the nearest Peacekeeper. It turned its massive head to look down on him, and he tapped his hat with his cane. "Hullo." He clicked his fingers. It reached out a hand and lifted him carefully, placing him atop its gleaming red carapace.

"Choose a conveyance, Ms. Havenhand. Or, if you prefer, pick a horse, Mr. DeWalt. We have a long ride ahead of us."

The cables detached as the last of the new instructions were fed to the Peacekeepers by the logic engine. They stomped forward, shaking the concrete floor of the warehouse with each step. The ones in the front row raised their massive claws, and the brick walls of the warehouse collapsed before them. The ones behind, including those carrying Ivan, Eva and DeWalt, scrambled nimbly over the rubble and kept going, heading for the streets of Malifaux and the mountains beyond.

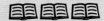

Epilogue

Solomon Pell awoke with a very sore head in a partially wrecked brick hut as the morning sun shed its light on a scene of destruction. Many fires still burned, and the roof of the hut had fallen in where tangled debris had landed on it, but other than his aching head, Pell was surprised to learn he was unscathed.

Knowing that his part in the night's affairs would doubtless come to light before long, he returned to his lodgings, planning to be very far away when the Guild came looking for him.

So it was with even greater surprise that Mr. Pell learned there had been a delivery for him the evening before. His landlady, who disapproved of practically everything, including, it seemed, deliveries, reluctantly handed him a note that had come for him just after dawn. It read simply, "A gentleman's promise kept. Enjoy your breakfast."

His landlady advised Mr. Pell that he could find his two boxes of billing records up in his room.

ANGELICA, MISTRESS OF CEREMONIES - MINION

Looking for an escape from Earthside drudgery, Angelica was quick to accept Colette's offer as her Mistress of Ceremonies at the Star Theater. From the time she could say "step right up," she had helped her father, a carnival barker, in his routine, and over the years, he taught her the art. From voice projection, to engaging a crowd and bawdy jokes, to the especially important talent of weaving a mystery for the rubes in a few short sentences, he passed all of his secrets on to her. After her father's death, Angelica carried on the tradition, the depth of her persuasive skills all but lost on the farmhands who wanted to see her legs more than hear her pitch. She thought she was doomed to live the same life as her father until Colette heard her performance.

She found the magic that her father had been lacking once she reached the Star Theater. Her voice had an even stronger persuasive edge; she could pitch a whisper to the farthest corners of the theater and could bend the crowd to every syllable she uttered. For a time, every rowdy tough with enough pocket money bought a ticket to the show and tried his best to upstage the Mistress of Ceremonies. None succeeded. Those rare times she was forced to deal with a heckler she could reduce him to tears with the force of will behind her words.

Having settled into her role at the Star, Angelica continues to aid Colette in the theater's operations. She gladly participates in any skullduggery her employer plans, relishing the time out of the limelight, using the gifts her father gave her to ensure the Star's continued success.

30MM BASE

SOULSTONE COST: 5

SHOWGIRL, UNIQUE

WK/CG	HT	WP	CA	DF	WD
5/7	2	5	5	5	6

HOOKED CANE	
RG	🗡 2
CB	5 📖
DG	1/3/4

PROJECTED VOICE	
RG	⌐8
CB	5 📖
DG	1/1♣/2♣♣

TALENTS:

Abilities

Commanding Presence: ⬡8. Other friendly Showgirls are immune to falling back. Other friendly Showgirls falling back immediately rally when entering this ⬡.

Duty: This model's Controller cannot be changed.

First to the Stage: After all models are deployed, but before the game begins, this model's Controller may exchange its position in play with another friendly Showgirl model.

Weapon

Projected Voice: Friendly Showgirls cannot be targeted by this Weapon and are immune to damage caused by this Weapon.

Actions

(1) Encouragement: ⬡6. Resist Flips made by friendly non-Construct Showgirls receive ➕.

Triggers

Cb (📖📖) "Get off the Stage!" [Hooked Cane]: After damaging defender, Push the defender up to 3".

Cb (📖♥) Showstopper [Projected Voice]: Instead of inflicting Moderate or Severe damage on non-Master defender or placing any ♣, defender must discard two Control Cards or receive **Paralyzed**.

SPELLS:

(0) "Bring Out the Next Act"
(CC: 11 / Rst: - / Rg: 18) Target friendly Showgirl that has not already activated this turn activates immediately after this model's activation ends.

(1) "Do You Want to See More?"
(CC: 12📖 / Rst: Wp / Rg: (↑)10) Only enemy models need to resist this Spell. Models losing their Resist Duels receive -2 **Wp** and lose any suits associated with their **Wp**.

(1) "Give Them an Encore"
(CC: 14 / Rst: - / Rg: 2) Push target friendly Showgirl up to 3".

BLESSED OF DECEMBER - MINION

"Blessed" by December's touch into a creature both more and less than human, Rasputina's Silent One must now contend with the warring urges fighting for control of her mind.

Transformed into a creature of hunger and desire, December's rapacious will amplified her baser instincts into overwhelming needs she can never satisfy. The hunger for flesh and thirst for blood December instilled in her constantly threaten to overwhelm the tenuous grip she has on her own mind. Only her devotion to her mistress prevents the beast within from completely suppressing her humanity.

Physically transformed into a ravenous creature closer to Wendigo than human, the Blessed of December's new body is well-equipped to tear through skin and bone. She leaps upon her prey, ripping into them with black claws and sharp fangs, consuming without satisfaction. Her gaze carries a hint of the strength of December's might within it, cowing the bold who would try to stand against her moments before her bite finds their throat.

For now, Rasputina's commands are enough to halt the Blessed's frenzy of violence, but she worries that when the war between the halves of the Blessed's psyche ends, the half in control will no longer attend to her orders.

40MM BASE   **SOULSTONE COST: 8**

BEAST, GRAVEROBBER, UNIQUE

WK/CG	HT	WP	CA	DF	WD
5/8	3	5	5	6	7

RAGGED CLAWS

RG	/// 2
CB	6 📖
DG	1/3/5

FERAL BITE

RG	/// 1
CB	5 🌀
DG	2/2/4

TALENTS:

Abilities
December's Pawn: When this model flips or plays the Black Joker, its Controller immediately draws two Control Cards.

Frozen Heart: This model is immune to Morale Duels.

Hard to Wound 1

Stalker: If this model is out of LoS from all enemy models at the End Closing Phase, Push it up to 6". This model must be out of LoS from all enemy models after the Push.

Terrifying → 11

Weapon
Feral Bite: This model heals 1 **Wd** each time it damages an enemy non-Construct model with this Weapon.

Actions
(+1) Melee Expert

(1) Ravenous: Discard any number of Corpse Counters carried by this model. Perform a Healing Flip for each Corpse Counter discarded.

Triggers
Cb (🌀📖) Gorge on Flesh [Feral Bite]: After damaging a living model, immediately make another Feral Bite **Strike** against the defender.

Cb (🌀📖) Grip of Winter [Ragged Claws]: This Weapon's Damage Flip receives ♣ ♣.

Cb (✗) Rip Throat [Feral Bite]: When damaging a defender without **Armor**, inflict +2 **Dg**.

SPELLS:

(0) Leap
(CC: 10 ♥ / Rst: - / Range: C) Move this model up to its **Cg**. This model receives **Flight** during this move. This Spell cannot be cast if this model is in melee.

(1) December's Gaze
(CC: 14 📖 / Rst: - / Range: 8) Target model performs a **Wp → 14** Morale Duel.

Fire Gamin - Minion

Taming the energies required to summon a fire gamin is akin to trying to tie the tails of two cyclones together. Manipulating the requisite aether is neither for the timid nor the lazy. Equal amounts of passion and ambition must be merged with an iron-willed concentration to call one into being. Ambition and passion are required to feed the fires stoked by the aether while a summoner without adequate concentration can find himself immolated mid-sentence as the gamin appears, but in its natural state, untamed and without a containing vessel.

Fire gamin are malicious and mischievous, creating all manner of trouble for their summoner and those he would send them against. Their imp-like features are wreathed in flames, their bodies constantly setting alight anything flammable their cavorting brings them into contact with. Fighting a fire gamin in close quarters all but ensures its foe terrible burns, either from its burning body or the gobbets of magma it can spit short distances. In fact, even defeating a fire gamin provides its own challenge. When a fire gamin's energy is extinguished, it explodes in a ball of flames as a final defiant gesture.

30MM BASE　　**SOULSTONE COST: 4**

CONSTRUCT

WK/CG	HT	WP	CA	DF	WD
4/8	1	4	3	4	4

BURNING CLAWS	
RG	///// 1
CB	5 📖
DG	1/2/3

SPIT MAGMA	
RG	☞8
CB	4 📖
DG	2/2☁/3☁

TALENTS:

Abilities

Ablaze: This model is immune to Burning Tokens.

Armor +1

Blazing Glory 2: (ʀ)2. **Dg** 2 when this model is killed. Models suffering 1 or more **Wd** from **Blazing Glory** gain one Burning Token.

Burning Blood: When this model is damaged by a melee **Strike** or melee Spell, the attacker suffers 1 **Wd** and gains a Burning Token.

Drawn to the Flame: This model may be hired by Crews led by Sonnia Criid or Kaeris. When hired by Crews led by Sonnia Criid, this model costs no additional Soulstones and gains Rare 3.

Smoldering Heart: When declared the target of a Duel, this model may suffer 1 **Wd** to receive +3 **Wp** until that Duel is resolved.

Weapons

Burning Claws, Spit Magma: A defender damaged by this Weapon gains one Burning Token.

SLATE RIDGE MAULER - MINION

Prospectors exploring the mountains north of the City first encountered a creature with a remarkable similarity to Earthside bears, except for the additional pair of legs and bony spines running along its shoulders and back. The creature was quickly named the Slate Ridge Mauler.

Recently, demand for four-armed coats made from the Mauler's unique hide has generated a brisk trade in the pelts. Experienced trappers and hunters search the mountains for their dens. Slate Ridge Maulers are aggressive, especially so when defending their den from would-be intruders. Rearing back onto its hind legs in a display of dominance, a Mauler towers nearly nine feet tall, bellowing out a roar audible up to five miles away. Thanks to their additional legs, they are capable of amazing bursts of speed, overtaking and attacking fleeing prey with ease.

The reward is well worth the considerable danger however. A single bear pelt brings in more Scrip than a month spent hunting Gremlins for their bounty. Men and women who have never hunted for anything more dangerous than an open tavern see the Slate Ridge Mauler as a fast and easy way to make money, far easier than slaving away in the mines or panning for 'stone dust or even gold in Malifaux's waterways. Many of these novices are never heard from again.

50MM BASE

SOULSTONE COST: 7

BEAST, RARE 1

WK/CG	HT	WP	CA	DF	WD
4/7	3	5	4🗡	4	8

CLAWS	
RG	⚔ 2
CB	6
DG	3/4/5

TALENTS:

Abilities

Bearskin Armor: This model may choose to ignore damage inflicted by (🜚), (◐), and (♟).

Enraged: While this model is reduced to half of its **Wd** or less, it gains +2 **Cb** and **Hard to Kill**.

Hard to Wound 1

Ornery: This model cannot be activated by another friendly model's Talents. This model cannot activate simultaneously with other friendly models.

Weapon

Claws: Paired. Enemy models damaged by this Weapon are Pushed 1" toward this model.

Actions

(+1) Melee Expert

Triggers

Cb (✗) Rip Throat [Claws]: When damaging a defender without **Armor**, this Weapon inflicts +2 **Dg**.

Cb (🗡) Shred [Claws]: After the defender suffers damage from this Weapon, defender receives **Slow**. In addition, until the Resolve Effects Step, defender receives -2 **Df** and cannot activate **Df** Triggers.

SPELLS:

(1) Bear Hug
(CC: 12🗡 / Rst: Df / Rg: ⚔ 2) Target small or medium based **Ht** 1 or 2 model suffers 1 **Wd** and receives **Slow**. At the start of each of the target's activations, it must win a **Df → 12** Duel or suffer 2 **Wd** and receive **Slow**. This Spell ends when the target wins the Duel, the target is not in melee with this model, or this model casts this Spell again.

Union Miner - Minion

UNFAIR!

Brothers of the Miners and Steamfitters Union, it is time for Labor to Rise Up and Be Counted!

For too long we have toiled under the Unfair working conditions put forward by the Guild Bosses!

For too long we have seen good brothers and sisters meet their Maker at the hands of Lethal cave-ins, "Accidental" Explosions, Dangerous Creatures while the Bosses watch us Suffer from afar!

NO MORE, we say! NO MORE! We must take our Fate into our own hands! RISE UP!!

NOW IS THE TIME TO STRIKE!

SOLIDARITY NOW!
UNION FOREVER!

NOT ONE MORE DEATH at THEIR HANDS!

THE M&SU CALLS FOR A STRIKE!! WHO SHALL ANSWER??

30MM BASE   **SOULSTONE COST: 4**

M&SU MEMBER, SPECIAL FORCES (M&SU ASSET)

Wk/Cg	Ht	Wp	Ca	Df	Wd
4/6	2	5	4	5	6

IMPROVISED WEAPON

Rg	〃 1
Cb	5
Dg	1/2/4

TALENTS:

Abilities

Companion (M&SU Member)

Rioter: This model's Damage Flips against game elements with Hardness, models with the Object Characteristic, and Markers receive 🂠 and inflict +1 **Dg**.

Smoldering Heart: When declared the target of a Duel, this model may suffer 1 **Wd** to receive +3 **Wp** until that Duel is resolved.

Stand Together: This model's Attack Flips receive 🂠 when the target is within 3" of one or more other friendly Union Miners.

Weapon

Improvised Weapon: Models may not declare **Df** Triggers when attacked by this Weapon.

Actions

(0) File False Claim: This model's Controller discards one Card. Bury this model. After all models have activated this turn, simultaneously Place this model and any other buried friendly Union Miners completely within 6" of a friendly Union Miner in play. If no friendly Union Miners are in play when buried Union Miners should be Placed, Place them completely within 6" of a friendly M&SU Member in play. If no friendly M&SU Members remain, these models are removed from the game as casualties.

(1) Union Benefits: This model heals 1 **Wd**.

(2) Wind Up: This model makes an Improvised Weapon **Strike** which receives 🂠🂠 to the Damage Flip.

Triggers

Cb (📖) Brutal [Improvised Weapon]

SPELLS:

(1) Menace

(CC: 10 / Rst: Wp / Rg: 6) Move this model up to 4" toward target model. Target may not take move Actions until the Start Closing Phase.

ARCANE EFFIGY - MINION

Arcanist Masters call upon the Arcane Effigy to aid them in their continual pursuit of aetheric knowledge. Arcane's natural affinity with the eddies and flows of the aether provides the Master who commands it with a conduit of increased mystical power as well as bends their ear with whispers of magical lore forgotten centuries ago.

The Effigy carries scrolls and books filled with spells and rituals from old Malifaux, memories pulled from the collective spiritual energy of the aether and made real. They are written in a language only Arcane understands and selectively doles out in cryptic whispers to its current master. The secrets it chooses to share allow it to subtly guide its master toward particular lines of study and experimentation, all intended to settle the raging aetheric tides created by the Event.

If and when Arcane's machinations are uncovered, it is not without the means to defend itself. Its aetheric bolts tap into the very stuff of magic, penetrating mundane defenses with ease. It can also tap the aether for its own well-being, rejuvenating itself with a quick dip in the magical streams.

30MM BASE

SOULSTONE COST: 4

OBJECT 1, SPECIAL FORCES (DOLL), UNIQUE

WK/CG	HT	WP	CA	DF	WD
4/-	1	5	6📖	5	5

WEIGHT OF KNOWLEDGE	
RG	⚡ 1
CB	4
DG	1/2/3

AETHERIC BOLT	
RG	⤙6
CB	*
DG	1/2/3

TALENTS:

Abilities

Aetheric Connection: One friendly model with the **Aetheric Connection** Ability within 6" of this model may activate after this model's activation ends.

Aetheric Demands: Non-Neverborn Crews hiring this model must nominate one leader per model with this Ability they hire. Those leaders cannot attach Totems.

Arcane Reservoir: Increase this model's Crew's Maximum Hand Size by +1 while this model is in play.

Magic Resistant 2

Other Allegiances [Neverborn]: This model may be hired by the indicated Faction's Crews at no additional cost.

Weapon

Aetheric Bolt: Magical. This Weapon's **Strike** Duels use **Ca → Ca**.

Actions

(1) Conduct Aether: Target friendly leader within 6" receives +1 AP on its next activation. This AP may only be used for **Cast** or **Channel** Actions. This Action may be taken only once per Turn.

Triggers

Ca (⚡📖) Drink Aether [Aetheric Bolt]: This model heals 1 **Wd** for each wound inflicted on the defender.

Ca (📖📖) Vicious Siphon [Siphon Aether]: If this spell inflicts Severe damage, target model's Controller discards another Control Card if able.

SPELLS:

(0) Siphon Aether
(CC: 14📖 / Rst: Ca / Rg: ⤙6) Dg 2/3/4. Target model's Controller must discard one Control Card if able if it suffers one or more **Wd** from this Spell.

(1) Aetheric Barrier
(CC: 14📖📖 / Rst: - / Rg: ⊙6) Friendly models receive **Magic Resistant 1**.

Neverborn

A Great Adventure

A Is For Awful, B Is For Blood,
C Is For Creature, A Thing That Goes Thud

All stories begin small, with a twist of fate.

The teddy bear was a little dirty, a little frayed, and its black, button eyes were a little loose. Someone had lovingly stitched and patched its fuzzy, brown sides, however, and it was well stuffed with straw. It lay on the floor in a slick of blood, its long muzzle pointing straight up at the ceiling.

The sitting room of the Grey family was low and cramped. A wood-burning stove stood in the corner, beside some brightly colored number blocks, a toy cutlass, and a wooden train. A table, chairs, and various ornaments lay broken or flung on their sides, and the yellow curtains were torn. The room was even more cramped with all the men in it, talking in tight, low voices above the muffled sobs from the back room. Guild badges hung from chests, beneath grim, vengeful expressions. The air was charged, like at a hanging. There was blood all over, but those present wanted more.

A tall man entered, as rangy and grizzled as an old mountain lion, and the voices hushed. Riding spurs clinked as he walked, and guns hung from his belt. He did not take his hat off. He spoke to a hefty man with a sergeant's badge, in a wilderness drawl that was soft and gentlemanly, with just a hint of menace. "Your man in back. He got a name?"

"Grey, sir. Phineas Grey."

"Has he talked?"

The sergeant glanced towards the back room. "Some of the men had a go at him. Didn't say nothin' worth repeatin', sir."

"The neighbors, they hear anythin'?"

"If they did–"

"–they ain't talkin'." Even behind his bushy, grey moustache, the man's expression told what he thought of the neighbors.

"They're scared, sir," the sergeant said. This was his neighborhood, and he felt an odd compulsion to rise to its defense. "Proper scared. Been a lot of sightings. Odd things. Then this."

The man looked at the sergeant for a while, his eyes hidden under his hat. "Y'all know this part of town. Seen many street kids hereabouts? The Wee Malkies? The Little Sisters? Crooligans?"

"Not now you mention it, sir, no. Is that important?"

The man considered this for a long moment, then gestured to the back room. "Fetch our Mr. Phineas Grey to the cells. Mind he doesn't fall down any stairs on the way there." He looked around. "The victim?"

"Well, just..." The sergeant pointed over by the teddy bear, and then at various other red, wet splashes around the room. The man with the spurs took a last look and left.

"Bleedin' Neverborn Hunters, thinkin' they're better'n us," Sergeant Kliegemann muttered, as he headed for the murderer in the back room. "This ain't got nothin' to do with him, anywise."

Not long after, the sun came up, and the men all departed, leaving a bruised, brooding emptiness in the house. Shadows came and went and came again as day passed and night fell. Flies clustered around the darkening blood in the silent rooms and crawled on the teddy bear's fur, but the house stayed still and dead.

And so things might have remained. If fate had not lent a hand, the house would have been cleaned and stripped and the teddy bear thrown away along with everything else. Things might have turned out very differently indeed had the rat not come along.

Drawn by the blood-soaked straw, the rat gnawed a hungry hole in the toy's side before picking it up in her jaws and running back down into the sewers with her treat. The sewers of Malifaux are home to things much worse than rats, and the sight of something raw and bloated eating an unwilling supper frightened the rat into dropping the bear into the foul water.

It floated for a long time, passing through unlit halls and old buried streets until a woman's hand closed over it and lifted it clear.

"Ah," the Widow whispered in a voice like twigs on a windowpane, "you're perfect. You've seen things." Fingers more like knives gently stroked its button eyes. "These remember, they do."

Crooning softly over the sodden bear, the Widow skittered up a long flight of steps, through a trapdoor, and into the back of a long-closed shop. An old spinning wheel and a stool sat surrounded by a carpet of white bones. She cleared a space for the bear on the rotted floorboards by the wheel, sliced a seam open with one of her sharp fingers, and lowered her black bulk onto the stool, folding her many legs underneath. She opened her mouth, which was round and full of needles, and exhaled an inky, dark cloud that she captured on the wheel and began to spin into a glistening black thread. She placed the end of the thread into the seam she had opened and continued to spin.

She was happy in her work. It had taken her a long time to gather all the precious material she needed for the black thread; many nights of clinging around eaves and windows, sniffing for the scent of a human child having a nightmare. There were quite a lot of those in Malifaux. Her whispers in their ears would make the nightmares worse, and then she could open her round mouth filled with needles, open it wide, lean close and breathe deeply of their fear. It was sweetness to her.

The black thread began to fill the bear, and her sharp fingers worked fast, loosening the stitches and letting the sodden fabric stretch. It grew larger and larger, impossibly so. Still the Widow exhaled the stolen terrors, and the black thread ran on and on.

Eventually the Widow sighed and sat back, aching and weary, but pleased with her night's effort. The floorboards creaked, and dust fell from the cracked ceiling as the teddy bear sat up, its massive bulk filling the back room. The fur was torn here and there, but instead of straw, what poked out look more like bones and gristle. The button eyes had sunk into the fabric and vanished, leaving stark, black holes like abandoned wells where something ancient and hungry waited at the bottom. The soft, round hands split as black shards of bone pushed out to form wicked claws, and the stitched mouth opened to reveal a nightmare smile of swords.

The Widow clapped in delight.

Teddy was in a toy room, bright and full of joy. He saw the woman clapping, and he smiled and clapped too. She must be a mummy. They were always kind and smiling. She was pleased with him, and he liked that. He played with the toys, while the mummy watched. After a while, his tummy got sore and rumbled. He cried, and tried to eat the toys, but they were dry and crumbled to dust. The mummy opened a door. At first he was a bit worried, but the mummy told him that outside was a magic kingdom, and he was going to have a great adventure. Teddy liked adventures, and waved goodbye to the mummy.

The Widow watched as the great creature lumbered off, wrecking a path through the deserted woollen shop and out into the empty lane beyond. She wiped a tear away from one of her many bulbous, white eyes. It was so hard to let them go.

D is for Doomed, Sentenced To Die,
E is for Endless, Death To Defy

Each minute in the cells lasted forever, but the days and weeks were stolen away as the appointed date drew nearer.

The condemned man's shouts and yells were louder and fiercer than any of the others, but the jailers were deaf to cries of injustice. Even so, they were glad when Phineas Grey left. He had arrived pale and shrinking, but the darkness of the jail had brewed something black in his soul. Some said it was his crime, eating him up. Others were not so sure. In his last days, those who met his hollow gaze under the lanky, brown curls chose to sleep that night with a candle burning.

The murderer was hanged for the crowd on a Friday. With his last words, Phineas Grey promised them all justice, in this life or the next.

On Saturday and Sunday, a cold rain fell as his body creaked on the Hanging Tree in a breeze that few could feel, and those who could chose not to speak of it.

On Monday, the body was gone.

F is for Fun, Toy Trains In a Station, G is for Grisly, A Nightmare Creation

Not all mummies were kind.

Teddy had learned this first hand, several weeks into his Great Adventure. To his delight he had found a toy train set just like one he remembered–

the night porters of Creepwood Station had run screaming as the giant Neverborn creature appeared out of the mists on the gas-lit platform

–and had played with the brightly coloured trains for a while, rolling them up and down the track, while their happy faces puffed steam and smoke–

the accountant dragged his elderly mother from the mangled wreckage of the sleeper car, amid the screams of the dying, while the abomination hurled another carriage at them along the tracks

--and then he played hide and seek with the people inside--

Rebecca knew she had to stop her brother's teeth from chattering, or the thing would find them both hidden away in the luggage compartment. So she wrung his neck. It still found her

–until they all fell asleep.

But then a mummy turned up, with hair as black as coal under a cowboy hat. Teddy had run to play with her, but this mummy did not want to play. This was an angry mummy, with angry friends. Pistols cracked, and made Teddy hurt. The black thread inside him tried to stitch his blood-soaked fur, but the onslaught of lead was more than even it could keep up with.

Frightened and confused, Teddy turned and ran.

He blundered through dark alleyways and down twist-back streets and hidden closes, until all sounds of the angry mummy and her bullies had gone. By the time he reached an expanse of waste ground, where the moonlit mist lay low like a patchwork quilt, he had quite forgotten about her, and was keen to continue his Great Adventure.

He set off, the mist billowing around him like a ship's wake. He passed a brightly painted wooden wagon, decorated with puppets, pirates and clowns, with colored bunting strung up on old washing lines, but no one was home. He sniffed the air, and could smell no one to play with, so he carried on sailing through the Magic Mist to the Kingdom Of Adventure, while far above Master Moon and Mistress Luna smiled down and whispered secrets only brave Teddies should know.

All was still and silent in the waste ground, until, that was, something the size and shape of a small boy appeared, following Teddy through the mist, its limbs clicking as it walked.

H is for Hired, A Gun That Is Peerless I is for Injured, But Nonetheless Fearless

The woman sank slowly to her knees, pain etched on her face, as blood ran from the wound in her side. Her broken swords lay on the corpses in front of her, her empty pistols on the corpses behind.

"Give it up, bitch," Scissors O'Doull sneered, stepping back and wiping her blood off his knife. Louden and Smalls, his two remaining companions gave a nervous laugh. "Lord knows, ah don't mind hittin' wimmin, but ah try an' avoid killin' 'em. 'Specially the pretty ones."

The woman said nothing, her head bowed, her face hidden behind long, red hair.

"It's Oriental Joe we want," O'Doull said. He was pointing with his knife at the man from the Three Kingdoms standing behind her, but O'Doull didn't move any closer. He had seen what the woman could do – the evidence lay cooling around her. "Step aside, an' we'll match whit he's payin' ye."

With gritted teeth, the woman slowly drew a long, stiletto blade hidden in her belt and dug the point into the cobbles to steady herself. She paused to draw breath, and O'Doull seized the moment. Springing forward he kicked the blade away, and then jumped back, a more bullish sneer on his face. "That's whit ye call a last warnin'."

The woman looked over her shoulder at her employer, Bai Jian. Her dark eyes pinned him to the iron gate he stood against. His meaty jowls trembled, and sweat stained his collar. He held up a hand, spreading all five fingers.

The woman shook her head.

Bai Jian glanced at O'Doull and his men, let out a whimper of fear and held up both hands. Ten fingers.

The woman looked away. Her hand reached into her boot, and came out holding a nail file. She dug the point into the cobbles to steady herself.

O'Doull started to laugh, but then she looked up at him, and his laughter faded away into the night. His face hardened, and the knife came up. Louden and Smalls hefted their brickbats, and charged, yelling. Bai Jian hid his face in his hands and curled up into a small ball until the sounds of violence were over and the only scream was the night wind in the chimney tops.

A rough hand grabbed his collar and pulled him to his feet. He looked not into the leering face of Scissors O'Doull, but the warlike face of the woman he had retained to protect

him, a woman he knew only as Zephyr. Eyes like gunmetal, and a countenance just as cold and hard, she wiped the nail file on the sleeve of her shirt and tucked it away. She held out a hand. "The deal was for ten hundred."

Stunned, Bai Jian handed over a neatly folded bundle of high-value Guild Scrip. He could not take his eyes off O'Doull. The man was still standing, his body shaking violently. *How could he still be standing?*

"Ten *extra*."

He paid, transfixed by O'Doull

"Expenses," Zephyr said, swaying on her feet, her voice cramped from the pain. "Broke my swords. That'll be another two."

Zian paid.

"And I'm out of ammunition. Another two. Call it two fifty."

To Zian's enormous relief, O'Doull's body finally toppled, crumpling next to his own head. The blood spurting from the stump slowed to a steady ooze. Zian paid again, without complaint.

As she stepped away over the pile of bodies, he called out after her. "That small fortune you have. You can do anything you want with it."

"No, sir," Zephyr said, stopping to pick up her pistols. "It's not nearly enough."

And she walked away, O'Doull's blood tattooed on her cheeks.

J is for Joke, A Trick That Is Cruel,
K is for Kids, Who Should Be In School

The lane behind the rows of terraced, brick houses was dark, cluttered with rubbish and shadows. Old bed frames leaned against piles of moss-covered slates, and ash bins overflowed beside reeking night pails. The cobbles were dangerously uneven, and in places, sinkholes stank of the sewers below. The lane was home to rats, cats, and other two-legged vermin.

"Hey, missus!" Callooh shouted, flinging another cracked tile to shatter a window of the house he and his brother had targeted for that night's fun. "What'll ye do when the Wee Malkies come? Hey, missus! What'll ye do?"

Lights flicked on, and Callooh snorted, ducking down behind the wall, crouching on a moldy mound of broken boxes. He was almost invisible in his filthy rags, and his skin was dark with dirt and ash. He turned to elbow his younger brother into action — the plan was to draw the housekeeper's attention out the back, and then his brother would nip round the front and nick the brass off their door, leaving the traditional Wee Malkie calling-card steaming on their front step — but Kallay wasn't there. All of sudden, Callooh felt a shiver run down his back, and he remembered what the older Malkies had said about going into this part of town. Boys and girls going missing. They didn't sound so stupid, now.

Then a pathetic, mewling noise made him peer down the lane, and there was Kallay, his tiny frame almost buried under a sack. A sack that was moving.

"Whit ye got there?" Callooh hissed, leaping down, all thought of warnings and Number 78B's brass door ornaments flown at the sight of the bag. "Show us!"

Kallay's face mirrored his brother's — a mischievous smile in a dirt-smeared face surrounded by long, filthy hair that might have been any color once upon a time. Both of them wore the black rag of the Wee Malkies around their necks. "Ah've only gone and found a sack of kittens, didn't ah?" he whispered, eager to impress. "Ah reckon a few are dead, you know, but ah figure we can fling the rest at whitever poor eejit they lock up in the stocks in the mornin'!"

Then a sound that did not belong in the lane made them both freeze. It sounded like someone dropping canes onto the cobbles, over and over, and it was getting closer.

"Whit's that, Callooh?" His younger brother backed off, the whites of his eyes bright in the darkness. "Whit's that?"

"Ditch it!" Callooh hissed. "Hide!" As his brother heaved the sack into a garden, Callooh ducked behind some rusted old pipes. Kallay joined him in a flash, wedging in tight against his older brother.

"Ah don't like it—"

"Put a sock in it!" Callooh put his hand over his brother's mouth as the sound grew louder. Trembling, he put his eye up to a rust hole.

It was hard to make anything out in the dark, but what he could see was small, like him, and fast, but moving all wrong. And there were a lot of them. He caught glimpses of colored cloth and enameled eyes. There was no sound but the soft clatter of wood on the cobbled lane, and he knew that if they spotted him or Kallay, it was all over. Whatever they were, they were hunting.

Callooh kept his hand where it was long after they had gone, until Kallay's tears had dried in the cold night air. Even when he and his brother crawled out, sprinted down the lane, and ran breathless back to Wee Malkies' territory, he was convinced he could hear the tap-tap-tapping behind him all the way.

L is for Lady, Gets Quite A Fright, M is for Master, Won't Outlive The Night

Teddy liked the house. The yellow curtains reminded of him of somewhere he once knew, and it had bright marble columns at the front, like teeth. It smiled at him, so he went in.

The LaGrange family, grain merchants with solid Guild connections, returned later that night from the opera. None of the servants were around. Everrard LaGrange called angrily at the back stair and rang the bell, but no one appeared. Alarmed, he took his children to the drawing room to get his gun

Teddy had found several people in the smiling house, but none of them wanted to play, so he had put most of them in the naughty box to teach them manners-

Lady Isabelle LaGrange entered the kitchen, and her look of fury turned to one of horror as she saw the blood slick on the tiled floor. A thick pool of it led back to the cast iron oven in the range. The door had been forced shut, and the parts of the servants' bodies that had not fitted fully inside were crushed around the edges. Hands, feet, and pieces she could not identify. There was always a low fire burning through the night, and the stench of cooked flesh turned her stomach. Then she heard her children screaming

–but he had kept a few of them with him to help him make number blocks. Teddy had always enjoyed number blocks, but it had been hard to get these ones square. They were a bit mushy–

The maids had fainted on the drawing room floor when the nightmare creature had plucked the butler's head clean off and started hammering it against the walls, forming it into a crude cube of mashed bone and brain. It had carved what looked like numbers into the sides with one jagged claw, before reaching for the maids

–but red was a good color, and he hoped the family who lived here would like them.

They did not.

Disappointed, Teddy showed them how to make more number blocks, but when he had finished, there was no one left to play with.

Outside the drawing-room window, something small watched him play.

N is for Nightwatch, To Guard Against Danger, O is for Outlook, To Watch For The Stranger

"One of the clock, and all's well," Sergeant Kliegemann called, feeling the rain trickle down the back of his neck. It sodding well was not all well, but every time he called out, as his deep voice echoed back to him in the narrow streets, he felt as if he had company on his patrol. A welcome feeling on a night like this.

It had not been a good spell for the Guild Guard, he reflected as he paced down Ambergris Street, the light from his lamp sweeping to and fro between the closed shops on either side of him. The cut glass of the windows flashed white as his lamp played over them. His cap was pulled low and his collar raised against the incessant drizzle.

There had been that unfortunate incident of the murderer going missing off the Hanging Tree two months ago. They never had found the victim's body, of course, but the blood in the Grey house had been enough for a conviction. Fortunately, that had been pushed off the front pages by the massacre at Creepwood Station. It had been released to the Malifaux Daily Record as a points failure on the track. No survivors meant no one to contradict the official version. A few more runaway kids than usual had been reported, but then the LaGrange killings, right in the heart of up-market Feverstone quadrant only a couple of weeks ago, had forced the Guild to put more feet on the beat in the areas around there. Specifically, his feet, for the use of which he was unlikely to get overtime pay. Being a sergeant was supposed to spare him this nonsense, but here he was.

The only saving grace was that the gangs of street kids had been unusually quiet recently, but all that meant was that the Guild would have a hard time pinning trouble on their frequent fights.

And then, although Sergeant Kliegemann was not keen on thinking about this alone at night, there had been the deaths of more than a few Guild Guard officers. No one was calling them murders, because the morgue had said 'heart attack' in every case. Still, Sergeant Kliegemann could not remember the last time a heart attack had caused a man to rip his own ears off as he died.

He shone the lamp beam over a patch of red brick wall next to Ormiston's butcher shop, where hand-printed bills curled in the rain. Missing children were buried under rugs for sale, and snake-oil sleep remedies were partially obscured by brightly colored posters for the puppet show out on the waste ground.

He walked on, swinging his lamp from side to side, the light flashing in the leaded shop windows. And then he caught a glimpse of his own reflection in one of the windows, and his thoughts fled, leaving only one remaining – *there is someone standing behind me.*

Sergeant Kliegemann whirled, his pistol raised. The street was empty. He stood for a long moment, watching and listening – he had been Guard long enough to know that some shadows should be jumped at. But the street held only him and the rain. The night air felt much colder now – he let out his breath and it fogged around him. A whiff of decay made his stomach rise. He glanced back at the window and his heart shrivelled in his chest – there it was again, closer this time. A dark figure, the rain glistening on its bowed head. *There was something wrong with its neck.*

He spun back, crying out, but the emptiness of the street seemed to mock his fright.

The rain grew heavier, hissing on the cobbled street, summoning a knee-high spray.

He looked back at the window, his pistol hand shaking. The figure was still there, only a few feet away from him. He could almost reach out and touch it. Then all sense left Sergeant Kliegemann as he realised its feet did not touch the ground. He screamed, dropped the lamp and ran.

He ran as if in a nightmare, the shops on either side hemming him in, the hiss of the rain drowning out the slap of his boots on the stones and the rasp of his breathing. In momentary pictures, each shop window he raced past contained only him and the thing at his heels, both blurred by the rain. In every reflected instant, it drifted closer and closer no matter how fast he ran.

A voice spoke, or it may have been just the hissing of the rain. "Jusss-tissss."

Sergeant Kliegemann stumbled, cried out and fell hard, skidding on the cobbles. His gun skipped away like a stone on a pond, lost in the dark.

The street behind him was empty, but in the tall, rain-streaked window of a tailor's shop, the dark figure floated slowly closer.

The rain hissed louder still, and it was all he could hear. Not even the drumming of his heart rose above it, and in the sound of the rain came the voice again. "Jusss-tissss."

The word was everywhere, carried on every drop of rain, in every bouquet of spray, repeated over and over by a countless choir. Kliegemann cried out, gripping his head, but nothing could keep the voices out.

In the tailor's window, the figure stooped over him. A rope hung from its broken neck, and long, curly hair hung heavy in the rain. Eyes burned with the fires of damnation.

"I know you," Kliegemann gasped, but he could not even hear his own voice any longer. "It – it can't be!"

"Jusss-tissss," the rain hissed, and Phineas Grey bent low over Kliegemann and whispered secrets to him with his dead, white lips and black, swollen tongue.

The morgue reported it as just another heart attack, although the Guard surgeon choose not to comment on why the late sergeant might have torn off his own ears.

P is for Plunder, Winnings Ill-Gotten, Q is for Quarrel, Needlessly Brought On

"Just give me my share, and I'll be on my way," the woman said, indicating the paired leather saddle bags stuffed with the stolen Guild Scrip.

Denver noticed that she protected her right side and wondered if she had an old injury there. It certainly hadn't slowed her up on the job, however, and the way she had dispatched those Union enforcers had been cool, clinical and impressive. Now, she looked pale and exhausted, just like the other four survivors of the raid on the Galestone Mine salary wagon, gathered in the abandoned trappers' hut.

Josiah Denver had a mean, narrow face, with a tight mouth and a head that seemed to come to a point under the slicked, black hair. Everyone but his mother thought he maybe had some bayou blood in him, and even some days she wasn't sure. No matter his expression, there was a sly hint of gremlin in those sideways eyes. He looked around at his hired hands, and wondered if he really wanted to share the proceeds with them at all.

He held up a hand to the woman he knew only as Zephyr. "In good time." He looked over at Roake, who had taken a mess of pellets to the face and was in a bad way. "Roake, it ain't right what done happen to ya, but don't'cha think y'all should've been watchin' that third wagon?"

Roake didn't look up. His voice was pained and slurred. "That was Jann's job."

Denver nodded, glancing very briefly at Jann as the thick-necked Swede bridled at the tarnishing of his name. "Maybe it was, maybe it weren't," Denver said, "but he told me he had to go help Ferris with the locks."

Now it was Ferris' turn to stir, and he fixed Jann with a cold stare. "Didn't need no help, didn't ask fer none."

The woman buttoned up her docker's coat, and said in a low voice that only Denver could hear, "It doesn't have to go down this way."

Denver just grinned. Sharing was for deadbeats and children. "Easy Ferris. Sounds like you're calling Jann a liar."

Had there been anyone outside the trappers hut a moment or so later, they would have heard gunshots, maybe a half-dozen or so, the flashes creeping through the cracks in the shuttered windows. They would have seen a man with shiny, black hair come out the door, saddle bags slung over his shoulder and a pistol in his hand. They would have seen him take a few paces, drop the pistol, and then fall, dead. And they would have seen a woman walk from the hut, pick up the saddle bags and head off down the trail towards the horses.

It was a lot of money, Zephyr knew, but it wasn't yet enough.

R is for Run, A Thing You Should Do,
S is for Scared, Of Things You Bump Into

It was too late to get away.

The lawman towered over Callooh and his brother. He had a face like the mountain lions outside the Malifaux Museum and riding spurs that clinked as he walked. Guns hung from his belt, catching the light of the gas lamps behind him.

"'Bout time I ran into yeh," he said in a prairie drawl. "You and yours've bin keepin' mighty quiet these past months. I reckon you're gonna tell me what I wanna know."

Callooh puffed his chest out but made sure his little brother was standing between him and the lawman. "Ah'm no tellin' you nuthin, bandy legs. Wee Malkies dinnae clipe. In't that so, Kallay?"

The man looked at the older child for a while, his eyes dark under his hat. "Ain't half the words comin' out yer mouth mean a dang thing to me, boy. Speak English, or I'll tan yer hide. There's things in the streets at night, got y'all runnin' scared. I thought I had 'em, too, not a few moments ago. Posse of 'em, but they up and gave me the slip." He smiled, but it was full of menace, and grabbed the knotted rag around Callooh's neck, twisting it tight in his big, gloved fist. "Then I got lucky and found myself a pair of jokers."

Tap-tap.

Callooh froze, but the big lawman mistook the fear in his face, and carried on talking.

Tap-tap-tap.

Callooh couldn't see anything of the street past the man's enormous frame. "Mister-" he began, and then the lawman stopped mid-sentence, his mouth open.

Callooh tried to pull away, but the lawman was holding him tight. "Mister?"

The man started to shake. A stick, with a sharpened tip, appeared inside his open mouth and slowly pushed out between his teeth. Blood poured down the man's chin, and his eyes rolled back into his head. His body jerked violently.

Callooh's little brother screamed and tried to run, but Callooh was still holding him and the lawman holding Callooh. Then the stick vanished with a sickening slurp, and the lawman dropped like a stone.

There was not one, but a dozen of the things crowding the narrow street. They were clad in garish colors, stripes and checks, some in jester's motley and one in the tricorn hat and black garb of a privateer. All had limbs and faces of wood, and they leapt on the body and hacked at it with their sharp fingers.

Callooh drew a broken-glass shiv and stabbed at the gloved hand that still held him tight, and then froze as the marionette with the pirate costume raised its carved, painted face towards him and his brother.

Its fixed smile and blood-covered hands were the last things Callooh saw.

T is for Torment, Secrets To Tell,
U is for Undying, Dry Whispers From Hell

Phineas Grey was dead. He had died on the Hanging Tree, three months ago or more. All that was left was his fly-blown body, warmed only by the fires of vengeance.

He could barely remember anything of his life, and even his existence now passed by in splinters of awareness, drifting through an endless night, dark fragments of the man he had been, held together by pain and anger.

His was the pain of the noose around his neck, the pain that a man feels when all hope is truly gone. A pain that not even death had eased.

The noose tugged at him, and he went. To officers of the Guild Guard who had been in the Grey house that night it pulled him, one by one. The whispers he had heard hanging on the Tree blew through his dry, cracked lips, caressing them with corpse-breath. He did not know who they were or why he spoke to them, only that he must. The noose tugged, the fires burned, and he must.

He spoke to the men who had walked him to the Tree. He spoke to the men who had locked doors and turned keys until none were left who had wronged him, but still, it tugged.

He came to an alehouse, tumbledown and rank with dead dreams, and he spoke to the men. None of them had been there that night, but his vengeance still burned all it touched, and he moved on.

The fragments of Phineas Grey wept in their cold, dead prison.

Time passed, or none at all. It mattered not. He came to a ward, where the sick lay. The soft, dry whispers beyond the grave touched them all, taking everything they had but leaving him only anger and pain.

He came to a house. All within heard his tales, from young to old, but it mattered not. The noose tugged, and he must.

One cold night, he passed a caravan on some waste ground. It was brightly colored, and beautiful to look at, but there was nothing alive within to whisper his secrets to, and he carried on past. His shrivelled, putrid eyes saw a small figure hastening away as the clouds hid the moon. The noose tugged in a different direction, but whatever was left of Phineas Grey recognized something in that small, running figure, and he drifted after it.

V is for Valuable, Things We Hold Dear,
W is for Wish, Heart's Desire Sincere

Alderman Abster Sinth awoke to see a pistol, and a face he knew. His mouth was dry from sleep, and his teeth were in a glass jar beside his bed, so it took a few attempts to get the name out. "Sheffir?" It was a question, and a curse.

"Alderman Sinth," Zephyr replied, with a small nod. Her red hair was tied back under a black scarf. She had a fresh scar on her right cheek, but she was as beautiful as ever. She put the candlestick down by Abster Sinth's bedside and gestured with the pistol at the glass jar. "Good evening."

Carefully, Abster Sinth plucked his teeth out of the jar and put them in his mouth, working his jaws a few times until they clicked into place. The movement let him shift the bedcovers enough that he managed to slip his right arm back under them. The mercenary he had hired at great expense two weeks ago did not seem to notice. "The Lorimer brothers?"

Her eyes never left his, and the gun did not waver. "Dead."

For a moment he felt a surge of vicious pleasure, and then swallowed. "I am surprised. I assumed they had offered you double to kill me."

"They did."

"I see. But you killed them anyway."

"I never walk away from a paying job. And I always take payment up front. You knew my terms when you hired me."

"I suppose that, once in your life, you might consider making an exception?" Abster Sinth's right hand moved very carefully, and very slowly, closing over the grip of the custom, snub-nosed Peacekeeper he kept in a hollow in his mattress. "Double it again. I know you're desperate for the money. Let me live. The Lorimers are dead, no one will ever know. Just walk away and let me live."

Zephyr lowered her gun to her side, and for a moment his heart leapt, but then she spoke. "I can't do that."

"Money's no object, dammit!" He covered the sound of the hammer clicking back with his raised voice. "Ten times what they paid you!"

"No, I mean, you're already dead." Zephyr said, at the same time as Abster's finger tightened on the hair-trigger, and a hollow click sounded, muffled by the bedclothes.

Zephyr tapped the glass jar with the tip of her pistol, and it rang softly. "Powdered bayou rose, applied to your false teeth. It's painless, and quick. And I took the firing pin out of your gun."

Abster tried to pull the trigger again, but his hands seemed numb and distant. "Curse you, woman!" he rasped. He fell back onto sheets that were suddenly damp with sweat. "I hope you choke on the damn money!" His breath was becoming heavier, and the candle seemed to be dimming. But he still had riches, and enemies he did not want gloating at his funeral. "There's a list," he said. "In the drawer by the window, on the left. A list. And there's a safe. In the room. I can pay you now. Get the list."

Zephyr shook her head. "You're a spiteful old man, when all's said and done, but with the scrip from the Lorimers I finally have all I need. Your sons will have to continue your petty feuds for you."

"All you need?" Abster gasped. "I'm offering you a fortune! Who ever has all they need?"

Zephyr's face grew terrible, and Abster shrank further into the bed. "I did, once. Then a man murdered my son, Dylan. Dylan Grey. Maybe you've heard of him?"

He could barely see her anymore, and no matter how deep his breaths, his lungs barely filled. "That was last year. They hanged him. On the Tree. Phineas Grey. I remember. He was – your husband?"

Her voice reached him across a vast and sluggish ocean. "Zephyr Grey, lady-at-arms, at your service. Oh, they hanged dear Phineas, but they didn't hang the man who killed my son. Although, in truth, I hear he is no man at all. Puppetmaster, I have heard him called. I really don't care what manner of creature he is, down in that caravan, putting on his sick shows. What I do know is that he came into my home and took my beautiful Dylan – tore his body apart and imprisoned his soul in a monster's plaything of wood and string and left my husband to hang for it. I came back from a job Earthside and found my husband dead and my son gone, and I want them back. I want to hold them again, more than anything in this world!" Abster felt a rough hand on his face, closing the eyes whose lids he could no longer move. "Now go to sleep, Alderman Sinth. Your money, the Lorimers' money – all of it is for my family. I was told it would take a king's ransom, and that's exactly what I have. I am going to get them both back."

X is for X-Ray, To See What Is Hidden, Y is for Yell, But Escape Is Forbidden

Teddy was disappointed. He had been looking for the House of Teddies and had run into one distraction after another. It was fun to stop and play, but he really wanted to find the House of Teddies that the little boy with the big knife had mentioned. There was something about being in a house that made Teddy's stitches tingle, and if it had yellow curtains that would be even better. Yellow curtains and a family would be best of all.

A couple of times he had seen – or thought he had seen – a small figure following him, but every time he turned it was gone. He was left with an impression of wooden limbs and strings, and a pirate hat. It seemed familiar, for a moment, but then he would find something new and wonderful and get all excited and his head was fuzzy at the best of times.

There had been the little girl in the blue dress. She and Teddy had played for a while – the little girl had found a daddy wandering all alone in the streets–

Resolved Jones had spent an evening drowning his sorrows, and was full as a tick, staggering from pillar to post trying to find a street he recognized. A girl child came out of nowhere, took his hand and spoke to him. She looked normal in all respects but one. The wisps of smoke coming from her empty eye sockets sobered him up but quick, but by then it was too late

-and asked him if he wanted to play hide and seek. Teddy liked that game, and it quickly got underway–

Resolved Jones screamed as the girl plucked his eyes out. In disbelief, he found he could still see through them, and watched himself clutching his own maimed face as the girl popped his eyes into her own vacant sockets. "You should hide," she said, and started counting back from twenty. Jones ran, and watched himself stagger away around a corner

–with Teddy carrying the little girl in the blue dress and her telling him where to go. The daddy wasn't very good at hiding, but every time they found him crouched under a cart or in a doorway he would leap up–

he had no idea where he was, and had tripped and fallen so many times his clothes were torn and wet with blood, but then he would see himself and know they had found him again – that girl and the monster she was riding on

–and run off again. This game was fun!

outside a ruined posthouse, Resolved Jones turned his ankle on a loose cobble and fell heavily, breaking through rotten wooden slats over a buried coal pit. His left leg and collarbone shattered when he hit the bottom. He tried to be quiet, but the pain came out in whimpers he could not stop. Then he saw a loose cobble, and the broken slats of a pit, and knew they had found him again. The girl-thing jumped down the pit, and he watched as she ate what was left of his face

The little girl in the blue dress skipped away into the night, and Teddy waved goodbye, another chapter in his Great Adventure complete.

In the ruins of the posthouse, a pair of painted eyes watched him go.

Z is for Zephyr, Bold, Quick and Brave, Summoning Monsters, Her Family To Save

The inventors-for-hire who had built the device for Zephyr, Dr Oldish and his shrewish assistant Mr Lemon, had told her it would work best some place high, so she carried it, piece by piece, to the top of the north towers on Hurrycross Bridge. She was sweating freely on the third trip up the narrow, winding steps.

It had cost her every cent of Guild scrip she had earned in the four months since her family had gone, and all their savings from before then. Dr Oldish had raised the cost at the last minute, but she'd been expecting that and had negotiated a six-chambered discount that the good doctor had been wise enough to accept.

She finished assembling the device at midnight, as the damp on the wind finally turned into rain and lightning flashed far off across the city. The device was about the size of four large traveling trunks stacked together. Most of its innards were concealed behind polished wooden panels, but here and there copper coils or brass buttons broke the surface. On top, complicated arrangements of glowing glass tubes reflected in gleaming black ceramic insulators. The raindrops hitting them sizzled into vapor. It looked expensive, and impressive, but the real cost lay in the customized soulstones hidden within.

Zephyr opened a wooden hatch on the front. "Resonances," Dr Oldish had said. "Something aetherically attuned to both you and the subjects." That meant personal belongings, and Zephyr placed her wedding ring – the one thing she'd refused to pawn – in one hatch and a lock of her boy's hair in the other. Times had been hard when Dylan was born, and she remembered repairing his favourite teddy bear's stitches with some of his own hair to save on thread. The memory hardened inside her, like all the others. She flipped the switches in the sequence Mr Lemon had written down for her, and waited in the rain.

–the noose tugged, but this was stronger by far. Phineas Grey turned and floated across the river. The rope around his neck dangled down, drawing a wake in the black water below his feet–

She did not have long to wait.

The air grew cold, and puddles iced over as her dead husband's lolling head rose over the tower parapet. He drifted up and over, towards the device, the wet rope around his neck trailing on the stones. Fear froze her, but only for a moment. It was working, just as they had said it would.

"Phineas," she called. "Phineas, it is me."

He turned towards her, and for a moment she thought she saw something alive in his dead, white eyes, but then the whispering began, and he drifted over the rooftop towards her, ice crackling into being beneath him. Before the whispers grew too loud, she flipped the first master switch and the device hummed anew. A blue light from a coiled tube pierced her husband through the breast, and he floated in silence.

–all strings led to the Puppetmaster, but this string was new. New and taut like iron on a cold day. The other strings

snapped, one by one, and Dylan Grey ran over the cobbles on wooden pegs, heading for the bridge–

She had only just flipped the switch when Zephyr's instincts told her to duck. As she did so, a small bundle of black cloth and sticks hurtled over her head to land, skittering and struggling to stand on the spreading ice. Painted eyes glared at her with a malevolence that chilled her soul, even as carved fingers, black with dried blood, reached out for her.

"Dylan!" she cried, one hand on the second master switch. Her mind rebelled at the thought that this murderous marionette could be her only son. It found its footing and advanced on her, but still she did not flip the switch. "Dylan?" she begged, looking for anything that might remind her of her child. "It's mama!"

The grasping hands were only inches from her face when she flipped the master switch. The puppet stopped, held up by a single thread of blue light from Dr Oldish's device.

"Dylan," she whispered, raising a hand to the marionette's painted face. It twitched, once, then nothing. She gathered her resolve and began the final sequence of the device.

–his stitches tingled as they had never done before. Something powerful was tugging at them, and not even the black, nightmare thread the Widow had placed within him could resist. Teddy reached the tower and started to climb–

The device was rumbling and hissing like an old boiler, and shafts of blue light lanced out into the rain-lashed night to rival the approaching lightning. Zephyr stood back, her heart in her throat, willing the device to work, looking from it to her husband and son and back again. She shouted at the machine, cajoling and begging it to complete its task, but she knew it was out of her hands now. Thunder rumbled as sparks flew, and she looked in astonishment as the noose around her husband's neck glowed blue, loosened and slid to the stones. The puppet's wooden limbs split, and layers of wood began to peel back. She had not dared to hope, not once, not since she had found her home cold and empty and her family gone all those long months ago, but now she did.

She did not notice the monstrous creature heave itself over the tower parapet behind her.

Teddy had once had button eyes, and those eyes had seen things. Images flashed before him; a house with yellow curtains and toys on the floor; a man, a woman and a child. A family. Not just any family – *his* family. Something bad had happened to them, but here they were, gathered on top of this tower to greet him! They were all together again. Teddy was overjoyed! And – he noticed the hissing, chugging device beyond the mummy – they had brought a toy to play with.

He knew what he had to do. He had to take his family back to the house with the yellow curtains. Everything would be fine then. Teddy smiled – he would show them what a good Teddy he was. He would carry the toy for them.

Zephyr was sent sprawling across the rooftop as the monster barged past her. Her anguished cry was lost in a peal of thunder. It all happened so slowly. The creature reached out two enormous claws, each ragged talon black as night, and plunged them deep into the device. Wood splintered. A pressurised container burst, and scraps of brass flew through the air. Sparks leapt from raindrop to raindrop as the blue light spluttered and died. The hulking creature, its filthy fur matted in the rain, turned towards her, the innards of the machine cradled in its claws. Eyes like stab wounds looked at her, and it bared row after row of vicious fangs. Zephyr screamed in disbelief, and drew her sword and pistol.

Something had gone wrong, Teddy knew. The mummy was angry, angrier than he had ever seen her.

Zephyr emptied her pistol into the huge head, each shot ripping tears in the sodden, patchy fur. Something black boiled beneath, dark and fearful. She leapt forward, slashing with her sword, but the nightmare thing raised its claws and blocked her blade. Then the thunder and her own cries faded away, and she could hear only the hiss of the rain on the stones. There was a voice carried on the rain, a voice she knew well, and it spoke only one word. "Jusss-tissss."

She turned, aghast. The thing that had been her husband was at her side, the stench of death overwhelming her, and knives of ice drove into her mind. She tried to push him back, and then the marionette was on her, clinging to her back and stabbing at her eyes with its sharp, little fingers

Teddy could not understand what he had done wrong, but now his whole family was angry. He had to do something.

Protecting her face with her pistol hand, Zephyr grabbed the puppet and hurled it into the undead body of her husband, knocking them both back. She staggered back a step, reeling from the wounds to her head and back and the unrelenting whispers that poisoned her mind. She fell to her knees.

Teddy reached out to help the mummy stand. He lifted her to her feet, and then realized he had made an awful, clumsy mistake.

Zephyr gaped wordlessly, gripping the black talons where they pierced her belly. The razor edges of the claws sliced her hands open to the bone, and her body shook as one talon grated against her spine. The creature stared at her, smiling as blood welled in her mouth. She looked over at her son and husband as her vision darkened. The riven wood of the puppet's limbs was smoothing over once again as the effects of the device faded. Her husband bent awkwardly and picked up the fallen noose. He tightened it around his broken neck with cold, dead fingers. Then the black talons slid out of her stomach, sawing against her bones, and she collapsed to her knees. With a herculean effort she rose to her feet, and took a step towards her family, but she had finally pushed her body to its limits, and she fell one last time. She could not move, but the rain felt cool on her face. The last thing she saw was three abominations gathering around her under a storm-bruised sky.

The mummy was sleeping on a red, red rug, and the daddy and the boy stood over her. Teddy looked at the daddy's white, lifeless eyes and grey, sagging skin. He looked at the boy's cruel, painted face and blood-stained hands. This was not what he remembered. Not at all.

–the noose tugged, and the thing that would never again be Phineas Grey felt the fires of vengeance kindle once more. A corpse, a nightmare, and a wooden doll that no longer sparked any memories in his rotten skull. There was nothing here to listen to the truths he must tell. The Hanged Man drifted away–

–the strings returned, one by one, and the puppet that only looked like Dylan Grey felt them pulling him back to the

gaily painted caravan on the waste ground. The lumbering creature took a step towards him. The puppet had been following it for a long time, whenever the strings had allowed him. It had reminded him of a toy he had once loved, but this blood-stained monster was nothing like the teddy bear whose memory was fading fast. The Marionette skittered off over the cobbles, returning to his true master–

Teddy ran after him, but he was too slow, and a moment later he was alone on the top of the tower.

He stood, trembling, his claws clenched. His stitches ached, as if they were being pulled out one by one. It had all been a lie! The house, the yellow curtains, the family. All of it was a lie! He swung both great arms at the wreckage of the device, sending fresh splinters of wood and brass out into the storm. He would never play with toys ever again! No one would! With a sky-splitting roar he brought fists like hammers down on the gutted remains, again and again, smashing it to pieces. He would never be friends with anyone ever again! He ripped stones and tiles from the roof and hurled them into the night, great inky streaks of black ooze running from his bullet-hole eyes. He hated them all, everyone! Then he heaved the buckled frame over the parapet.

Lightning flashed overhead. A fissure of light touched the soaring frame and Teddy gaped in wonder. A thousand sparks burst into life in brilliant hues, crackling and fizzing in a kaleidoscope of stars. Fireworks! Beautiful fireworks! It was the most magical thing he had ever seen.

He spread his arms as the incandescent motes drifted down around him, twirling and swirling like fairies in the night. It seemed to go on forever, as if the stars above had come down to dance, just for him, and he danced along with them, turning and whirling across the rooftop. Where the stars touched him they tickled, and he laughed, spinning and swaying all the more.

When it was over, and the last of the twinkling fairies had gone, he walked to the parapet and looked out over the city. The rain eased and stopped. The storm passed and faded from memory. Teddy smiled as he thought of all the excitement and wonder that awaited him in his Magic Kingdom. This truly was the greatest of adventures.

Iggy - Minion

Iggy, the Woe of Consuming Neglect is filled with a white-hot resentment. Unable to see right from wrong, he embodies the fiery pain of malice caused by a lifetime of parental disregard, the burning anger seething in a youth forced to raise himself without guidance, love, or support.

Acting as a free spirit, he blithely wanders Malifaux doing what he pleases, without regard for the consequences. Caring adults witnessing his actions mistake them for those of a human child without a firm guiding hand at home. Any effort by an adult to exert some manner of discipline for Iggy's own good (such as stopping him from setting a cat on fire), are met with terrifying repercussions. His skin quickly reddens; warming hotter than a furnace, then erupts with bursts of murderous flame. Screaming profanities at his victims, Iggy punctuates his tirades with cries of *"You don't love me!"* and *"I hate you!"* as they burn.

Once Iggy has satiated his rage on the unfortunate Samaritan, his mood brightens before he skips along to his next distraction. Even other Woes give Iggy a wider berth than they give one another, none quite sure what words or deeds might next trigger his immolating tantrum.

30MM BASE **SOULSTONE COST: 6**

WOE, UNIQUE

WK/CG	HT	WP	CA	DF	WD
5/7	1	5🐾	4🐾	6	6

SMOLDERING FIST		BURNING RESENTMENT	
RG	🔥 1	RG	⌐8
CB	6🐾	CB	4
DG	1/2/4	DG	2/3/4☠

TALENTS:

Abilities

Ablaze: This model is immune to Burning Tokens.

Animosity [Hamelin]: This model cannot be hired by a Crews containing the indicated model.

Affinity [Kaeris]: This model may be hired by Crews containing the indicated model.

Burning Aura: Bulletproof 1. When this model is hit by a melee **Strike** or melee Spell, the attacker suffers 1 **Wd** and gains a Burning Token.

Martyr: When this model is hit by an attack, but before applying the Duel's results, its Controller may nominate a friendly Woe in base contact. The Woe is now the target of the attack.

Weapon

Smoldering Fist: Models damaged by this Weapon gain one Burning Token.

Actions

(+1) Ranged Expert

(0) Incite: Target enemy model unaffected by **Incite** or **Pacify** within 12¨ performs a **Wp→Wp** Duel with this model. If the target model loses, it must activate before any other model in its Crew which has not been affected by **Incite**. If this model wins the **Wp** Duel, it may choose to take the **Incite** Action again this activation.

(2) Flurry

Triggers

Cb (📖🗡) Seethe [Smoldering Fist]: This Weapon inflicts +1 **Dg** for every Burning Token on the defender before making the Damage Flip.

Wp (🗡) Uncontrolled Rage [Incite]: After this model wins the **Wp** Duel, Push it up to its **Wk** toward the target.

SPELLS:

(1) Playing With Matches
(CC: 12 🗡 📖 / Rst: Df / Rg: (Ɏ)4) **Dg** 2. Enemy models damaged by this Spell gain one Burning Token.

Spawn Mother - Minion

50MM BASE

SOULSTONE COST: 8

BEAST, GRAVEROBBER, SILURID, RARE 1

Wk/Cg	Ht	Wp	Ca	Df	Wd
4/6	3	4	6 🦇	5	8

TALONS	
Rg	🗡 2
Cb	5 🐾
Dg	2/3/5

CORROSIVE SPIT	
Rg	⌒8
Cb	4 🐾
Dg	1/2/3

TALENTS:

Abilities

Amphibious: This model ignores movement penalties from water terrain. This model receives +2 **Wk** while moving in water terrain if it was in water terrain at the start of the Action.

Feed the Young: While this model is in play, all friendly Silurid models gain the **Graverobber** Characteristic. Friendly Silurid models carrying Corpse Counters may **Walk** up to 4" directly toward the Spawning Pool at the end of their activations.

Mama: The listed Soulstone Cost is for this model and one Gupps model.

Mother's Rage: Whenever a friendly Gupps model within 6" of this model is killed by a melee or ranged attack by an enemy model, this model may immediately **Charge** the model that killed the Gupps model.

Silent: Models cannot ignore cover when targeting this model.

Unstable Evolution: This model suffers 1 **Wd** at the End Closing Phase if it is more than 6" away from water terrain or another Silurid.

Weapon
Corrosive Spit: Poison 2

Actions
(+1) Instinctual

(0) Chameleon: This model receives soft cover until it performs any Action other than **Walk** or **Pass**.

(0) Self Preservation: Push this model up to 6". This Action may only be performed if this model is in an enemy model's melee range.

SPELLS:

(all) Spawning Pool
(CC: 14 🦇 / Rst: - / Rg: C) AR: *Place a 4" circular Spawning Pool terrain piece (**Ht** of 0, water trait) centered on Spawn Mother. Discard all Corpse Counters on the table within 3" of this model and those carried by this model. At least one Corpse Counter must be discarded. Place one Egg Counter on the Spawning Pool for each Corpse Counter discarded. Friendly Silurid models within 3" of the Spawning Pool can discard any number of Corpse Counters they carry as a (0) **Interact** Action and place one Egg Counter per Corpse Counter discarded on the Spawning Pool. During the Resolve Effects Step, this model's Controller may discard two Egg Counters on the Spawning Pool to Place one Gupps model touching the Spawning Pool. The Spawning Pool and any Egg Counters on it remain in play until this Spell is cast again.*

(0) Rain Dance
(CC: 13 🦇 / Rst: - / Rg: ⊙12) Friendly Silurid models, including this model, ignore the effects of **Unstable Evolution** during the End Closing Phase.

Gupps - Minion

40MM BASE

SOULSTONE COST: 3

BEAST, INSIGNIFICANT, SILURID, RARE 4

Wk/Cg	Ht	Wp	Ca	Df	Wd
3/5	1	4	4 🐾	5	5

VESTIGIAL CLAWS	
Rg	🗡 1
Cb	4 🐾
Dg	1/2/2

TALENTS:

Abilities

Amphibious: This model ignores movement penalties from water terrain. This model receives +2 **Wk** while moving in water terrain if it was in water terrain at the start of the Action.

Pack: When activating this model, its Controller may simultaneously activate any number of friendly Silurid within 6" that have not already activated this turn.

Regeneration 1

Silent: Models cannot ignore cover when targeting this model.

Unstable Evolution: This model suffers 1 **Wd** at the End Closing Phase if it is more than 6" away from water terrain or another Silurid.

Weapon
Vestigial Claws: Poison 1

Actions
(0) Mud Bath: This model gains **Armor +2** while it is in base contact with a base with the water trait.

SPELLS:

(0) Leap
(CC: 10 🐾 / Rst: - / Rg: C) Move this model up to its **Cg**. This model receives **Flight** during the move. This Spell cannot be cast if this model is in melee.

(1) Juvenile's Wail
(Cast: 10 🦇 / Resist: - / Range: (ϒ)10) This Spell may only be cast when this model is engaged with an enemy model. One friendly Silurid with the **Leap** Spell per 🦇 in the casting total may immediately cast **Leap**. That model's **Leap** move must be toward this model.

The curious lifecycle of a Silurid begins in a stagnant pool deep within the Bayou. There, the female of their species, the Spawn Mother, comes to give birth to her brood. She selects the spawning pool with care; the pool's composition right down to the temperature of the mud must be perfect for the immature Gupp Silurid to have a chance at survival. Centuries of instinct honed to ensure her species' continuation ensures her choice is a good one.

Once the perfect spawning pool has been chosen, she then calls to her attending males. Their task, seek out incubators and food for her soon to hatch babies. The male Silurids eventually return to the spawning pool, bearing with them carcasses in which the Spawn Mother will lay and incubate her eggs and which will also serve as food for the ravenous Gupps when they hatch.

The egg laying leaves a Spawn Mother weak, hungry, and temperamental, but she dares not eat any of the carcasses for fear her babies will not have enough to eat. Before long, the Gupps begin hatching. A Gupp's accelerated growth pattern demands immediate fuel, and they eat quickly, tearing their way out of the bloated carcasses before pulling themselves free of both the remaining gristle and the mud.

Not every Gupp survives the migration from the pool. Some become tangled in the slimy remains of their egg and suffocate or drown as their amphibious lungs confuse the pool's water for air. Others are maimed or killed by their brothers and sisters as they fight for scraps of food at the pool's edge. The strongest eventually pull themselves from the pool, ready to seek their next meal, hunger and instinct pushing them to hunt down the largest food source they can find.

Tuco - Minion

After his capture by Nephilim ambushers, Tuco took strength from his faith in his family. They would never stop searching for their cousin. For days his captors drove him mercilessly. They seldom rested, and fear gripped his heart. He knew what Nephilim did to their captives, and his imagination ran wild with the tortures they would visit on an Ortega.

When they arrived at the coven, he was placed before the largest Nephilim he had ever seen. A massive creature, Nekima, the leader, informed him in halting English that he would tell her the Ortega's secrets.

Tuco refused.

So the Nephilim tortured him. His resolve flagged, but never failed, knowing his family would come for him...soon.

Tuco overheard reports of Ortega attacks, renewing his hope, helping him withstand the torture just a little longer. The reports became less frequent and then stopped altogether. What had happened, Tuco wondered.

Nekima saw the opportunity. "They have given up on you, my friend. You are dead to them. Your life is mine. Even who you are, *what* you are has changed. "

Recently, horn nubs had begun pushing painfully from Tuco's forehead, and a boiling in his blood was too strong to ignore. "How would they take you back now? You withstood my interrogations, and it has changed you. They did not do this, *you* did it. You are stronger than you think."

She was right. His captors taught him to rely on himself and his own strengths. His family had deserted him. Tuco's resolve wilted, and he discovered the freedom of doing what was best for him. Seeing her captive's change of demeanor, Nekima removed his chains and welcomed him.

Now Tuco fights with the Nephilim against the Ortegas, aiding with his knowledge of humanity. Encounters with the Guild have brought Tuco close to his former family, but he remains in the shadows for these encounters. When the time is right, he will reveal his presence to Papa and the others, to see what faith in family has done for him.

30MM BASE · **SOULSTONE COST: 7**

NEPHILIM, UNIQUE

WK/CG	HT	WP	CA	DF	WD
4/6	2	5	5 🦇	5	8

CLAWS

RG	⚔ 2
CB	4 🦇
DG	2/3/5

SHOTGUN

RG	🔫 8
CB	5
DG	2/3♣/4♣♣♣

TALENTS:

Abilities

Black Blood

From the Shadows: This model may be deployed after all other models, in or behind any terrain more than 12" away from an enemy, or the objective of any strategy or announced scheme. This model may not be targeted by **Charges** or ranged attacks until it takes an Action other than **Pass** if deployed this way. If multiple models with this Ability are in play, players alternate deploying them using the deployment order for Crews.

Hard to Kill

Nemesis [Family]: This model's Attack and Damage Flips receive ♦ when attacking a model with the indicated Characteristic.

Regeneration 1

Scout

Stubborn

Terrifying → 11

Actions

(+1) Nimble

(0) Deranged Laughter: Increase this model's **Terrifying** by +2.

(2) Run and Gun [Shotgun]: This model performs a **Strike** with this Weapon that receives -2 **Cb**. After resolving the attack, this model may move up to its **Cg**.

Triggers

Ca (✗ 🦇) Disillusion [Taint Loyalty]: Defender must discard two Cards after losing its Resist Duel or the effects of the Spell last until the end of the Encounter.

Cb (🦇 🦇) Flay [Claws]

Cb (🦇) Sepsis [Shotgun]: Poison 1

SPELLS:

(0) Veil Appearance
(CC: 12🦇 / Rst: - / Rg: C) Push this model up to 3". Enemy attack Flips targeting this model receive ⊟ until the Resolve Effects Step.

(1) Taint Loyalty
(CC: 12 / Rst: Ca / Rg: 8) Target model loses its Faction affiliation and is not considered friendly to any other model in the game.

Weaver Widow - Minion

Hush-a-bye, baby, don't you cry, The Weaver's sung you a lullaby,

The threads of fate run all through Malifaux like dreams in the night. Some navigate the complex, ever-shifting weft and weave to see the unfolding of great events, but there are other creatures that have been drawn to these threads, who live in and upon them, and who pull and pluck them for their own, mysterious ends.

The Widow Weaver is one such creature.

What she does is known to but a few. Why she does it, to none but herself.

Folklore has it that she will come to a crying child in the night, creeping through the darkness to cling outside the window. In some tales, she enters the house. In other, more twisted tales, a family member will let her in, lest she visit her horrors on them instead.

However she comes, the result is the same. The children's nightmares darken and terrors grip their minds. All their primal fears are brought screaming to the surface and become food for the Weaver. She eats her fill as the child cries and the household stirs. And then she is gone.

Hush-a-you, baby, don't take fright, The Weaver comes but just one night,

Legend has it that the Weaver will never return to the same place twice. She uses the nightmares she has taken to spin new threads in the skein of Malifaux, to weave new fates from the dark dreams she has stolen, all toward some purpose she tells to no one.

Hush-a-now, baby, soon be dawn, The Weaver's dreams will all be gone.

Some say that the Weaver's victims are cursed, and that bad luck will follow them all their days. But there are some who suggest the Weaver is a blessing in disguise, and that, in Malifaux, a child with dreams dark enough to interest her is probably better off without them.

40MM BASE · **SOULSTONE COST: 9**

GRAVEROBBER, NIGHTMARE, SCAVENGER, UNIQUE

WK/CG	HT	WP	CA	DF	WD
5/-	2	7	5🐾	4	10

KNIFE-LIKE FINGERS			NEEDLE-FILLED MOUTH	
RG	2		RG	1
CB	5🐾		CB	6
DG	2/3/5		DG	1/3/6

TALENTS:

Abilities
Affinity [Collodi]: This model may be hired by Crews containing the indicated model.

Arachnid

Inhale Terror: Whenever a model fails a Morale Duel within 6" of this model, this model's Controller draws one Control Card.

Terrifying → 13

Weapon
Needle-Filled Mouth: This Weapon ignores **Armor**.

Actions
(1) Thread from Nightmares: This model may discard two Control Cards to gain one Corpse or Scrap Counter. This Action may be taken only once per activation.

Triggers
Ca (✗ 🐾) Mortify [Exhale Terror]: After defender is damaged by this Spell, it receives -2 **Wp**.

SPELLS:

(0) Create Plaything
(CC: 15🐾 / Rst: - / Rg: C) *AR: Discard any combination of four Corpse and Scrap Counters.* Summon one Teddy.

(0) Gruesome Stuffing
(CC: 14🐾 / Rst: - / Rg: 2) Target friendly Construct gains "**Rotten Contents**: When this model suffers 1 or more **Wd** from a melee **Strike**, flip a Fate Card. If the flipped card is a ✗, living models within (✗)2 of this model suffer 2 **Wd**."

(1) Breathe Life
(CC: 15🐾 / Rst: - / Rg: 12) Target friendly Doll and one additional friendly Doll per 🐾 in the casting total gains one of the following: (+1) **Melee Expert**, (+1) **Ranged Expert**, or (+1) **Casting Expert**.

(1) Craft Doll
(CC: 12🐾 / Rst: - / Rg: C) *AR: Discard one Scrap Counter.* Summon one Wicked Doll.

(1) Exhale Terror
(CC: 13🐾 / Rst: Wp / Rg: ⤳8) **Dg** 1/2/5. A model damaged by this Spell must perform a **Wp → 11** Morale Duel.

Mysterious Effigy - Minion

The Mysterious Effigy was created by Zoraida for use against her own kind, the Neverborn, if the need arose. Since its awakening by the Event, the Mysterious Effigy has chosen a path of obfuscation and subterfuge. Unlike the other Effigies, it prefers manipulating its pawns to actively engaging with them whenever possible.

The Neverborn have worked with the aether over centuries, and the familiar tug of their will was an almost welcome caress to the Effigy. Despite its original design as a weapon to be used against them, Mysterious is now pulled to the Neverborn, instinctually aware of their natural distrust of anything *other*, which suits it fine. Only after ensuring it has their commitment to its purpose is it willing to expose its identity.

Its plots provide allies with a crucial edge, concealing their intentions from their foes the instant before they strike. Its persuasive whispers confuse and misdirect its enemies as well. It is capable of magically planting a suggestion in the mind of whoever hears those whispers, giving it the edge it needs to lash out with its well-concealed dagger. When Mysterious is forced to defend itself it does so with deceptively fast reflexes, making a quick escape if the cut alone is not enough. It knows well that it is responsible to a more pressing concern than the lives of any of its pawns and will abandon them at a moment's notice to preserve itself.

30MM BASE

SOULSTONE COST: 4

OBJECT 1, SPECIAL FORCES (DOLL), UNIQUE

WK/CG	HT	WP	CA	DF	WD
5/6	1	5	5 🐾	6	5

HIDDEN BLADE	
RG	〰 1
CB	5
DG	1/2/4

TALENTS:

Abilities

Aetheric Connection: One friendly model with the **Aetheric Connection** Ability within 6" of this model may activate after this model's activation ends.

Aetheric Demands: Non-Neverborn Crews hiring this model must nominate one leader per model with this Ability they hire. Those leaders cannot attach Totems.

Harmless

Weapon

Hidden Blade: Magical. After wounding a target, Push this model up to 1" per **Wd** inflicted.

Actions

(0) Beguiling Litany: This model's Controller flips one Fate Card. Opposing models with **Wp** lower than the Card's value within (〤)3 of this model receive **Slow**.

(0) Rapid Acceleration: The next **Charge** Action this model takes during its activation receives **Wk/Cg** +0/+3.

SPELLS:

(1) Disguised Fate
(CC: 15🐾 / Rst: - / Rg: 6) Once per turn, when target friendly leader in Mysterious Effigy's Crew Cheats Fate, it may do so by playing its Control Card facedown. The Control Card is then revealed when determining final Duel totals.

(1) Obfuscate
(CC: 14🐾 / Rst: - / Rg: ⬤6) Friendly models receive +2 **Df** when targeted by ranged attacks.

(1) Suggest
(CC: 12🐾 / Rst: Wp / Rg: 8) This model's Controller nominates one of target's printed Actions or Spells. That model cannot use the nominated Action or Spell until the end of its next activation. This spell may be cast by Mysterious Effigy once per activation.

WORLD IN CHAOS

The world was chaos and doubt, and so she climbed.

Misaki Katanaka scaled crumbling brickwork, watched by alien constellations. A restless energy powered her higher, fueled by lungfuls of cold city air and a gnawing anger she couldn't escape.

She prowled the top of the bell tower among the gaping gargoyles and raptor filth, seeking clarity amid the rough, stone heights. In her charcoal gray silks and with her long, black plait tied up, only her beautiful, pale face and jade eyes stood out in the shadows.

Exertion burned her blood, her breath steaming silver in the moonlight. She was free up here, away from the demands of the Trading House and the Ten Thunders. Free to explore the mystical energy that had coursed through her veins the moment she'd arrived in this wonderful, terrifying place, an energy that channelled through her to make her one of the most fearsome fighters Malifaux had known. Up here, with the world at her feet, she felt like a god.

Misaki stopped, a flare of light in the nightscape snaring her hunter's eye. Another Guild train puncturing the Breach between the worlds. A lead downspout looked secure, and she swung across to a ledge thick with droppings. Always moving on.

Far below, the city's lights burned blue and yellow in the dark, a dark that held more than its fair share of monsters and nightmares and terrible things.

A cloud passed over the moon and she stole its shadow to flit unseen, stepping silently up a crow-stepped gable. Ever upwards. The stern lights of the night boats glittered off the river that split the city in two. Dark docks and unlit piers hid midnight commerce from prying Guild eyes and behind them lay Little Kingdom. The Gateless City-within-a-city, part of it but always apart. She knew what that felt like.

And at the heart of Little Kingdom lay the Katanaka Trading House, her headquarters and the base of operations for the Ten Thunders in Malifaux. And now it also held her Brothers, arrived just this week from Earthside. She had not been back there since they came.

With the thought returned the anger, and Misaki raced down the gutter and leapt, suspended for a moment between twinkling lights above and below, landing with a whisper on a bronzed eave. Her bisento, a long-hafted weapon with a wicked blade, had been on her back when she started the leap and in her hands when she touched down. The blade hummed the soft song of steel as she held it outstretched, chest heaving, the razor-point motionless in the dark. Control. In a cruel and random world, control was everything.

But she could not control her feelings the same way she could her bisento, and the choice before her seemed an impossible one. One way lay the path of family, duty, and loyalty. Obey her father, the Oyabun. Pursue the interests of the Ten Thunders, and do what she knew was right. The other – the other was a path that struck out on its own. It led up and kept on going, knew no summits or heights, and its call had grown stronger with every passing day. But it was a path that would take her away from her family, and there could be no going back.

Once more the city below tugged at her, calling out duties and responsibilities. The liquid fires of the newly-installed Geissler tubes atop the Katanaka Trading House bathed the rooftops around them, the familiar kanji letters burning in electric shades of red, green and blue. Modern, lurid and expensive – her Brothers would have slapped each other on the back when they first saw them. Her Brothers, who had swaggered unwanted and unannounced through the Breach, made no effort to pay their respects, and wrecked so much in a single night. Always, no matter how high she climbed, they pulled her back down.

She descended into the chaos of the city, to greet them.

The night was cold, but so was the sake – the Trading House was serving them the good stuff.

Aki Taoka of the Ten Thunders emptied the choko, then returned the small porcelain cup to the bamboo mat. His silence told the serving girl she could continue, and soon Aki and his eleven Brothers were toasting one another and calling loudly for more. The fight with the Dervish Swords had ended only a few hours before, but soon it was so embellished and gilded in the telling and re-telling that few of the Brothers could agree on anything except that they had fought bravely against impossible odds.

Satoru Moriya's shoulder had been cut near the bone by one of the Dervish Swords' hired muscle, and he was struggling to raise his arm to the toasts. Seeing this, the others redoubled the number of toasts, the serving girl came round again in the blink of an eye, and the sake flowed as Satoru groaned.

"And where is Big Sister?" Aki Taoka demanded, slamming his choko down, his face red. "Huh?" he barked, as heads up and down the long, low table nodded in sympathy. All but one. "She is supposed to be in charge here. Does she pay her respects to her Brothers? Does she tend to our wounded?" Heads shook. All but one.

All but Shigeo Inagawa, a young man whose handsome, tattooed face looked haggard and worn. He wiped sake from his moustache and gestured at the empty seat at the head of the table. "Big Sister—"

"—is probably working on her back at the Qi and Gong!" roared Hideki Tsukasa from behind his dripping, black beard, slamming the table with his fist as he choked with laughter. Others doubled up and hammered their cups also, while the serving girl skilfully refilled them without spilling a drop.

With a black, glowering frown Shigeo ignored the belly-laughs around him and carried on. "Big Sister holds our Oyabun's seat at this table, and must have the same respect—"

The table creaked as Aki leaned across to Shigeo, real anger in his watery, blue eyes now. "And maybe she'll have it, the day she remembers her place and stops waving that horse-cleaver around like she—"

But a stunned silence had fallen, and Aki and Shigeo turned their heads to see why. The serving girl. She had filled the only unused cup in the room and then sat down before it,

at the head of the table. Misaki Katanaka untied her white serving apron, handed it to the slack-jawed Hirofumi Nomura on her left and downed the sake she had just poured.

Beside her, in an iron stand, her trademark bisento stood, and not one man present could remember how it had got there.

She drew a cold look across them all, and then nodded her head a fraction, not taking her eyes off them. They were trapped, and they knew it. They had criticised a superior to her face, while accepting her hospitality. As social taboos went in the Ten Thunders, well — fingers had been cut off for far less. Misaki had outmaneuvred them, but she felt no great satisfaction in it — dealing with them was simple compared to the adversaries she faced daily in Malifaux.

The real serving girl hurried in, placing a bowl of cherries in front of Misaki. She slowly savored a handful, giving Aki Taoka her full attention as she spat the stones into a cup. Despite the sake, he retained enough good sense not to look her in the eye. None of them did.

"I hear you all won a great victory over our rivals tonight," Misaki said, in the manner of a spider to a fly trapped in its web. "You are to be congratulated. From the sound of it, the Dervish Swords are no more, and the stragglers have been run out of Malifaux with your katanas jabbing their fat behinds. Is this true?"

Aki paused, and then grunted, "No."

"I see." Misaki downed another cup, the sake as cool as her voice. "Then they have at least been put out of business, and I will never have to concern myself with their enforcers taking protection money that should be going to my Trading House?"

Another pause. "No." Aki's eyes were trying to drill a hole in the wooden table before him.

"Indeed. Then your attack on them struck a mortal blow, and our Ronin can deal with what's left without any significant unpleasantness?"

A longer pause. "No." Aki's mouth flapped open and shut a few times before, "Also, we lost the Ronin tonight."

"So, allow me to draw fact from the fiction I heard earlier. You attacked the Dervish Swords tonight, disregarding the careful plans I had laid for dealing with them. Your attack failed utterly, the Dervish Swords are not only still a threat but are alert to our intentions toward them, and you got my Ronin killed. I had intended to take over their operations, and their best people, and you have just turned what was an opportunity for expansion into open warfare. Am I being unfair in my assessment?"

"They had fifty swords—!" Aki began.

"You were unprepared and hasty."

"—and our Brother Satoru has been badly injured!" As if a desire for vengeance would redirect Misaki's anger.

She smiled coldly. "You'll all think yourselves lucky if you reach morning with an injury like Satoru's. Very lucky."

Shigeo Inagawa was the first to realise what she meant. He looked up at her. "We're going back? Now?"

Misaki stood in one fluid motion. She had always liked Shigeo. He had been one of the few who'd sent congratulations when her father had appointed her his First Lieutenant in the new dominion of Malifaux. "What you don't know, since you're all new and stupid, is that the Dervish Swords have been busy making friends in low places. Dangerous friends. Right now, they are running to those friends and demanding support against Ten Thunders' aggression." Before her Brothers could blink, she snapped up her bisento and brought it scything down over her head. The enchanted blade stopped dead an inch above the heavy wooden table, which split in two down its length with a crack like thunder, the cups and mats flying in the air. Misaki grinned a snake's smile. "They have no idea. We're going to show them just what Ten Thunders' aggression looks like, and this time we'll do it my way."

Ramos could barely make the woman out. In the red glow from the distant furnaces she was little more than embers and shadow, smoldering beneath the enormous, dark crucible. Oblivious to his presence she moved, raising a hand to touch the cold skin of the smelting vessel that hung above her like the belly of an iron giant. This forge had been closed down for repairs, and the unpoured zinc in that vessel was cold and hard.

Ramos waited, willing her on. His companion held patiently beside him as the woman stood unmoving, the three as still as the machinery dwarfing them in the disused forge. From the other forge halls beyond the firebreaks and baffles, distant sounds of heavy industry roared and rang.

Ramos shook his head. Despite the soulstone harness, and his training, she still lacked the raw power.

Then, a smile crept across his face as a ruddy light glimmered into being from the lip of the smelting vessel. A moment later, he had to turn his head as white-hot metal spilled from the gaping spigot and splashed in a waterfall of eye-searing stars and sparks into the empty mold tracks below. Sweltering heat filled the forge.

The woman approached, seeming to emerge from the infernal glow itself, and stopped in front of him and his companion. Her usually pale face was flushed with effort, glistening with sweat beneath her short, blonde hair and her eyes filled with an exhilarating light. Ramos fancied he could see embers dancing in their depths.

"Impressive," he said, "and timely. Certain friends in the city have asked for aid. I thought of you." Ramos indicated the other man, his face hidden behind a set of polished goggles. Elaborate pistols hung from a leather harness. "This is 74 Victor. You may find him useful."

The woman turned to the gunman, and the light from the cascading metal was blotted out as brass wings sprang from her back and flexed purposefully, eagerly. She leaned forward, the smell of smoke and blistered steel like perfume. "So. 74 Victor. Are you in?"

There were two ways into the Dervish Swords' warehouse complex; by well-guarded canals from the river, or through the front operation – Madame Chin's Teahouse. Either way, Misaki knew, they would be waiting.

Reckless and hasty they might be, but her Brothers were also proud and fierce warriors who had served the Ten Thunders faithfully for years, and Misaki had no desire to see any of them cut to pieces in the dark, winding waterways, or in a frontal assault. But even if they got in, they had no idea what awaited them in that warehouse. They were skilled, fearless fighters, that much was true, but that was not enough amid the perils of Malifaux. Where these Brothers had come, soon her father would send more, and more, and they would always need her to get them out of situations like this. She would never be free.

It was still dark, and from her vantage point atop Stricken Mews clock tower, she watched by gaslight as the two hand carts made their way along the cobbles towards Madame Chin's. On the open backs of each cart, nestled in thick straw, sat branded barrels of sake, fresh from Earthside. The runners moved cautiously: fine sake needed careful handling, and was sensitive to bumps and jolts.

Much like gunpowder, mused Misaki, as the runners deposited the carts outside the teahouse, lit the hidden fuses and sprinted away. Too late, shots were fired at them from the dark windows of the teahouse and then the ornate wooden building vanished in a billowing column of dark smoke. The *thump* of the blast arrived a fraction of a second later, and Misaki felt it in her chest. Glass shattered up and down the street, and the bell in the clock tower rang softly.

As thick pieces of timber rained like rice at a wedding, her Brothers broke from hiding and raced towards the fresh ruin, their battle cries thin on the night breeze. Shigeo and Aki were vying for the lead, Shigeo with his battered katana and blunderbuss pistol, and Aki waving a long-handled cleaver in each hand. The other ten Brothers followed close behind, screaming and brandishing naginatas, clubs, chain-scythes and pistols. They vanished amidst the smoke and the cries of the wounded.

Misaki leapt from the clock tower. There was a third way in, although only birds, the wind and Misaki herself could use it. She landed running, flitting silently across a tiled ridge like a rogue breeze.

She hadn't told them the whole truth, of course.

A row of weathered statues provided a series of stepping stones beneath a copper-sheeted eave.

There was something black at the heart of the Dervish Swords.

She jumped across the gap between buildings, springing off a crumbling course of projecting brickwork on the opposite wall and climbed quickly up a series of ornate corbels carved with crows.

There was a reason Baojun Katanaka, her father and Oyabun of the Ten Thunders, wanted to expand into Malifaux. A reason beyond money. A darkness had infected the Three Kingdoms, a darkness that no outsider was permitted to know, and one that her father wanted no part of.

A bird does not twitch at a falling leaf, and Misaki ran right past a row of pigeons before they even noticed she was there. With a leap she landed on the sloping, tiled roof of the Dervish Swords' warehouse, clinging on as her feet threatened to slip on the polished surface.

She had to know if that darkness had come here, too. And that was why she was up here while her Brothers were in the thick of it. They would draw out the poison, if it was here, and she would lance it.

The night still shuddered to the gunpowder blast, and the cracks and booms of the still-collapsing teahouse would lead the Guild right to them. Time was tight. Just audible, coming through the skylight nearby, were the sounds of battle from the warehouse floor below. Misaki prised the wooden lid open and lowered herself inside for a proper look.

The warehouse was sprawling and dark, lit intermittently by gas lamps strung around iron pillars that held up the broad roof. Piles of bales and crates dotted the timber floor. Off to her left, yellow gaslight glimmered on water where the narrow canals came right into the warehouse, and to her right, smoke billowed from numerous doorways and passages leading towards the stricken teahouse.

Her Brothers were almost directly below her, and she could not help the stab of pride and relief to see they were all still standing, although bloodied. Back to back, the twelve held their ground in a tight knot, surrounded on all sides by the foot soldiers and hired hands of the Dervish Swords. Beyond them, Misaki could just make out a woman and a man, standing together in the shadows, but before she could position herself for a better look, the Oyabun of the Dervish Swords arrived.

As soon as she saw him, she felt a sour taste in her mouth, and a pain behind her green eyes. Her father had been right. The poison had spread to the Dervish Swords. The Thirsty Glass was here.

The Oyabun was naked and shackled, his frail, white body covered with self-inflicted wounds and weeping sores, but that was the least of it. He was held behind glass, four thick walls to make a cage carried on the shoulders of four sturdy slaves, the inside smeared with blood both fresh and dried. There was something embedded in the glass she could not quite make out. The slaves placed the cage on a stone plinth and moved to surround it, one standing on each side facing outwards. The Oyabun raved wordlessly within, as the Dervish Swords around fell silent. Misaki could not help noticing that they kept their distance from their own Oyabun.

Then she looked closer at the slaves and recoiled in disgust. Each had a hole the size of a fist in their chest where their hearts should be. Leading from the ragged black wound, a gossamer-thin cable led behind them and into the glass of the Oyabun's cage. More gas lamps were lit, and Misaki could see what was embedded in the glass. Four hearts, red, raw, and beating.

The Oyabun placed one trembling palm on the glass, above one of the living hearts. It convulsed, but kept beating. The slave linked to it spoke at once, his words jumbling and tangled. --

"--weavinganddancingbutnowthedanceisoverKILLbe-foremidnightchimesonceandthelastnamesarecalled-ofthosewhoremain--"

The Oyabun cried out and flailed against the walls, and the slave fell silent. One of the Dervish Swords spoke up, a Korean giant with arcane tattoos across his cruel face, addressing the surrounded Ten Thunders. Misaki recognised him as Ssang Kal, the second in command.

"The Oyabun is generous. He will grant a swift and honorable death to those who put down their weapons now."

The Oyabun placed a hand on a different heart. The slave's head snapped up.

"--talecarvedthriceistrueKILLevenfromaliars'tongue--"

Ssang Kal spoke again when the Oyabun stopped. "Select one of your number to live. He will return to your master with a message from the Dervish Swords." He drew a wicked-looking knife and leered. "His tongue will be cut out, and the message carved into his flesh, but he will live."

Shigeo stepped forward, an insolent smirk on his face. He had lost his pistol, and his katana was a little more battered than before, but he rested the bloody blade on his shoulder in an insultingly casual manner as he looked at the giant and tapped his chest.

The giant Dervish Sword spat. "A volunteer? So *these* are the mighty Ten Thunders we heard so much about? I had not thought you could be such cowards."

Shigeo's smirk vanished and he whipped the tip of his sword round to point at Ssang Kal. "I volunteer to be the one to cut your head from your shoulders, unless Big Sister takes it first."

"--toagirlwhorunsandrunsbutKILLcrieswhenherhairiscut--"

No sooner had the slave fallen silent than Ssang Kal threw his arms wide and crowed, "And where is the Lady Misaki, the Oyabun asks? Where has she vanished to?" The Dervish Swords howled in derision, brandishing their weapons. "I think she has fled, rather than face the-"

"--tigerspiderturningburningKILLonthewall--"

One of the Oyabun's slaves was looking right at her, and Misaki didn't need a tattooed giant to translate. She was already moving, dropping fast, her sandals scraping against one side of an iron pillar while her bisento held fast against the other. Ten feet above the floor she kicked off, cartwheeling through the air to land, crouched, at the feet of a shocked Ssang Kal, her bisento held straight out behind her.

A hush fell over the assembled Dervish Swords. A hush that seemed to grow as a single drop of blood swelled at the tip of Misaki's weapon, holding the attention of everyone in the warehouse, until it finally dropped. When it hit the sawdust, chaos erupted as Ssang Kal's body toppled to the floor, preceded only moments earlier by his severed head.

Several things happened at once. Shigeo and the other Ten Thunders drew round, red objects from beneath their robes and hurled them at the feet of the Dervish Swords. They exploded on the warehouse floor in a flash of fire and smoke, blinding their enemies, as Misaki's Brothers charged.

The man and woman standing back in the shadows exchanged a glance and split up without a word, a matter-of-fact look of determination on the face of the man, and a barely contained look of excitement on the woman's. The man's cloak flicked open to reveal an array of weapons holstered on his wiry frame, complicated optics glinting in brass tubes.

Misaki ignored them and pointed herself at the Oyabun, racing forward towards the towering glass cage. A howling Dervish Sword got in her path, and she cut him from shoulder to groin. She smashed the iron-shod butt of the weapon into the bearded face of another on the return swing, and then used his collapsing body as a springboard to leap high above the fray. She emerged from a column of acrid smoke, dark coils trailing from her charcoal silks and drove the point of her weapon into the glass of the Oyabun's cage.

It did not even scratch the surface.

Undaunted, she landed with another strike already underway, and brought the long blade of the bisento scything down overhead. Once again, it rebounded from the glass, and she had to duck and roll to avoid a hooked blade on the end of a chain as it sought her out. A lunging thrust pierced the lungs of the man on the other end of the chain, and he died with blood frothing at his lips.

"–holdwithinthefirethatburnsKILLtimeonlyendingwillsto-pit–"

The slaves reached for her, jabbering their nonsense, but they were too slow and Misaki easily evaded their clumsy swipes.

"–overlybrokenKILLmarksthelimitsof–"

The glass was clearly enchanted, if it was glass at all. A glimpse of the gossamer threads joining the slaves to their master gave her an idea, and she cleaved the head of the nearest slave from crown to breastbone. He collapsed immediately, blood fountaining from his cloven face. Immediately, the glass around the heart cracked.

Misaki was fast, lightning fast, but the Oyabun was prepared. His hand was over the heart before the slave had fallen and the crack sealed up a fraction of a second before the bisento struck it. Again the blade bounced off.

At Misaki's feet, the slave's sundered flesh and shattered bone re-knitted, and he stood back up, babbling anew.

Three Dervish Swords rushed her at once, one swinging a machete, one a nail-studded club, and the other with matched sai daggers. She cut the club in half, along with both arms wielding it, while she kicked the one holding the machete in the throat. She had to leap backwards as the twin daggers stabbed at her face, and the slave behind wrapped his arms around her.

"–whiletheironishotKILLnownownowME–"

Misaki froze in her struggle, twisting round to look at the slave. Had it really said that? Its empty face continued to babble as the Oyabun looked on, chewing the ragged tatters of his own lips.

"–fabricunravellingKILLcrumblingtodustnoroominthe-bloodUS–"

The two remaining Dervish Swords renewed their assault as Misaki spun her weapon to break the slave's grip and ducked away from the blows. She sent the bisento lancing backwards, and it spitted both men through their bellies. With a twist and a wrench, she loosed their innards and pulled the blade and haft free.

With the slave's words ringing in her ears she set off, racing around the glass cage on its pedestal faster than the wind, her weapon joining her in a blur of leaping, spinning, deadly motion. She flowed through the fray like water through reeds and her strikes were like lightning, but as fast as she killed the slaves and fractured the heart-glass, the Oyabun re-knitted them and healed his protective cage. Heads split and chests ripped asunder once, twice, three times and more. Faster and faster she sped, the blade of her bisento humming a lethal song, but still the frail madman kept his defenses renewed, and a drooling grin spread across his quaking features.

And then, instead of making the last strike, she hurled her weapon away like a bullet from a gun. It struck one of the iron columns side on, perfectly balanced, the hardwood haft bending like a bow, before streaking back through the air towards her. Towards the heart pumping in the cage and the Oyabun's grinning, insane face.

A fraction of a second before it reached its target, she brought a wooden-sandaled foot sweeping around and crushed the skull of the slave standing before her. As he died a crack appeared in the glass and the tip of the bisento plunged through it and lodged right between the eyes of the Oyabun behind.

The glass fractured all over with a crackle like winter ice. The four hearts withered to autumn husks in their last beat. The slaves collapsed, dark blood oozing from the holes in their chests, and the Oyabun hung motionless, pinned like a fly in amber by four inches of folded steel embedded in his skull.

The fight slowed to a halt around her, the din of battle ebbing as the Dervish Swords saw what had become of their leader. Putting her back under one of the carrying poles, she toppled the glass cage off its pedestal with a hoarse cry. The warehouse held its breath as it tipped, and the sound of the glass shattering into a thousand glittering shards echoed off the far walls. Bestride the corpse of the wretched Oyabun, she wrenched her bisento free and stepped back as the body went the way of the glass. Fractures spread outward from the neat wound, speeding over the white flesh, and the remains fell apart at her feet, noxious, yellow gas seeping loose as it was riven from head to foot.

Springing atop the now vacant pedestal she held her weapon aloft. "The day is ours!"

Her words had barely left her mouth when a spear of flame flashed out the shadows. Misaki leapt away just in time, seeing her own shadow painted black on the crates before her as a blinding blaze burned where she had stood. White-hot fire consumed the remains of the cage and the

Oyabun with a dragon's roar, flames searching for the roof as the updraft tugged at Misaki's grey silks. Knives of glass caught up in the heat began to redden and sag.

A winged figure stood atop a pyramid of huge, ceramic jars. Blue fire lingered at the ends of her outstretched arms, a cold light that glimmered in the brass of her wings and the curves of her face. She spoke English, her tone cool and measured. "I don't speak your language, Lady Misaki, but I wouldn't start counting heads just yet."

Misaki motioned at her Brothers to hang back. This was bigger game than they could bring down, and she cursed herself for having ignored the woman. She had recognized the power the woman held in just that fleeting glimpse earlier in the battle, but had been too focused on confirming her father's suspicions about the Dervish Swords. She started circling left. So where had the western woman's friend disappeared to?

Misaki spoke in English, too, watching the corners and keeping the woman in sight. "Bodyguard, I have left you no body to guard. Who are you?"

"The name's Kaeris."

It meant nothing to Misaki. Those brass wings spoke of money and Arcanist connections, and Misaki had known enough Ronin to recognize a hired sword when she spoke to one. But she was out of the Dervish Sword's league, so who was paying for her? And now she had the edge on Misaki – not because of her weaponry, but because she had seen Misaki fight. Misaki knew nothing in return, and that was dangerous. Any crumb of information would be useful. "This fight is not your fight."

"No, but a lady needs a hobby."

Cocky. Arrogant, perhaps. But still holding back. She was careful, too. Precise. She was not the only one playing a waiting game, Misaki realised, as she moved from cover to cover. "And yours is being too late to stop me killing your employer?"

"Him? He's nothing. He was an indentured slave until the Investors gave him to the Thirsty Glass. Poor sod. No, I'm here for you."

"You missed."

"Did I? First rule of business. Leave nothing behind." The fire was spreading now; contortions of scorched metal in a puddle of smoking, molten glass was all that remained of the Oyabun and his conveyance. Burning scraps had scattered small fires all around the warehouse.

Misaki reversed course for an instant, just to see what would happen. Kaeris raised an arm and then let it drop as Misaki resumed circling left, keeping in cover. So the woman wanted her going this way. That answered Misaki's question about her friend.

The surviving Dervish Swords had fled, and she was approaching an open stretch of the warehouse near the canals. She was about to run out of cover. A glint of reflected firelight caught her eye, coming from deep shadow near some wine barrels. She looked for Shigeo, found him watching her, weapons and Brothers at the ready.

She was within three paces of the open stretch when Kaeris opened up, just as Misaki had anticipated. And, just as anticipated, she aimed to Misaki's right, trying to drive her into the open area. Instead of dodging left, Misaki leapt towards the bolt of flame that would explode the instant it touched her. But a kestrel diving on prey does not snap at the wind, and Misaki swept her bisento through the air to match the speed of the bolt, catching it from behind and spinning, turning in mid-air with bolt and blade as one and then released it with a cry.

If the look on Kaeris' face was priceless, what value the look on the face of her friend as the fireball slammed into the barrels where he hid? *Should have shielded those optics better, Gunsmith.* Wine geysered, most flashing to steam in the intense heat as burning wooden slats danced Catherine Wheels through the air.

"Take him!" Misaki shouted to her Brothers, already darting towards Kaeris. "Leave her to me!"

But the Arcanist woman was firing again, a rapid stream of angry red comets hurtling through the air, forcing Misaki to jump two steps to the side for every one forward. Wherever they landed, the fireballs burst, spilling greedy flames over the dusty timber boards that sucked the fire outwards in ever-expanding pools. Heat washed over Misaki as she flew past an iron pillar, and still the onslaught of flame continued.

Shots and cries sounded, but she had no time for her Brothers now. She paused behind a stack of ceramic tiles to chase away motes burning in her silks and noticed a neat hole through her scarf. A shot she had never seen had just missed her neck. That man must have taken it while she was in mid-leap, before she sent Kaeris' fire his way — his was a rare talent indeed.

It was time to take the fight to the Arcanist witch. She scaled the stack of tiles like a cat going up a curtain. Kaeris glimpsed her as she reached the top, and the twin streams of fire started to converge. Misaki sprinted forward and leapt off the stack. She fell through heat-hazed air and slammed her bisento down flat-bladed onto the timbers. Furious energy coursed through her, discharging with a thunder-clap as a wave of pure power flowed outwards, rippling the timbers in a massive, outrushing disturbance. Dust and dirt exploded upward from every joint in the floor in a punishing grey cloud, lit blood-red by the fires. A cloud that hid her from Kaeris' sight.

Fast as a breaking wave, she raced forward, not even slowing a fraction as she shot up and over the pyramid of urns Kaeris had been on. She jumped off the pyramid a second before a searing spear shot out of nowhere, aimed more by anticipation than sight. It scorched the air as it passed her by, and pain burned down her side. She landed clumsily, gasping and rolling clear as another dragon's breath flamed towards her out the dust and then a shadow loomed and Misaki brought the haft of her bisento squarely down on Kaeris' left hand.

The woman cried out in pain of her own, clutching her hand and twisting away as the blue flames on the injured hand flickered away to nothing.

Misaki's hand flicked out, flinging a round, red object at Kaeris' feet as the mercenary prepared to retaliate. Kaeris jumped back in alarm, then stopped, a look of bewilderment on her face.

Misaki shrugged. "Just a cherry." But she'd bought herself an opening and only just had time to dive behind some sturdy winch gear as Kaeris brought her uninjured hand up and split the air with a beam of fire so white-hot it felt as though the sun had been rent asunder. The scream of anger that accompanied it was just as furious.

Misaki kept moving, fast and low. The smoke from the dozens of fires was adding to the dust cloud, reducing visibility to only a few feet.

Straining to listen over the rush and crackle of fire, she heard a roaring *BA-BOOM!* and a scream from one of her Brothers. The Gunsmith was still alive, then. She tried to put him from her thoughts – Shigeo and the others would have to handle him alone.

As if reading her mind, she heard Kaeris call out. "What are they to you, Lady Misaki? These so-called Brothers of yours? People like me and you are made to shape this world, but they're just murderers and thieves."

"While you burn everything around you in the name of peace and tranquility?" The smoke and flames were confusing the air, making sounds come from all directions. Misaki kept low, circling outward.

"You're telling me you have something in common with them?"

"I wouldn't expect your kind to understand," Misaki replied.

A laugh, but from where? "I may have my price, but I know about loyalty."

Misaki answered with a laugh of her own. "As you know my name, and yet I am a complete stranger to you, so it is with your kind and that word."

"The man who made these wings for me, and trained me in the ways of power, would prove you wrong!" There was fresh anger there – she'd struck a nerve.

An avalanche of noise sounded from off to one side, a splintering, crashing torrent that had to be the remains of the Tea House collapsing. It gave Misaki her bearings for a moment, just as a red-wreathed silhouette loomed in the swirling smoke. Kaeris. She scythed her bisento as Kaeris sprung forward. Fire blossomed, meeting the magical blade, and then both women were grappling, their hands on the hardwood haft and their sweat-streaked faces inches apart. Flames poured like molten steel but were harnessed by the power of the bisento and instead of searing Misaki's flesh from her bones, they raced along the blade and lashed outwards harmlessly.

Misaki shifted, trying to unbalance her foe, but the mercenary moved with her. More crashing sounds came from the ruins of the Tea House, along with heavy, clanking sounds. Was something coming through the wreckage?

"Loyalty has to cut both ways," Kaeris panted, the effort of maintaining the flow of fire sending tracks of sweat through the ash on her face, "or it is just chains by another name. And I'm certain the Ten Thunders are getting a lot more out of you than you are of them."

"And what of the company you keep?" Misaki spat back. "These so-called Investors? Did you gag at the foulness when taking orders from that thing in the cage, or did you not notice after a while?"

"Today they are our friends, tomorrow who knows? That is freedom!" Kaeris' eyes were glowing with the energies pouring out of her, her frustration at Misaki's ability to deflect them clear. "But what of the Ten Thunders? What does it feel like, to wield power like this and live among scum? Do you still feel them dragging you down, or do you not notice after a while? What can they offer you? Ancient traditions? Duties and responsibilities? Babysitting those fools?"

"Discipline," Misaki said, as Kaeris' fires flew ever more violent and directionless, burning great avenues of flame in the air and setting the ceiling ablaze. "Mastery." Swift as a snake, she released her grip on her weapon and delivered a savage flurry of jabs to her opponent's midriff, just below the harness. As Kaeris recoiled in pain, Misaki snatched her bisento back and spun it around her shoulders before stabbing it forward. Kaeris only just rolled aside in time. "Control."

The mechanical clanking sound increased as Kaeris sprang to her feet, but she did not strike out. Warily, they circled one another, the smoke making ghosts of them both. Kaeris was smiling.

"And at last I have the measure of you, Lady Misaki. *Control.* I should have known. I tried to control the power, too, at first, but that's not the way it works here." Flames like snakes unravelled from her uninjured hand and entwined themselves languidly around her. "You think I am controlling this? Control is a myth unless we embrace the chaos. Control is impossible unless we revel in uncertainty and doubt. That is the paradox of power in this land." The snakes eyes glowed white-hot and furious. "You have revealed yourself to me, and that will unmake you."

The snakes struck, their heads splitting like hydras in mid-air. Misaki had been expecting the attack, but the nature of it surprised her. She fell back, scorched and warping timbers shifting underfoot. The flame-serpents were a flurry of motion, spending and renewing themselves from Kaeris' hand in brilliant bursts of light, but there seemed no sense or skill to their onslaught. Misaki moved with perfect timing, catching tongues of flame on her bisento and snuffing them to nothing, moving to intercept the next one in flawless harmony. But always falling back, because the next one was never where it should be, never where any skilled assailant would strike next. Most of the attacks were easy to repel, but a few came at her from improbable angles, their sheer randomness making them deadlier than anything Kaeris had flung at her before. In moments, her silks were smoking and charred in a half-dozen places, and she could smell her own singed hair. Off balance, and losing ground, her skill was working against her.

With a titanic groan, an iron column collapsed and fell between the two women. Layers of roof and glass smashed down with it, and Misaki turned to see an enormous construct emerging from the smoke and flames where the Tea House had been. Metal beams and chunks of masonry bounced unnoticed off its armored shell. Brass cogs ground their teeth and steel talons glinted with malicious, mechanical intent as the Peacekeeper ripped up fistfuls of aged timber, its great head hunting for targets through the smoke. The Guild had finally arrived.

"Time to be leaving," Kaeris said, coiling vines of flame around her body and across the floor, "but first things first."

The looping tendrils of fire exploded outward, lunging for Misaki in an immolating embrace. But the interruption of the Guild machine had given her a second to think. Kaeris' assault embraced chaos and confusion to devastating effect, obliterating Misaki's superior skill. The very concept was anathema to her, but her only hope was to do the same. Abandon perfection. Let chaos reign. Fight fire with fire.

She charged, screaming, before she knew what she was doing. That choice saved her life. She moved without thinking, abandoning her training to become as unpredictable as a force of nature. One moment as fluid as water, the other as highly sprung as steel, she changed

in the blink of an eye to the whiplash motion of a striking mantis. The fires of Kaeris could not find her, could not touch her. She reinvented her style with every heartbeat, drawing inspiration for the next lunge from a coil of smoke, the next block from the feel of the timbers under her feet, the next strike from the sound of her own breathing. Every stitch stood apart from the others, and yet knitted into one perfect whole. Chaos was pitted against chaos, and Misaki's was the most thorough and inventive. She was advancing now, her bisento describing blinding arcs in the air she had never seen before and – wonderfully – had no idea if she would ever see again.

Kaeris screamed in rage and frustration and backed off, spawning a kraken of fire to encircle Misaki, but whatever gaps the flames left, there she was, impossibly leaping and spinning through them unhurt, every step bringing that sweeping blade closer to Kaeris.

The paradox, Misaki realized as her steel bit the air inches from Kaeris' neck, was to achieve mastery through both harmony and anarchy. Exhilaration flowed through her as she understood the potential of what she had unlocked. She did not know what her next move was until she made it. When the Peacekeeper's chain spear exploded through a wall of burning barrels, it became simply another note in the symphony she was building, one whose final movement was now inevitable.

Kaeris was spent. She had nothing left. Misaki poised and leapt, blade drawn back, and then the Peacekeeper crashed over them both like a wave of iron. Misaki danced anew in a forest of pistons and armour, thunderous clanking over the hateful hiss of steam, rising up over its great, red carapace among the soot and oil and beyond the grasping claws to launch herself once more at Kaeris.

But Kaeris was rising. Borne aloft on brass wings and roasted air, she crashed into Misaki and kept on rising, one hand grasping Misaki's silk robes. Her feet left the Peacekeeper's back as it reared up, enraged at their escape, swiping its railroad spike-claws at them, but catching only smoke. Kaeris rose higher. Her brass wings heaved, steadily gaining height. Misaki struggled, but she was tangled, and could not bring herself about to strike. Patches of night sky sucked the smoke out of the burning warehouse, with more and more appearing as the building's death hastened.

Misaki saw her fate; a short fall and a quick end once Kaeris gained clear skies. Then a familiar cry and a pair of strong arms wrapped themselves around her waist. She looked down into the blood and ash-streaked face of Shigeo, hanging on for grim life, and behind him the burning stack of shipping crates he must have launched himself from.

Immediately, the three of them began to drop back into the smoke.

"No!" Kaeris screamed, her wings unable to bear Shigeo's extra weight.

Misaki felt the grip holding her loosen, and looked up into Kaeris' eyes. They burned with bitter hatred.

"You still feel them dragging you down, Lady Misaki?" Then Kaeris let go.

Misaki and Shigeo fell. Before the smoke swallowed them up, her last sight of Kaeris was of the bronze wings rippling with blue fire as they powered the woman out a rent in the warehouse roof. Misaki hit the ground hard, rolling through burning wads of packing linen and sprang to her feet before the flames could take hold. She grabbed Shigeo's hand and hauled him upright, slapping at the fires that licked at his robes. Thunderous crashes sounded all around them, and the doomsday clank of the Peacekeeper was not far off.

"Time to leave, Big Sister?" Shigeo shouted.

Misaki nodded. "What about the Gunsmith?"

Shigeo shook his head and winced, grabbing his arm at the shoulder. Misaki noticed the blood soaking the silk. "He got away. Left me one of his bullets. I left him a limp."

"Who did we lose?"

"Satoru. Hideki. And the big Guild engine put its spear through Hirofume."

It could have been a lot worse, but her Brothers had fought fiercely and bravely and had made amends for their earlier disaster. Misaki was satisfied honor had been restored, and the Dervish Swords had been wiped out in the most emphatic fashion. Come morning, everyone in Little Kingdom would be reminded why not even a brave man crossed the Ten Thunders.

"There's no way out through that!" Misaki shouted, pointing towards the fury of the Peacekeeper and the raging fire. Wherever the Peacekeeper led, other Guild constructs and forces were not far behind. "Come with me."

Misaki and Shigeo gathered the surviving Ten Thunders at the waterway at the rear of the warehouse. The rear wall was a blazing sheet of flame, burning timbers dropping into the oily, black water, but they could swim out, and the Guild would not have been reckoning on a pursuit to the river. They would take whatever boats they could find and be long gone by the time the lawmen caught up.

Misaki was the last to leave, watching impassively as the great, dark shadow of the Peacekeeper raged amid the hungry flames. After a short underwater dash, she hauled herself up green-slick stones and onto a narrow tow-ledge. Ahead, her Brothers were still swimming, aiming for the Harken Docks. Out of sight behind her, the warehouse burned. Great blankets of smoke spread across the night sky, lit blood red from below. She looked up at the old stone and timber wall beside her, working out the best route to the top.

A splash from below made her turn. Shigeo was stuck, unable to climb after her. She leaned down and gave him a hand up.

"I owe you thanks," she said.

"Less than we owe you." His shoulder was bleeding freely, but it did not look broken. He would mend. He glanced up at the wall she had been about to scale. "Are you leaving us?" The question was a loaded one. He knew, she realized. He'd always been the smart one.

"I thought I had a difficult choice to make, Little Brother. Whatever path I chose, I would lose something very important to me. But in the fight with that woman, I found a way to fight and win I could never have imagined before. It was as if the north wind and the south wind blew as one. Two forces in opposition that came together. It should not have worked, but it did. I have much to think about."

"And have you made your choice?" He looked away, unwilling to meet her eyes.

She shook her head. "No need. I am trying to tell you I have found another way." She put a hand on his uninjured shoulder. "Go. We will meet back at the Trading House. As much as I respect my father, our Oyabun, this is a new world with new rules. So I will lead the Ten Thunders, as he asks, but I will do it my way, and I will take you all with me. To the very top. This world will not know our next move until we make it. It should not work, but I have a feeling it will."

Shigeo nodded. He gave a short bow and leapt into the canal, his battered katana between his teeth. She watched as he paddled away out of sight, and then began scaling the wall.

The world was chaos and doubt. Misaki Katanaka smiled to herself, and climbed.

LAZARUS - MINION

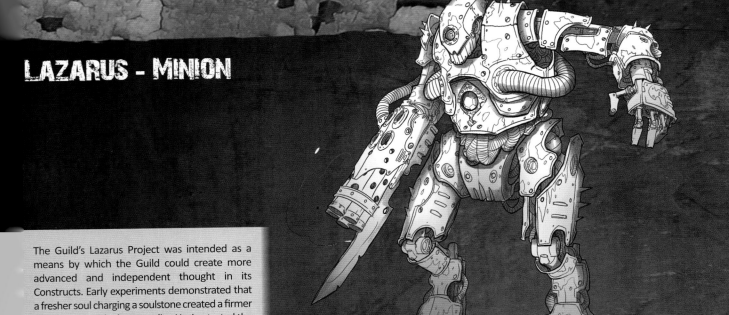

The Guild's Lazarus Project was intended as a means by which the Guild could create more advanced and independent thought in its Constructs. Early experiments demonstrated that a fresher soul charging a soulstone created a firmer grip for the residual personality. Having tested the theory and resulting charging process, Guild researchers sought a Guard volunteer who naïvely believed their assertions that they could reinsert his spirit into his body once the experiment was over.

Once the volunteer's spirit had powered the soulstone and was connected with the experimental Lazarus Construct's logic engine, the test began. At first, the Construct performed as expected, accepting the edicts the researchers programmed into it as would any other Construct. Verbal revisions to the edicts were also followed as expected; the Guardsman's spirit reacted within the expected parameters, demonstrating that his personality remained more or less intact. Then, slowly, certain verbal commands would be ignored, or in some cases, the programmed edicts themselves circumvented in what the researchers could only attribute to the Guardsman's spirit fighting for command of his new body. They had not anticipated its quasi-state of self-awareness would lead it to realize it had been tricked, the spirit now trapped in a body of metal. When the researchers attempted to shut Lazarus down and remove its logic engine for analysis, the Construct rebelled, smashing equipment and wreaking havoc before breaking out of the research facility.

The Guild pursued Lazarus, dogging its flight into the Quarantine Zone, but lost their target in the warren of tumbledown buildings and rubble-strewn streets. Since then, despite their failures in locating the Lazarus Construct, the Guild continues to search for it, investigating rumors of its appearance. Lazarus, however, continues to elude them. With its unique blending of human and Construct intellects, Lazarus plots the next move against its betrayers, instinctually collecting what it needs to augment and improve itself while allying with anyone willing to stand against the Guild.

40MM BASE

SOULSTONE COST: 8

CONSTRUCT, MERCENARY, SCAVENGER, UNIQUE

WK/CG	HT	WP	CA	DF	WD
4/6	3	6	5	4	9

BAYONET	
RG	1
CB	5
DG	2/3/4

GRENADE LAUNCHER	
RG	10
CB	6
DG	2/3/4

TALENTS:

Abilities

Constant Upgrades: If this model discards two Scrap Counters when performing the **Assimilate** Action, it gains the **Assimilated** Talent or Spell until the end of the Encounter.

Evasive 2

Hate the Maker: This model cannot be hired into Crews that contain Guild models. This model's Attack Flips receive against non-Construct Guild models.

Immune to Influence

Reinforced Patchwork Armor: Armor +1. This **Armor** cannot be modified or ignored.

Ruthless

Actions

(+1) Melee Expert

(0) Assimilate: This model gains one Talent or Spell possessed by target Construct within 6". Effects that reference a model by name cannot be **Assimilated**.

(0) Self-Repair: This model performs a Healing Flip.

(2) Automatic Fire [Grenade Launcher]: Discard one Control Card. Target a model within range and LoS. This model performs a **Strike** with this Weapon against that model and up to two other models within 2" of the initial target which are also within range and LoS with this Weapon. This Action may be performed once per turn.

Triggers

Cb ( ) Unload Ordnance [Bayonet]: After damaging an enemy defender with this Weapon, place with at least one in base contact with the defender following the normal rules for placing . Models other than this model and the defender touched by the suffer 3 **Dg**.

LENNY - MINION

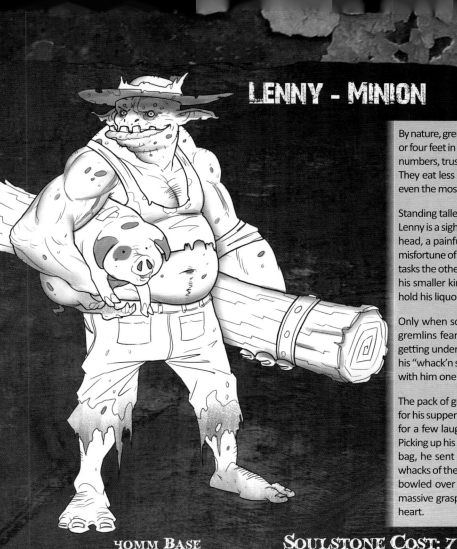

By nature, gremlins are slight in stature, seldom growing taller than three or four feet in height. What they lack in physical size they make up for in numbers, trusting in a flood of green bodies to overcome any obstacle. They eat less than a human, due to their size, but can easily outdrink even the most seasoned saloon regular. Then there's Lenny.

Standing taller than two gremlins sitting on one another's shoulders, Lenny is a sight to behold. His gnarled hands are larger than a gremlin's head, a painful fact more than one of his dim-witted kin has had the misfortune of learning. He can do the labor of five, accepting whatever tasks the others pile on him with a blissful smile. Lenny can also outeat his smaller kin, devouring entire roasted pigs at one sitting, and can hold his liquor after lesser gremlin have long slid under the table.

Only when something riles Lenny enough to lash out do the other gremlins fear his height and strength. They do their best to avoid getting under his skin, having witnessed his disturbing accuracy with his "whack'n stick" and a few well-aimed piglets he happened to have with him one afternoon.

The pack of gremlin youths who came across him trying to catch fish for his supper thought an afternoon of mocking Lenny would be good for a few laughs; that is until they ribbed him one too many times. Picking up his stick and digging his snack of three piglets out of a burlap bag, he sent the piglets squealing toward the gremlins with three whacks of the stick. After being pelted by flying pork, the youths were bowled over by Lenny's massive form before being crushed in his massive grasp. A lesson every gremlin in his kin took very quickly to heart.

40MM BASE

SOULSTONE COST: 7

GREMLIN, UNIQUE

WK/CG	HT	WP	CA	DF	WD
5/-	2	4	3	3	9

WHACK'N STICK			WHACKED PIGLET		
RG	///	2	RG	⌐	8
CB	5		CB	4 🐗	
DG	2/4/5		DG	1/2/3♣	

TALENTS:

Abilities

Dumb: This model receives **Slow** at the start of its activation unless its Controller discards one Control Card. If the card is a Joker, this model receives **Fast**.

Hard to Wound 1

Numbskull: Armor +1. This model is immune to **Paralyzed**.

Pitiful: Until this model activates each turn, models targeting this model must win a **Wp → Wp** Duel or the Action immediately ends.

Stubborn: This model receives +2 **Wp** when defending in a Duel.

"Woops!": When this model misses with a Whacked Piglet **Strike**, the closest other friendly model within 8" and LoS suffers an unmodified Damage Flip of 1/2/3♣. If there are no other friendly models within 8", there is no effect.

Weapon

Whacked Piglet: Enemy models damaged by this Weapon can be targeted by **Swine Dash** Actions even if they are not the closest model to the Pig performing the **Swine Dash** Action.

Actions

(+1) Reckless: This model may suffer 1 **Wd** to receive **Fast**.

(1) Big Target: 🐷3. Friendly **Ht** 1 Gremlins targeted by enemy ranged attacks gain **Armor +1** until the end of the attack.

Triggers

Cb (🖐) Hugs and Squeezes [Whack'n Stick]: This Weapon inflicts +2 **Dg**. Defender cannot disengage from this model.

Cb (🐷) Off Balance [Whacked Piglet]: After hitting defender with this Weapon, Push defender 2" before the Damage Flip.

Df (🐗) "Quit Pickin' On Me!": After this model suffers **Wd**, all models within (x)3 must win a **Wp → 12** Duel or receive **Slow**.

McTavish - Minion

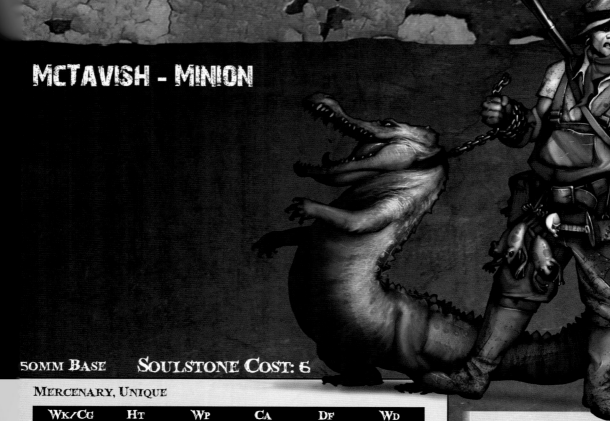

50MM BASE **SOULSTONE COST: 6**

MERCENARY, UNIQUE

Wk/Cg	Ht	Wp	Ca	Df	Wd
5/7	2	4	4	5	8

"GIT 'EM!"			HUNTING RIFLE		
Rg	///// 2		**Rg**	⌐ 14	
Cb	5 🍂		**Cb**	5 🍂	
Dg	2/3/4		**Dg**	1/2/3	

TALENTS:

Abilities

Covered in Muck: This model counts as a Pig for the purposes of **Stampede**.

Hunter

Low Standards: This model may be hired by Gremlin-led Crews.

Scout

Stubborn: This model receives +2 **Wp** in Duels where it is the defender.

Weapon

Hunting Rifle: This Weapon's Damage Flips receive 🃏 against Beasts or Nightmares.

Actions

(+1) Reckless: This model may suffer 1 **Wd** to receive **Fast**.

(0) Give Her Some Slack: Increase "Git 'Em!"'s **Rg** to 3. This model's Hunting Rifle Attack Flips receive ⊟.

(0) Guide: (Ϫ)4. Friendly models gain **Scout**.

Triggers

Cb (🍂) Critical Strike [Hunting Rifle]

Cb (🍂🍂) Death Roll ["Git 'Em!"]: This Weapon's Damage Flip receives 🃏. End this model's activation if the flip inflicts Severe damage.

SPELLS:

(1) Shrug Off
(CC: 10 / Rst: - / Range: C) Discard one Token or end one effect on this model plus one effect or Token per 🍂 in the casting total.

(1) Wrangle Critter
(CC: 11🐗 / Rst: Wp / Rg: 8) Target non-Master model with the Beast, Pig, or Vermin Characteristic immediately performs a **(1)** Action or a **Charge** controlled by this model's Controller. The Action selected may not cause the model to be killed or sacrificed as part of the Action. This Spell may be cast once per activation.

People go missing in Malifaux all the time.

Near the Bayou's edge, when a body (kicking or not) needs disappearing, you visit McTavish. The desperate can find his "place" located on a spit of land which stabs out into the Bayou's murky waters. Little more than a shack, McTavish is quite happy to be left alone by, well, everyone. Only if his mood is right and a person has brought enough gin to satisfy him will McTavish grunt an agreement and help out with whatever skullduggery his visitor proposes.

When McTavish has disposing to do, he drags out a stained and scarred chopping block, setting it at the water's edge, humming tunelessly while he works. Gators are drawn to his humming; it sings to them of full bellies, calling them close until they are packed tight enough they can barely move. He feeds them the fruits of his labor, one unidentifiable chunk at a time.

The "kickin' ones" cost extra, McTavish will tell a visitor, expecting adequate payment for any additional labor involved. He typically demands his employer assist with the job, directing them with terse comments such as, "feet, get 'em," or "gimme 'at rifle."

Occasionally, one of McTavish's employers thinks they can get the better of the "rube from the swamps" and tries to stiff him on his payment, or make him disappear. So far, none have been as crafty as old McTavish but asking them will be difficult. People do, after all, go missing in Malifaux all the time.

SUE - MINION

He comes out of the setting sun, clothes as black as the night which follows, a six-string slung on his back. He walks slowly, but with a roll and a rhythm that eats up the miles. He finds the places where men and women gather, where the lights are low and the drink is cheap.

He tells them his name isn't his, that it's just one he found along the way. He tells them a man can be judged by the wrongs he's done, the people he's loved, and the price he's paid. A name, he says, won't let you judge the man.

He plays, and it is music they have heard before. A long time ago, when things were different, and they were not the people they've become. Music like the whistle of a train they've missed, an urgency of hope that's fading, drawing away and leaving them behind.

He plays, and they talk and drink and remember the wrongs they've done and the people they've loved. They remember the long and lonely trails they've walked, all leading back to the places where the lights are low and the drinks are cheap. And somewhere, they know, there's a train they should be on, but there's a price to pay and they're paying it.

He leaves, during the night, when everyone is sleeping and their dreams run low. Who did you love, asks the boy at the door, and what wrongs did you do? And the man in black picks up his six-string, pulls his hat low. "That don't matter no more," he says, "but this is the price I paid." He walks slowly, with a roll and a rhythm that eats up the miles, and he's gone.

30MM BASE

SOULSTONE COST: 7

MERCENARY, UNIQUE

WK/CG	HT	WP	CA	DF	WD
4/6	2	6	5📖	5	8

PISTOLS
RG	↗10
CB	5🟣
DG	2/3/4

TALENTS:

Abilities

Gunfighter

Hard to Kill

Lifer: This model is immune to Morale Duels caused by **Terrifying** effects.

The Man in Black: This model cannot be hired by Crews containing one or more models with the **Ruthless** and/or **Wicked** Abilities.

Weapon

Pistols: Paired.

Actions

(0) Disrupt Magic: ⚫6. Enemy models' Casting Flips receive ⊟ until the Start Closing Phase.

(1) Hurt: Inflict up to 3 **Wd** on Sue. Draw one Card for each **Wd** inflicted. This Action may be performed once per turn.

(1) Six-String Inspiration: ⚫5. Friendly models, including this model, receive +2 **Wp** during opposed Duels.

Triggers

Ca (📖📖) Rising Higher [Circle of Flames]: Increase the **Dg** Flip to 2/3/4.

Cb (🟣) Critical Strike [Pistols]

SPELLS:

(1) Circle of Flames
(CC: 15📖 / Rst: - / Rg: ⚫2) Models moving into or performing an Action within the ⚫ suffer a 1/2/3 Damage Flip which cannot be Cheated. Models suffering 1 or more **Wd** from the Ring of Fire also gain a Burning Token.

(1) Shrug Off
(CC: 10 / Rst: - / Range: C) Discard one Token or end one effect on this model plus one effect or Token per 🟣 in the casting total.

(1) Tread the Line
(CC: 13🟣 / Rst: - / Rg: ⚫8) Friendly models, including this model, gain "**Duty:** This model's Controller cannot be changed." Friendly models are immune to effects which restrict when they can activate during the turn. These effects on models within the ⚫ when this Spell is successfully cast immediately end.

Ten Thunders Brother - Minion

30MM BASE

SOULSTONE COST: 5

MERCENARY, TEN THUNDERS

WK/CG	HT	WP	CA	DF	WD
5/7	2	5	4	6	6

THE TEN WEAPONS OF WXU-SJU

RG	/// 2
CB	5
DG	1/3/5

TALENTS:

Abilities

Companion (Misaki, Ten Thunders)

Diversion: An enemy model engaged with two or more friendly Ten Thunders Brothers must discard one Control Card when declaring an **(0)** Action or the Action immediately ends.

Expert Defense: While this model is affected by **Defensive Stance**, increase the Defense Flip modifier by an additional ⚔ and reduce its **Wk/Cg** by only -1/-1.

Actions

(+1) Melee Expert

(2) Run Through: Push this model up to its **Cg**. This model may interrupt the Push to perform one The Ten Weapons of Wxu-Sju **Strike**. Continue the Push after resolving the **Strike**.

Triggers

Cb (🗡) Ten Thunders Strike [The Ten Weapons of Wxu-Sju]: When damaging defender with this Weapon, this model's Damage Flip receives ⚔ for each 🗡 in its attack Duel total.

Cb (⚔) Trip [The Ten Weapons of Wxu-Sju]: After inflicting damage on enemy defender, Place defender anywhere in base contact with this model. Defender receives **Slow**.

Df (📖) Bend as the Willow: After resolving an enemy melee or ranged attack, this model immediately gains the benefits of the **Defensive Stance** Action as if it had taken that Action.

SPELLS:

(0) Martial Artistry

(CC: 11⚔ / Rst: - / Rg: C) This model receives one of the following effects until the Start Closing Phase:

  Crab Style: This model receives **Hard to Wound 1**.
  Snake Style: This model's **Wp** and **Ca** Resist Flips receive ⚔.
  Tiger Style: This model gains **Terrifying → 11**.

Brothers in thought and action, the men who serve the Ten Thunders in Malifaux are disciplined warriors. All hail from the Three Kingdoms where life for those born without rank is a continual struggle, so they choose to throw in with a powerful criminal clan for brotherhood and money.

Expanding its empire into Malifaux, the Ten Thunders has brought its finest through the lesser breach they control. Trained in the martial arts from childhood, these hardened fighters have mastered the *Ten Weapons of Wxu-Sju*, each representing a distinct martial discipline, each a sacred weapon of the Ten Thunders clan. Brothers employ these weapons only on the orders of the clan, knowing full well to wield one without the clan's approval would bring dishonor that could only be redeemed by the wielder's death.

Brothers disguise their faces behind leering *oni* masks when operating under the clan's orders. Anonymity is as deadly a weapon in the Ten Thunders' arsenal as a *bisento* or *katana*. Doubt as to who does and does not serve the clan maintains a culture of fear among the locals. It also provides witnesses with no distinct features they can provide the authorities.

Disciplined, lethal, anonymous, the Brothers of the Ten Thunders clan strike out from their Katanaka Trading House headquarters, advancing their clan's interests in Malifaux much to the Guild's growing concern.

HODGEPODGE EFFIGY - MINION

Traditional practitioners of magic routinely tell the uninformed there are four conduits of focus through which one can control aether. Those who know better can name literally dozens of minor channels by which one can shape and control Malifaux's magical energies.

The Hodgepodge Effigy was born from these lesser energies, woven into being from several strands of aether and made stronger for it in the weaving. Unlike the other Effigies, Hodgepodge is not so closely linked to a major aetheric conduit that it is drawn solely to practitioners using that conduit. Its affinity is for magical misfits, those who tap into the aether knowingly but do so in unconventional ways. It has served gremlin kin, its misshapen body and erratic behaviors paralleling their strange cultural norms. It has also found purpose alongside such personalities as the Steampunk Necromancer, Leveticus, the latter's grasp of the breadth of aetheric diversity staggeringly complete for a human. Hodgepodge has been attracted briefly to the unique manner in which the Viktoria twins weave the aether into their martial dance. These individuals have, for their part, entertained the gibbering effigy's presence, feeling the tangles of Fate around them unravel and straighten while it is near. They choose not to question the Hodgepodge's involvement in their affairs, willing to accept it as one of Malifaux's many anomalies.

30MM BASE

SOULSTONE COST: 4

OBJECT 1, SPECIAL FORCES (DOLL), UNIQUE

WK/CG	HT	WP	CA	DF	WD
4/6	1	5	5	5 🐾	6

OVERSIZED KNIFE	
RG	〰 1
CB	5 ✗
DG	2/2/3

RANDOM GIBBERING	
RG	↰8
CB	5
DG	1/2/3

TALENTS:

Abilities

Aetheric Connection: One friendly model with the **Aetheric Connection** Ability within 6" of this model may activate after this model's activation ends.

Aetheric Demands: Non-Neverborn Crews hiring this model must nominate one leader per model with this Ability they hire. Those leaders cannot attach Totems.

Always a Chance: Jokers used by this model are shuffled back into its Controller's Fate Deck instead of being discarded.

Fate is Fickle: Draw one Card when another friendly model flips or uses the Black Joker.

Misfit: Crews led by Outcast models may hire this model ignoring any Abilities that would prevent it from being hired.

Other Allegiances [Neverborn]: This model may be hired by the indicated Faction's Crews at no additional cost.

Actions

(0) Foretell: Look at two random Cards in an opponent's Hand. If either of the Cards is the Black Joker, that opponent must discard both Cards. If either of the Cards is the Red Joker, that opponent draws one Card.

Triggers

Cb (✗) Mismatched Arms [Oversized Knife]: When declaring this Trigger, this model's Controller nominates one of the following effects per ✗ in its total. The indicated Weapon gains these effects until the end of the Action.

- Ignores **Armor.**
- Ignores **Hard to Kill.**
- Ignores **Hard to Wound.**
- **Magical.**

Df (⋈) "It Won't Stand Still!": If an attacker successfully hits this model, the attacker must discard one Control Card or suffer 1 **Wd** or the attack misses.

SPELLS:

(1) Keeping a Balance
(CC: 11▤ / Rst: - / Rg: C) This model's Controller searches his or her discard pile and shuffles all Jokers found back into the Deck. This Spell may be cast by the Hodgepodge Effigy once per turn.

Because I Could Not Stop For Death

Months ago – Early October

"It usually does this when I'm about to die," Leveticus had said, looking at the throbbing green light emanating from the large gem on his staff.

Alyce wasn't surprised by such a statement, nor was she terribly upset. Looking around, however, she said, "So what're you going to do about it? None of your hollow girls about that you dote over, and don't even think about trying to claim *me* when you die."

The orb continued to glow eerily below his face, casting shadows above his bushy brows and crooked nose. "No, dear. Not you. You're too precious to be discarded so, and your spirit is far too strong to be shunted aside by one such as mine. Besides, I'll be fine."

She was skeptical, he could see, as she regarded him coldly. "You'll be fine?" she asked, but it was more of an accusation.

He laughed, low and wheezy. "They couldn't kill me the first time. Not here. Don't think they could do it back Earthside, either, but I don't remember testing the theory." He smiled at her as if the reassurance was enough.

"Does anyone *ever* know what you're talking about?" she asked spitefully.

He shook his head, wondering if she deserved the leniency he always offered. He could never be angry with her, though. "I don't speak to many people, now do I?"

She rolled her eyes. "I wonder why."

He ignored her. Something had drawn him to this spot, and he felt the sense of urgency and anxiety mount. As the sun crested the horizon, spilling its pale light upon them, a bitter wind picked up, whistling at them as if trumpeting the dawn. It was biting, even for that time of year, and the dawn brought no warmth.

Surprisingly, Alyce offered no complaint. She stepped closer to Leveticus, eyes wide as she began to sense the dread he could already feel. "What's going on?" she asked in a whisper.

"I've been telling you. Trying to explain. Death is approaching."

"Death? Uh...should we leave?"

"We cannot run from this."

"You sure?" she asked, her voice rising. "I'm pretty sure we can try!" The feeling of desperation grew within them both. "Are we going to fight, at least?"

"I'm not sure we can."

"Maybe you can't run and maybe you're not going to fight, but I'm kinda sure I can do both." He loved her naïve innocence and foolhardy bravado. She readied her pistol, locking the firing gears in place.

The sun's light broke the shadows for only a moment before an unnatural darkness descended from the twisting boughs of the Hanging Tree looming above them. It was a shadow that moved like smoke or fog but was not blown by the wind that intensified around them.

Neither had heard the mysterious figure, riding a large white horse, approach from behind the great Tree, but its massive bulk and shoed hooves should have rung out upon the rocks and sticks around them. "Tyferal mogul muertano," it said from the depth of a shadow beneath its wide-brimmed hat. His voice was at once a coarse whisper but also resonant and booming, like thunder carried on the winds of a storm from far distant. Alyce spun quickly, her pistol leveled upon his narrow chest, but the Rider made no move in response. Leveticus turned slowly, the glow from his staff gently pulsing, as if in time with his slowly beating heart.

He glanced at Alyce and saw she was afraid but her gun was held firm, aiming it steadily at the Rider that looked like a man, but both knew immediately he was not. He was not alive, but he did not look like a paltry reanimated corpse such as a Resurrectionist might create, risen in parody of life.

The man atop the horse seemed very much alive. His clothing looked modern, his leather vest buttoned with the gold chain of a pocket watch dangling across his breast. Upon his other breast was fastened a Death Marshal's badge, and Leveticus, at least, knew he may once, recently, have been a living, breathing, warm-blooded Marshal for the Guild. Now he was Soulless. His face, exposed only in a narrow band above the blue bandana he wore around his lower face, was pale, but not the odd color of a risen cadaver that had the blood and necrotic fluids beneath the skin slowly decaying. This flesh still pumped blood. But the lack of the soul left it oddly insipid. Leveticus could feel that void left from the empty vessel that once contained the Marshal's soul. It drew in the brightly luminescent spiritual energy that flowed through the cemetery. That emptiness longed to be filled. Leveticus, alone aware of the imbalance and eternal struggle toward entropy, had come to see the desire for equilibrium sought by the loosened spirits of Malifaux.

The horse, too, looked unnatural with its stillness, as if it were half asleep. Its sides rose and fell with breath, but its sheen was off – the very hairs of its coat simply devoid of color and as pale as its Rider's skin. Its long mane was matted against its thickly muscled neck and protruding randomly about its skull. Down its back, close to the spine, were thick quills, long thorn-like spikes that erupted from its flesh.

The Rider spoke again, its voice like a whistling wind that carried the echo of distant thunder. Alyce had no idea what it was saying. "Do you understand it?" she asked Leveticus.

"No, my child. I haven't the faintest clue."

"He says you are the key," the high voice of a young girl said from behind Alyce.

Leveticus remained stoic, but Alyce, typically combat-ready and seasoned beyond her youth, jumped and spun to face the girl just behind the gravestone near her. "Jessica!" she said, recognizing one of the empty vessels Leveticus acquired and tethered like an anchor between this world and the luminous world beyond. Jessica shouldn't be here, both of them thought, but, as Alyce was about to ignore the girl and turn back to their formidable adversary, an even larger, more gruesome horse and Rider stood enshrouded in the deepening darkness beyond her, the feeble light of the morning sun glinting off armor patinaed with age. This horse stepped forward, the lingering flesh attached to exposed bone, leathery and long dead. As the dead hoof hit the ground, it pressed against a taut wire Alyce had set up earlier – just in case. It triggered a catch on a mechanism hidden behind a nearby tree that released a thick branch that had been pulled far back around the tree. Under such tension, the branch swung around with enough force to break a man's neck. It flew too fast for the Dead Rider to dodge and caught him full in the chest. He didn't move, and the branch hit him as though he were a well-mortared wall. He didn't even seem to notice, though it should have cracked his open ribs at the least. His skeletal hand brushed it aside where it shook behind him.

"He found me," the girl said, her voice as calm and flat as always.

"Yes, my dear," he said to the young lady he had prepared as a possible vessel, "I suspected as much." Leveticus always wondered why she had been changed over so much easier than the others, almost willingly giving up her spirit to his necromantic arts. She was already likened to death, and damnation, he realized. She was long ago destined to find him, though he had always thought she had been his discovery. All the while he thought about Jessica being a tool for a higher power, he never took his eyes from the Pale Rider that first approached them.

Alyce shot a nervous sideways glance at Leveticus. "You knew about this?" she exclaimed.

"Not exactly. Though I've been expecting something for a long time."

"Maybe you could have offered a bit of a warning?" and she took a step toward him.

His eyes still unmoving, he held out his mechanical hand, stopping her as he said, "I *have* been trying."

The Pale Rider spoke again in his breezy whisper, and Jessica translated automatically. "The Red Cage has fallen," she said in echo of the Rider. "It has torn a hole between this world and the next." Her voice flat and her face as emotionless as always. The Rider continued, "It was foretold. The end has come. You are the key."

Alyce's eyes widened as she stepped back, planning to escape beyond the Hanging Tree if it came to that. Never taking her eyes from the two Riders confronting

Leveticus, she did not know that a third stood silently behind *her*. As soon as she stepped against the muscular chest of the animal, she spun quickly to face the new threat, nearly tripping on a gravestone as she stumbled backward. She looked up into the dimly glowing red eyes of a monstrous creature that may once have been a horse but now looked much more like a walking nightmare. Like her, its body was a combination of metal, wires, gears, and pistons, held together with a little flesh. It snorted hotly upon her, and she staggered back. The Rider, though, did not acknowledge her, instead facing Leveticus. She could not see its face, obscured by a great hooded cowl surrounding the head, bathing it in deep, impenetrable darkness. The thick hood was attached to a tattered cloak that fluttered behind it in the wind, but billowing slower than it should have, as if it were out of step in time, and the Rider rested a sword upon his shoulder.

"The one that has crossed into the aether," Jessica droned on.

The massive sword of the Hooded Rider was easily as long as a full grown man, but its mass was not what startled her most. Where the tattered cloak billowed slowly behind it, the sword's metal reflected the sky and sun above. But the sunlight could not penetrate the darkness that had descended and enveloped them, and even more remarkable was the reflection, disjoint from time, reflecting the passing sun far too quickly as it arced on the gleaming surface in seconds rather than hours.

"You are the key," Jessica said. "The end is nigh. The dead have returned to this world. There will be pain. There will be suffering. We are awake as was foretold."

Leveticus studied the Pale Rider from beneath thick bushy eyebrows. He asked, "And me? What's my role in this?"

Jessica spoke as the Pale Rider said, "You will direct us." Then the Hooded Rider spoke, his voice like rocks grinding together, and Jessica said, "But first you must die."

So startlingly fast was his lunge forward that Alyce had no time to move at all and did nothing to protect him. His great sword, now abnormally reflecting the darkness of night as the blade slid easily through Leveticus and out the back of his torso. Leveticus looked down at the dark blade sinking through his stomach.

"Ah, dammit," he gurgled, and blood spat from his mouth. "I hate this part." The blade sank deeper, its width nearly severing him at the waist. The Hooded Rider jerked and the sword came free of Leveticus' body, which fell, dead, his blood flowing freely beneath the Hanging Tree. Its roots greedily drank the blood, drawing it into the soil as quickly as it poured from the great wound in his torso.

Alyce stood between the three and Leveticus, her pistol ringing.

With Jessica there, he'd have a few moments to fulfill the necromantic purpose he had conditioned her for. He could already feel that undeniable pull, drawing him inexorably toward that comfortable and eternal bliss where he would join the multitude of voices and thoughts of all those that had already found solace in the rainbow world of the aether. But he was not ready. Unlike so many that died before they were ready, Leveticus had determined the answers regarding life and death. As one that experienced the rapturous joy of that otherworld and renounced its lure, he alone mastered the return to the life he had left behind. He had first done so long ago. At that time, he had a vision that needed to be fulfilled and a girl he loved that needed his protection and guidance. Now, so many years later, most of his original schemes had been fulfilled or, he would admit, were forgotten. And the girl? As decades piled upon decades, he would also admit that perhaps she was gone, too, though he still tried to convince himself that she was still there with him, as pure and innocent and unharmed as always.

Time was distorted while he lingered between worlds. It stretched out in a patient crawl as he could perceive them, those in the world of the living, moving like lazy, languid sloths, ironically like ghostly apparitions from his point of view, though it was he who was the disembodied spirit.

He would need to move quickly if he were to save Alyce from the Riders. He saw Jessica's tether line; her soul pulled from her and stretched out from this world and into the aether. It was thin, fragile, and almost imperceptible, but he would grasp hold of it with his spirit, clutch tight as the great void of the aether dragged him into its warm embrace. Then, if he could maintain his wits, focus, and will, drag his way back, pulling his tired spirit out of that beautiful place hand over weak hand, back into the cold and dying world again, into the empty vessel of Jessica to live once more.

They moved so slowly, and he was so fast now, in death, but it would still be many moments later in their world before he could return. It would be a long, long time for him. And it would be excruciating.

As he latched onto that faint tether connected to the girl, he let go of his hold on the real world and his life, prepared to be consumed by the aether. As his spirit flew toward the pinhole tunnel, the gray fog image of the Hooded Rider swept around, pulling his sword from the remains of the body that was no longer of any use. It swung before Leveticus' spirit, still slowly, but his own spirit dragged to a halt just as it passed. The weapon, out there in the real world, should have had no effect on him or the shadows to which he now belonged, but it struck the transparent spiritual tether, pulling it in its wake. As the sword completed its arc, the tether had grown taut and dense. It quivered in space before him as he moved down its length, heading into the aethereal abyss, vibrating slower and slower as his spirit grew closer to the sword. Quick thoughts stretched into seconds which dragged into minutes.

The Rider's sword began to pull away, but Leveticus could do nothing save hold tight to the tether. If he released it, he would be gone forever, lost in the void.

He braced himself, trying to close his eyes though that was impossible in this place. Perception was not conducted through the traditional senses any longer.

The sword would not be drawn away quickly enough, and Leveticus struck it. As he did, the tether snapped, cut, impossibly, and the line flew toward the aethereal gulf, finally released.

He would be lost, he knew immediately, in the endless abyss. He was helpless to stop it this time and tried to think of a fond memory of his life, now about to be torn from him, finally. No fond thought came. Not even of the girl he so adored.

But his spirit, striking the massive weapon of the Hooded Rider that existed in both worlds at once, did not continue toward the aether. Instead, it was like he struck a solid barrier and bounced back with a jarring lurch. It was another impossibility that he added to the bewildering circumstances befalling him.

Panic mounted. No other tether lines were near him, none of his hollow vessels prepared to receive him, to give him life again, were close enough for him to latch onto. And he seemed stuck in that shadow place where images of the Riders, Alyce, and Jessica were wispy and dream-like visions. Lines and shapes of those in that realm, the real world of Malifaux, blurred and stretched, even shook in a vibration that made it difficult to perceive one object from another.

He had no heart to beat in pace with his growing anxiety, which only added to his feeling of separation and isolation.

When the face of a Rider leaned close to his disembodied apparition, coming into clarity and seeming to stare right at him, he wanted to scream or flee but could do neither. It was the cold clean face of the Pale Rider, he realized, staring at him with soulless eyes from that other world. The other two Riders came closer as well, and their features clarified as they regarded him. They spoke with one another in the alien language he did not know. He had thought, before, that it was an ancient Neverborn tongue, but now realized it was very different. They conferred with one another, and he was sure it was in judgment of him. Was this how his final judgment was to come, he wondered. By Riders of death sent to drag him to hell for what he had done?

He deserved it; that was certain.

The Pale Rider spoke to him, his voice terrible and commanding. A faint echo followed, carried from Jessica into this world like a daydream. He could not be certain of what she said but thought he understood her to say, "They must be punished. They have brought imbalance." Her voice was too weak, too far away, and too damned monotone for him to really understand. That was his fault, though, tearing her spirit out made her apathetic. She might have said, "You will lead us. To bring an end," but couldn't be sure.

"How?" he asked, meaning he couldn't currently do much at all.

"Go to her," the Rider said.

"Who?" he asked, but he knew already and did not like the answer.

"The one who commands life."

His spirit lurched, flying through that misty world without substance like a bullet, though he did not will it. In fact, he fought to stop the flight that brought him quickly to the bayou and the Hag — one of the few people that might deserve both death and damnation even more than himself.

There was no deceleration when he came to an abrupt halt. He had traversed many miles in the span of several moments and then simply stopped. The movement and sudden lack of it did not jar him physically, of course; the movement was merely perception for him, now, although his mind tried to translate what it might have expected or understood about movement, which added to the foreign experience.

His surroundings were still that jerky fog of shadow and mist blurred and blended with hints of images from the world of the living that existed just beyond his full comprehension. Still, he could see the vague shapes of the foliage, dense and vibrant and full of life. He could sense it even more acutely in this disjoint world between life and death. He was in the heart of the bayou.

Finding Zoraida would be nearly impossible, especially now, with his perception of her world so full of static and confusion. But his vision seemed to come slowly into focus, almost incrementally allowing him to see some of his surroundings if he remained still and calm. Before him, he was now certain, was her hut raised above the bog on thick poles, with vines snaking up and around them as if longing to reach the woman above. He could see the aura of life emanating from them like a faint green glow. The living had an aura that pulsed and throbbed, and he could see it, but only in his mind. It was very much like perceiving the power of a soulstone, he realized, and understood at once how logical that was. Only a rare few could perceive that power, even when holding one in their hands, much less understand how to draw the released power of a broken stone into their being, to fuse the power to their own spirit and harness it. Even when crushing the milky white stone in their hand, they'd feel little more than a quick shock as though it were the snap of static electricity. He could feel it all around him now. All the life energy enervated him, thrilled him, and called to him.

He understood that the problem with "looking" around him for visual clues was so confusing because he was trying to perceive things with human perception, eyes that he no longer had. Focusing on the power of the spiritual energy that surrounded living things allowed him to see much more clearly though, at first, it seemed very much like trying to read a book with his eyes crossed and confused him as he tried to refocus his vision.

To his left, just within his peripheral perception, near a mound of soft mud and dirt, the surface quickly frozen over by the snap of frost that had descended upon Malifaux, he saw the bright green glow of someone clearly infused with great life. No doubt, one still young and vibrant and full of that energy of youth. But no young human should be near Zoraida's hut, and a Neverborn would not emanate as a human because their life forces were measured much differently. He studied the glowing figure more intently, and the soft feature of a young woman slowly became clear. She was beautiful, too, he was pleased to see. Further pleasing was her noticeable lack of attire, even in such frosty cold. Mere rags covered her upper body and around her shapely hips, leaving so much of her bare flesh for his thirsty eyes to explore. She was held aloft, nearly a foot above the ground, by the throbbing green glow of life that both emanated from her and was drawn to her from the bayou, itself. Her head was thrown back and her soft arms were outstretched and back, calling his attention to her every womanly curve.

"Heh," he spoke. "Even in death I've time for a beauty like this," and he chuckled, finding amusement even in his own lecherous attitude.

In his disembodied state he did not believe he could be heard nor seen, but the girl's head snapped forward toward him, and her eyes popped open, glowing brightly with the same pulsing energy that enveloped her. When she spoke, her voice resonated, infused by that power. "And you haven't changed a bit, old man," she said, which caused him to start.

Still having no control over his movement, he didn't realize that he floated away from her, scrambling back, as it were.

How did she see him? Hear him? Recognize him?

She smiled sinisterly, still staring at him with glowing eyes.

"Who? Who are you?" he asked.

She laughed, loud and hearty, and her voice was deep and sultry. He tried not to notice how intoxicating she was. Her hair was pulled up tightly and wound on her head in a bun, clearly to get the thick black locks out of her way although stray strands fell about her round cheeks. The insects, amphibians, and small bayou reptiles moving around below her finally made him realize: this was Zoraida.

"I don't understand," he spoke, baffled at her youth and, now he hesitated to think it, her great beauty.

"He said you would come," the young Zoraida said.

"Who?" Leveticus was growing exasperated. His mind was fatigued, and he had gone through such a bevy of emotions in such a short time that he was frankly no longer used to experiencing. He just wanted answers. "Who?" he demanded, no longer concerned at all about *how* he spoke, much less how she could hear him.

"The Hooded Rider."

"You understand them?"

"No. But 'Leveticus' translated well enough. I guessed they'd be bringing you here kicking and screaming."

"I would have come along on my own."

She laughed again. "I see they had other plans for you. Stripped you of your ugly parts," she said, meaning his mechanical limbs and organs that she found so repulsive. "Just the raw man." She laughed again, warm and thick, but he recognized the familiar intonation of each note and how it would eventually grow dry and shrill, becoming the cackle of the old woman.

"Very raw. Why is this happening?"

"Oh, how the tables have turned! Now it is Leveticus asking *me* for answers! How delicious. How thrilling. I'm more surprised you didn't recognize me. Isn't this the memory you have of me? How you found me so long ago?"

"No. I've forgotten. Forgotten all about you."

"Lies. Like I said: you haven't changed at all."

"Just tell me what's happening!" he snapped. The glow of her eyes slowly subsided, returning to the deep, dark brown that regarded him with far more warmth than she genuinely felt toward him. "And no lies from you, either. No manipulation. Just the truth."

"Ah," she said, sneering at him as she floated closer, her toes dangling below her. He pushed the inviting image of her ankles, calves, and thighs from his mind, chastising himself for being so distracted by her. It was very difficult. "Truth is but perception. Manipulation is just encouraging another to make the decision they already want to make. Free will."

The Riders were coming, he knew. He could hear them, or feel them – *perceive* them, at least, galloping toward them.

"Perhaps they've given you to me, like this, knowing that *your* spirit is still very strong, filled with the lingering power of the aether that you've waded through time and time again. But you're powerless to defend yourself against me. Imagine how easily I could take you in, twist you into my spirit, absorb you like a soulstone. Wouldn't you give quite a rush?" He knew she wasn't lying. She could do that. Any who had mastered soulstone use could do that to him now. He couldn't get away. He still could not control his movement and merely hovered in place futilely, hoping desperately that she wouldn't do it. Being absorbed into her spirit, to be consumed by her, was loathsome despite the allure her new body presented. She said with a grimace, "But absorbing you into my spirit sounds fairly loathsome though you do look a bit more inviting without all the mechanika." It was an odd reflection of his own thoughts and he wondered if she could read his mind like she could read the cards.

"I believe I'm meant to teach you what I've learned," she continued, "though I'm unsure of your role in this."

"They said I'm supposed to lead them. To bring about an end. To punish those responsible for the imbalance." His words stripped the smile from her face and seemed to genuinely shock her.

"Perhaps so," she said at last. "Perhaps that is what this is about after all."

"I don't think we can stop them. Not willingly. 'Free will,' you had said. Funny that one such as you, us, in fact, might still believe in free will. Fate rules our every action."

She continued his thought, "And evoking our free will, twisting fate, that has led to this, the end we must face. The end we must bring about."

"What are you supposed to teach me?"

She smiled again as the three Riders found them, two glowing spirits facing one another in the cold bayou. "I'm not sure what they hoped I would teach you. But, I intend to learn how to stop a Tyrant Entity."

"I did not think that was possible. You tried to do that to December with the girl and her sword. It failed. In fact, I think it only pissed Him off."

Zoraida nodded, not even trying to defend herself against the accusation of failure. "I said 'stopped'. I no longer think they can be killed. Not like we think of death. Actually, now it makes sense, your part in this. They are like you."

"What? Me? How?"

She regarded him coldly, accusing him of something with judgmental eyes. "Yes," she said, her eyes squinting, her lips pursed. "Like you. They are not physical. Not any longer. Not even when they take physical form like December did at Kythera or the Plagued did just months ago. They draw their power from the aether and from us, like we draw it from the stones." She looked away from him, thinking, and then spoke more to herself. "Is that what happened to this world? They devoured it, spirit by spirit?" She seemed to jump, her eyes growing wide. She looked to her hands and down her body at the glowing spiritual energy she drew from the bayou, feeding upon its energy, consuming it and twisting it into her being. She bowed her head as if ashamed at her new understanding. She turned back to him, angry, but at herself. "They're like us. Like us all. Feeding off of the power without regard for our actions. It's no wonder we will pay." She looked at the Riders and their unnatural mounts beyond the floating apparition of Leveticus. "But I don't intend to go without a fight. I don't intend to pay more than I must." She turned back to Leveticus. "Soulstones are easy," she said. "You hold them, break them, release the spiritual energy they contain, and absorb it. But *you*, more than any other, know this isn't the source of greatest power."

"The aether," he spoke.

She nodded. "The aether."

"It was torn. The fabric separating it from this world and from Earth. Its power spills into this place. But for the Tyrants. It fuels them because this world has grown so barren. There is not enough to feed the appetites of the Tyrants. They need the power of the aether to give them strength. So that they might ascend. Become independent of life and the world of the living, but not lost – absorbed by the multitude in the aether. To resist it, feed on it, rule that place."

"But they aren't the only ones that can use that power. We learned to use soulstones," she said with a smile. "We can use this, too. To siphon it from the world even as it gets absorbed into the fabric of this world."

"But they're using it already. I feel it. And they know how to use it already."

"True. But we're linked to them even if we don't know it. They choose us. Use us. Like we often create or summon totems that allow us to harness our power through them."

"I don't. I'm not a fool."

She regarded him again. "No, you don't, do you? Never a totem like the rest of us. Is that why you were chosen, I wonder? Connected to life and death but never the compulsion to link with a manifestation of your own spirituality? Has no Tyrant found you, drawing from you your power, I wonder? We can leech the power not just from the world being flooded by that spiritual energy; we can take it from *them*, harness it. Just as they hope to leech from us and consume us, to walk among the living by subjugating our bodies and minds as their own."

"You think we can learn to do this?"

She motioned toward her own body which he was all too willing to look at. He wondered briefly why she wasn't cold. She sure wasn't wearing much.

"Why did you make yourself young? Never mind *how* you did it."

"I needed to revert to an earlier time when I had different mastery over Fate. Before the threads became too entangled. When I could see the fabric more clearly. I didn't actually set out to become young."

"Fine. We gather more aetheric power than we've ever harnessed at once. And then what? Once we learn how to do this we fight the Tyrants? Teach all the others how to do this?"

"I don't know. Let's begin by learning how to manifest this power and become something even greater. See if we can master this."

"Something's in this for you. There's always something you're plotting."

"Yes, always something."

He would listen to her, see if he could absorb the aether flooding the world since the event. More than anyone, he knew of it. Now, disembodied, just a spirit himself locked in the world of the living, he could see the pools of aether coalescing around them. Around all things. Longing to be part of that great collective voice they were now separated from.

The Bigger They Are

December 21
Minutes Before the Winter Solstice

Rasputina knelt at the edge of the cliff, near the spot where Joss had climbed and also where she had kicked him off to die of blood loss or exposure. She could have killed Joss, of course, just as she killed the priests. Certainly she had no qualms about killing. Not anymore. Part of her wondered why she didn't. She tortured him and left him at the edge of death but stopped there. But she knew Mara would defy her, would save him. Why did she let that happen, she wondered then and many times since.

Perhaps she tested herself. To see if she could stop. To see if she were still in control.

There were more priests down in the temple she planned to educate. Men who used their combined might to subjugate the women drawn to December's call, just as she was. It could have been her, she knew, that fell victim to their misguided attempt at keeping the mighty Tyrant December from fulfilling His ancient machinations. It was a lie they all told themselves, selling it so fervently that they came to believe it themselves. She wondered what might have been accomplished if they'd chosen to guide the girls, taught them to use their formidable power to stand against December, together.

She knelt with her bare knees buried in the snow. The Silent Ones and acolytes believed she was meditating. It had been many days since she had eaten. The only water they could give her froze as it touched her lips, yet still they pressed the frozen slivers into her mouth, hoping it would be enough. Her skin had grown more pale, more cold in touch and appearance. Her fur cloak billowed gently behind her, leaving the bare skin of her shoulders exposed. It didn't matter. Cold no longer affected her. It hadn't for quite some time. Frozen veins, twisting tendrils of blue lines just below her skin, snaked out from the edge of her bodice below her chest and up to her neck. They were faint, beneath the skin, but growing more visible every day.

One of the lesser priests came out of the depth of the shadows from within the cave. He was terrified and slinked along the wall, hoping to go unnoticed. One of the two Silent Ones attending Rasputina jerked upright, prepared to fight. The expression on her face and in her posture conveyed her intent. She was not as defiant nor as trained as Mara, but she had grown much more confident in the recent months since Rasputina had come to deliver them. He shrank back into the cave. The Silent One recognized him as he poked his head from the darkness. He was on Rasputina's list, though not a priority as some were. He probably guessed as much, hiding deep in the bowels of the mountain, in some unused and forgotten chamber. They would have found him when Rasputina called for him. Now, he surfaced, hearing rumors that perhaps Rasputina had left the conclave since she hadn't called for another priest in days.

At least a few other priests had made a run for it and might have made it out alive.

The Silent One moved to confront him, to send him scurrying back into the heart of the mountain to await his turn before Rasputina. The hand of the other woman in attendance touched her upper arm, stopping her. The second motioned for her to wait. The Silent Ones had learned to communicate with one another very quickly, and almost imperceptible facial gestures allowed her to convey her thoughts immediately. The first girl slowly nodded in apprehensive agreement and, still angry, motioned for the priest to come out. The second pointed toward the other side of Rasputina – the cliff face that would drop to the path some twenty feet below.

He watched them from within, no doubt gauging their strength against his own. He also wondered if it was a trick Rasputina was playing and she'd spring to life when he wasn't expecting it. He nearly gave in to his fears of a painful death, almost returning to his hiding place beneath the mountain. But that would lead to his inevitable death, and he knew it. Hesitantly, he stepped into the light. He squinted and blinked, shielded his eyes against the glare from the snow and ice. Although the swirling mass of clouds above was dark, he had not been out of the shadows since September. When *she* had arrived.

The Silent One, with a cold and distant expression, pointed toward the cliff edge again. In desperation, he had surfaced with the hope of escape, and now that the girls commanded him to leave, to banish him, he hesitated once more and looked back. The Cult of December had inhabited the ancient caverns here for just over a year. But the sensation of dread stayed his footsteps. He longed for the comfort of the conclave, of the group dedicated to December. But more, he hated to admit, of the promise of power that had been dangled before him. It was gone. She had stripped them of their power and position. Even as the higher priests moved to silence her she had acted, freezing them in ice, though the lower chambers were dry. It was as if she had been warned of them. And they had celebrated her coming – it was a portent of the power amassing around them. Lost, alone, and near death after her escape at Kythera, she should not have been able to traverse the twisting path up the mountain. Yet she had. Alone and without a guide and without even knowing of the hidden temple.

Just her and the strange furry pet she called her Wendigo. Of course the skittish beast had fled as she had fallen exhausted in the very spot she now knelt.

Mere months ago he had thought they would control December by controlling her. Their power and illusion of dominion were dispelled within hours of her waking on that fateful day of deliverance.

He approached apprehensively. Either of the Silent Ones could dispatch him rather effortlessly without the other priests to fuel him with their arcane mastery. They clearly knew this and stood fearless.

The temperature plunged with each step toward Rasputina and the ledge. Also, unlike the Silent Ones, he had no natural protection against the cold and pulled his thick bearskin parka around his torso and face. He passed Rasputina without looking at her. At the edge, the wind raged violently just beyond him, and he could feel its unnatural force buffeting his fur-lined boots. It drew all heat from his toes, and he knew that a deeper cold awaited him below.

He turned back once more to the temple entrance, still reluctant to leave. As he turned, Rasputina's eyes snapped open and fixed on him without lifting her head. She made no move to attack him, but rumors of her unspeakable methods of torture were enough to terrify him beyond reason. Hesitating no longer, he plunged into the gale beyond the ledge. It was instantly numbing, and the power of the wind threw him against the jagged rocks. As despair set in with the realization he could not survive the rage of this unnatural force, he hoped he would succumb to it quicker, more gently than his death at her unmerciful hands.

Acolytes had said she was in a trance for those days she knelt beneath the fierce dark eye of the storm, that she wasn't even aware of them any longer. That wasn't true, although she did slip in and out of perception as others might understand it. She spoke to Him, to December. She taunted him, threatened him. 'You are weak,' she had repeated over and over. 'I have grown strong.'

YOU ARE NOTHING TO ONE SUCH AS I.

'Lies. You know I know you now. You promise an end to the hunger. Gorging until we are sated. I have fed on the weak without you. I have consumed their inner spark, more filling than a soulstone. I have felt you there, hungry, wanting to feed on them yourself. But I wouldn't let you.'

I TAKE WHAT I WANT.

'Then take me. If you can,' she taunted. 'You scoffed at the Plagued, said He was impatient and that was His undoing. That you knew the path to ascension. You were afraid I'd know the truth, and I do. His failed ascension did not leave the way open for you, but for me. It freed me. The power of the Event fed me, and I gorged upon it.'

That's when she had opened her eyes and looked upon the priest at the edge of the rock wall.

'You're hungry for it. Thirsty,' she said as the Priest dove into the howling wind below. 'You smell his spirit and have starved in your weakness. It wasn't the Plagued whose impatience was His undoing. It was yours.'

FEED UPON THEM. WHEN I CONSUME YOU, THEY WILL BE MINE. I WILL LEAVE NOTHING OF YOU BUT A SHELL.

She ignored him. 'You were impatient at Kythera. Taking a form used all the energy you had absorbed this last century. But they closed the Breach and left you desperate for more. Aching. They opened it again and fed you those spirits. You were a fool. You were afraid they'd shut it again, weren't you? You became the Wendigo, and they nearly undid you.'

IT DID NOTHING.

'But that was not the end of your mistakes. You were already in my head. Telling me lies. Making me weak. But I wasn't weak, and you knew that, too.' She awaited his response as she thought of the image of the little girl that lingered always in the back of her mind, always tormenting her. He said nothing. 'You attacked me. Thought to subjugate me. To walk again in my body since the Wendigo was severed from you. But you were weak!' she suddenly howled in her mind.

I WALK AGAIN NOW. I AM THE WENDIGO. He spoke as calmly as ever, just a whisper on the wind, but she heard the fear that he desperately tried to hide.

She spoke no longer in her mind, but screamed out loud, "The Wendigo, Storm? He is but a pale reflection of the power I expected! He obeys Snow as you will obey me!"

He said nothing, but she felt him recoil at her dismissal of the massive brute that walked among them.

She stood, controlling her fear and anger. Calling forth the spiritual power she had been feeding on for those months, she turned to a Silent One who shared her anxiety but was ready to fight. Rasputina said, "Go below. Gather our Sisters. The Acolytes and Priests, too, if they can be found. Let them know that they have nothing more to fear from me." The girl moved quickly, at a run, but Rasputina halted her, saying, "There is no need of haste. December does not come for me. I'm going after Him." The Silent One's eyes were wide, but she nodded. Rasputina's strength and confidence thrilled her. Rasputina turned to the other girl. "Bring Snow here. Be ready. We may need to slay the Wendigo Storm if December does not give in to me quietly." Her teeth clenched, and she growled, "You and our Sisters will indulge upon his flesh. We will quench our great thirst with His spirit. It will be a feast unlike any you have imagined." She spoke more for December to hear. She hoped her actions could match her bravado. But she could wait no longer. She was filled with the spiritual energy of the priests, which gave her the understanding of how to use the power spilling into this world from the puncture of the Event. She must be careful though because December would continue feeding and gathering his strength.

She watched as the Silent One ran across the ledge and around an outcropping of large rocks to retrieve Snow and Storm. It was a mistake on her part to send both girls off at once. The moment the girl was out of sight, December struck with the full fury of a Tyrant determined to see His ancient plans fulfilled. The large swirling mass of dark clouds that had spiraled above the mountain since his physical dispatch at the Masamune of Viktoria in the ruins of Kythera suddenly unleashed its pent up fury. A thick column of blinding blue energy erupted from down upon her from its center. Wind and lightning and the very air froze as the fury crashed into her, driving her into the ground with enough force to shake the temple below. She felt her bones break as the pressure lacerated her shoulders and cheeks in long blue lines.

She couldn't breathe as the pillar of energy burned through her chest. He was far stronger than she might have imagined. Underestimating the power of a Tyrant such as December would be a mistake she could not overcome.

Pain rippled through her body in waves. The weight upon her chest prevented any hope of breath, and the bright blue energy raining down was constant and strong, showing no sign of faltering until long after she had succumbed to suffocation. He was filling her with his own great and invasive spirit. Deep into her chest he poured, fusing his spirit to hers.

Any normal person would not resist as she did; it was futile in the face of one so powerful. But Rasputina was strong. She had felt his vile spirit and knew the loathsome presence. She knew how he would try to consume her, twisting her spirit into his own.

She understood starvation and thirst, too. But where that might weaken others, she knew it made her stronger.

As He pummeled her with His ancient will, she realized something else. He had waited for her attending Silent Ones to depart before attacking. When He had last attacked her, months earlier, she had used the gathered power of the Event to push Him aside at the last moment, driving Him into Snow, a girl possibly equal in power to her, but silenced by the Priests of December. Had He fully embraced Snow as his vessel, He would never have ascended, never have grown at all. But, releasing His own infused will after the Event, He manifested once again as the Wendigo Storm, hoping that He could control both it and the invigorated Snow. He was wrong. They were powerful incarnations of Him, but they demonstrated his weakened state. Storm was as inferior to Him as Snow was to her.

She recognized His fear as He saw her thoughts. It was foreign at first, different than the fear of a human. He was so confident and proud but too anxious, and that anxiety gave her hope.

The wind was greater than a hurricane and roared deafeningly against them.

Unable to breathe, hardly able to concentrate, her arcane will was more emotional than intellectual, and Rasputina was consumed by rage and hatred. She didn't try to stop his assault but redirected the energy pouring into her chest, turning it into a mighty and massive pillar of ice. As it bore down upon her, its colossal weight would have crushed her, killing her instantly she knew. But she felt December pull it aside at the last moment. She was not shocked. As she guessed, he could not let her die. Too much of him had been invested in her and bending her to accept his great being. The pillar crashed like a cannon blast near her, sending shards of ice into her side. She gasped quickly for air since the weight of the torrent was momentarily diverted, but he redoubled the raging wind.

She was dizzy from asphyxiation but used what she had to twist that energy as it came at her, drawing it around herself. She made it hers for a moment and created more ice, but a quickly forming column that lifted her from the ground. When December took his driving force back from her, to lash into her, he could not hit her directly now, and she pushed at it with her mind, attempting to deflect it as she had done months before. But he was too strong. The ice sheath and oblique angle helped stave off the full brunt of his assault, but it would not save her. The spiritual well within her was brimming with power of her own, accumulated and stored like no other in Malifaux had learned to do. She couldn't focus as well as she would like but compensated with an outpouring of hatred and defiance that directed her counter-assault. Such power had never flowed through any human, and the lashing blast of energy was directed at December's attack, breaking the coursing energy into tendrils. But her collected power, vast as it was, paled in comparison to December's. Even weakened after his body fell at Kythera and weakened again when she redirected his consuming will into Snow, he was still many times more powerful than she could comprehend.

Her own small lashing tendrils of power dissipated and the washing column of wind and sleet and crackling energy redoubled against her, slicing through her flesh. She was numb to the physical pain and only instinctively struggled to catch her breath, gasping as her head was knocked around in the gale.

The Silent Ones had joined her struggle, but she did not know it. Acolytes, too, were beside her, hurling harpoons ineffectually into December's manifestations. Two priests also joined her, adding their spiritual power and arcane understanding to Rasputina in the trance-like ritual that made them collectively so formidable. Even with them sustaining her, December's assault continued undaunted.

A Silent One saw Rasputina struggle for breath, eyes rolling into her head as it lolled back and forth. The Silent One leapt into the torrent and pulled the attack into herself, dragging the beam of energy from Rasputina. December pulled the attack from the brave young girl, but the priests understood what she had done and refocused their combined will against it, holding it against the girl for an additional second before December could wrest it from her and drive it back into Rasputina. As the power of December ravaged the girl's mind, she flailed on the ice, struggling against the pain that wracked her. Where Rasputina had withstood his assault for minutes, it took only seconds to break this weaker vessel, and the mind of the Silent One disappeared beneath the monumental weight of an ancient Tyrant.

Her body stretched and twisted. Her arms and legs grew long and reshaped to those more of a wolf than of the woman she was. Her fingernails, very much like claws, thickened and blackened into true sharp talons protruding from her flesh. Her face, once beautiful, became elongated and fanged. She lay there, panting from the wracking change that had ravaged her and consumed her. December's attention had already shifted back to Rasputina. The Silent One was blessed with His presence, but He had discarded her as mere nuisance.

Rasputina had only a few seconds to catch her breath. In that small window, she understood how easily this victory would be for Him. He would not kill her, could not, but He would suffocate her and break her ribs until she fell unconscious. Once unconscious, He would deliver himself unimpeded into her, bridging the divide between what He was and what He would be. To truly live again through her would mark the end of the world – He would devour it all.

Storm and Snow were there. Snow was deep in meditative thought, more like Rasputina than any of the others. Arms outstretched, fingers like talons toward the ground, she fought against the gale pummeling Rasputina. The shards of ice within December's attack tore through her flesh, and she gasped at each deep cut, making it more and more difficult to hold her breath. Rasputina pulled ice from the ground in a sudden jerk of her arms, in mounting desperation. The ice formed thick around her body and up over her head in a protective sheath. A small chamber within the ice allowed a few quick breaths. Her head fell weak against the ice as she gathered her strength and steeled her will. December's fury raked long gouges out of her ice encasement, quickly eroding it before Rasputina was ready. Within seconds, it would leave her exposed once more. She braced herself, but there was little she could do to stop it. It grew more and more obvious that their struggle against December was truly futile. She lifted her encased arm, and the ice around it followed her movement. She shielded her face with the armor of her forearm against the onslaught.

Unexpectedly, Storm pounced forward, long black talons gleaming in the blinding light of the unleashed energy, tearing huge chunks of ice to reach Rasputina. Rasputina turned in surprise, and the Wendigo howled, its voice long and rumbling. Its eyes flashed with the same blinding blue energy that beat down upon her, now bathing her in its brilliance. As it stared at her, its howl sustained, Rasputina gasped and clutched at her chest in pain that struck her more violently than any she had yet felt. Before the eyes of the acolytes and Silent Ones, her body suddenly changed. Her limbs elongated explosively, and her face, too, narrowed and stretched. Hair thickened and grew upon her back, all very much like the Silent One that had been briefly touched by December's vast mind and changed by Him.

Her will was suppressed by a feral need to feed, an uncontrollable instinct. Weakened already, and exhausted in body and mind, Rasputina was losing herself, consumed by the greater ocean of thought that was December. She was becoming the Wendigo, herself – a creature that harnessed the incomprehensible power of an ancient Tyrant. She would walk and feed like a creature never sated, devouring everything.

It was another surprise when the thick harpoon head of one of the acolyte's weapons burst from Storm's midsection, near his side, startling it. The howling caught in his throat, and Rasputina, still changing, fell against the remaining ice of her protective shell, clinging to the last remnants of her self. The harpoon was not nearly enough to fell the beast, but it was Snow that leapt upon the thick harpoon shaft protruding from its back, and jumped to the back of its head, holding herself there by a large clump of its fur. In her other hand, she lifted a long dagger, carved from some mineral found in the heart of the mountain devoted to December. It was ceremonial, but strong and sharp. The blade descended, and Snow drove it through the side of Storm's throat. Storm gurgled and recoiled in shock, the glow of its eyes dissipating as the howl rumbled away. She hadn't hesitated and showed no regret at killing the beast that was part of her own psyche. She thrust the blade outward, severing the rest of its throat and its dark blue blood trailed the dagger. As it fell lifelessly to the ice, Snow stepped off of its back and stood defiantly near Rasputina as she fought to revert to her natural form. Cold tears froze to the side of her eyes at the terrible sacrifice of Storm.

Rasputina's and Snow's eyes met, each filled with determination and hatred of the Tyrant. They understood one another better than any other around them might. But both knew the end was quickly approaching, and they were feeble obstacles still struggling against a hopeless fight.

They readied themselves for the end. Their final struggle against December.

Storm's howl was silenced, but December roared on around them.

Rasputina loathed Him. Despised the thought of Him consuming her mind and spirit. Loathed the idea of watching His actions from beyond a mental barrier of ice that would forever keep her from living again.

She thought of what he had said to her just those few months earlier when she had first come to the temple. When he had first pushed his mind and will against hers. He had said of the Plagued, "He does not have my piece of the key." She never knew what he meant. Never knew what key he needed. But, in the cloud of her memory, she remembered he had also said, "You must be protected." She never understood that, either, but assumed she had some artifact yet to find, like the

Plagued had the box, or the serpent ring that December had shown her in her mind. But she had no item of any physical consequence and refused to hold any of the ceremonial items from the temple like the dagger Snow used to fell Storm.

The last of the ice was torn away from the front of her, and she was again fully exposed to the blinding and terrifying might of December as he struck her chest, tearing into her, consuming her anew.

Even knowing its futility, those around her were determined to continue fighting, and even die, to stop December's rise, and they renewed their counter-attack.

The blue veins that snaked through her upper chest and throat pulsed brightly as her veins pumped the glowing icy fluid that was His blood. Hers had frozen many months ago. His blood coursed through her, changing her into the monster that could house his mind, merely a tool for him.

And realization struck even as her mind withered beneath His.

The key was not some artifact that might free him like other Tyrants needed. She was the key! More specifically, she realized, it was not exactly her, but her frozen heart. It held her spirit like a cold, living soulstone. It was the vessel December poured his form into. She felt it throbbing, pumping the frozen essence throughout her wounded and broken body.

Within her, she understood his predictions were playing out. He fed off the great power she had been consuming herself these past months.

Weak, exhausted, even moments from suffocating, she confronted Him within her mind.

'I will never be yours,' she snarled.

I TAKE WHAT I WANT.

Aloud she screamed, "Never! You will not have me!"

She harnessed those spirits within her, focusing one final strike at December. December saw it and might have laughed at her ineffectual efforts. She was no danger. Rasputina though, knew that attacking December was wasted effort, He had no physical form to injure. So she drove her power deep within her frozen heart, which accepted the power, as it was meant to. Her last act was a defiant scream, "Never!" against the invading presence. She released the totality of the spiritual force within her, erupting the frozen vessel in an explosion that blasted from her chest. Shards of diamond-hard crystals tore out her chest and back. Several of the Silent Ones were caught in the explosive force and were thrown back, dead. Others were struck by the shrapnel and spun away from the impact.

As the sound of the blast echoed around the mountainside, the cascading violence of December's will blinked out of existence. The silence was instant and terrifying. Her followers watched her, standing for a second with her chest torn open. She fell slowly to her knees, and the darkness that had loomed above them for so many months since Kythera broke. Thin patches of pale sun bathed the icy ledge.

Her defiant "never" echoed back from the surrounding mountains as she collapsed, face down on the ice.

From the Red Egg Rises the Bird of Paradise

December 21

Not far from where she stood, the darkly swirling mass of clouds that had loomed for half a year above a tall mountain in the distance flashed with a bright blue light. Even at this distance the light was blinding, and she had to shield her eyes from the brilliance. She had no time to wonder what it was. Seconds later, however, the frigid air around her was sucked toward the light. It was so sudden and strong that it momentarily knocked her off balance. As the wind subsided, the air left behind was temperate and calm. Looking once more at the light upon that mountainside, she saw the snow that had been dancing on the wind drawn from every side into that dark cloud.

It was an omen, she knew; a portent of something horrible that was about to befall her, possibly all of those in Malifaux. "That can't be good," she muttered.

Sonnia found the cave entrance easily enough with the ancient glyphs that she could now decipher almost automatically. Of course, many of the images had been befouled by that bastard Seamus. As Hopkins had relayed, there were quite a few lewd images as well as equally offensive limericks and rhymes. Hopkins may have sought to keep the images from her as he still maintained society's notions of propriety. She smiled at his chivalry, though she hardly acknowledged the graffiti save the irritation of not being able to see the true symbols correctly. Samael had dutifully recorded as many images as he could for her interpretation, but now, studying the wall illuminated by a small orb of flame she held aloft, she found several more images in shadowed recesses that offered even more information to her understanding of what was about to befall them. Those new signs and symbols disheartened her further, though they merely reinforced what she had already come to expect.

Still, it was difficult for her to proceed, knowing that deep beneath the surface Cherufe waited, an ancient Tyrant so feared that It was imprisoned in the spirit cage by Its own peers.

Sonnia found the entrance to the subterranean labyrinth. Lava flowed openly in a deep channel, more than a dozen feet below her. The heat was intense, especially given her acclimation to the severe cold that had enveloped all of Malifaux since the cage had fallen.

No one understood what that cage contained, not even the native Neverborn, some of which were partially responsible for entrapping Cherufe. Sonnia knew. She had searched obsessively for ancient books recording Its destructive deeds, written by the ancient Neverborn that fought against It and the other Tyrants as they devoured this world, its inhabitants, and themselves. They raced toward ascension – to abandon the last vestiges of their mortality. Those ancient texts were written over the span of many centuries, by those just wanting to survive across this world. But, even as their world fell beneath the weight of that monumental conflict, those texts migrated here, inevitably toward Malifaux, where they were lost in forgotten temples and ruins near the city.

She was drawn to the books. And the words therein were as familiar to her as they were alien. More than once she had thrust a newly discovered book away as she looked through it, certain she had read it before. And though the words were written in a language no longer known even to the Neverborn, she seemed to instinctively know what they said.

Once, while perusing a small, seemingly unremarkable book, she had dropped it and staggered back, knocking a full stack aside as she stumbled. Samael had been there, concerned, but she had assured him it was merely fatigue. The truth that she never spoke of, never even allowed herself to think again, was that the book was *so* familiar to her that it was as if she had written it herself. She knew each page before turning to see it. From her surprise, she purged the book in flame. It was the first, but only the first of many times, she unearthed a tome that spoke to her with such familiarity. It became so frequently disconcerting that she had come to expect that dreaded sense of knowing with each new written discovery. It wasn't merely the books, either. She was frequently drawn to some remote ruins in the bayou, overgrown with vines to the extent that it was otherwise undiscoverable. Or, some building now buried in the badlands beneath a makeshift mining boomtown. She'd go there on a 'hunch' and remarkably find the one missing piece to a puzzle she didn't even know she was working out.

Like this cave.

She stood in the center of the narrow chamber. Stalactites stretched from the ceiling, no more than eight feet above her, to the uneven and rocky floor below.

How Seamus was connected to it all she could never fully understand. Like her, he had a strange affinity for these places, leaving his mark more than once for her to find. Samael knew he was pursuing the same written works as Criid, but he did not fully understand the degree to which Seamus, too, was drawn. Usually a step ahead of her, too, which perplexed her to no end. His befouling the wall with limericks and graffiti were taunts for her, and she knew it. It was merely a game for Seamus, and, now that she descended into the narrow passages below, she realized that she had come to anticipate the game, to enjoy it on some perverse level. She had thought that, someday, he and she would ultimately meet for some kind of showdown. That notion always seemed to linger in the back of her mind.

Her sword, strapped to her back, caught on the protruding rocks of the tight crevasse descending into the tunnel below. She backed out, and removed the sword slung to her back, so that she could more easily squeeze through. Down the center of the bale was a faint blue glowing line. It throbbed brighter then grew dim again with the rising and falling of her breath.

She was delivering the sword to its rightful owner; returning it, finally, to the hand meant to wield it. Cherufe. The terrible and malevolent Tyrant that nearly destroyed everything. Where December devoured everything, consuming, growing stronger, never sated— Cherufe, it was written, seemed to take pleasure in destruction. And that was all. It demonstrated no lofty goals of ascension save, perhaps, to ravage the next world beyond the aether. Earth, maybe?

Even other Tyrants stood against It, aligning with the lowly inhabitants of a once thriving Malifaux city, and possibly other cities just like it, now lost in the barren landscape of the scorched Badlands or the even less hospitable wasteland beyond the Northern Mountains.

But they could not kill It. In an elaborate twisting of complex promises and betrayals and false unions, they did manage to trap and expel It, but at the cost of countless lives. This was long before the Breach.

She stepped down into a more open cave system, lit eerily from below as the lava flowed, hot and orange. She coughed, gagging upon toxic gases from the molten stream. Her eyes watered and burned, and she stepped back into the cool passage between the upper cave and the winding lava flow below to catch her breath.

The ground rumbled, slowly at first and just a tremor. Before she could run out of the narrow passage and the cave, the tremor erupted in a violent quake that knocked her to the ground. It was deafening, and she was battered back and forth against rocky protrusions. Streams of lava shot upwards in the tumultuous quake. Rocks fell from above to crash violently and thunderously nearby. She feared she would be crushed by falling debris or the walls so close to her. She braced herself for the inevitability.

Even though the quaking continued, she was not crushed. She found herself in a sort of trance, possibly caused by the heat and vapors washing over her from below. As she succumbed to unconsciousness she had a final thought. *'This has nothing to do with the heat,'* she thought. *'You're here, aren't you?'* she asked in her mind.

Yes. The voice of Cherufe responded in her thoughts. **I have waited long for your coming.**

Cherufe guided her unconscious body out through narrow tunnels and into the greater channel of lava flowing southeast, toward Malifaux. She fell to the rocky floor beside the quickly moving river of lava.

Sonnia awakened some time later. She had no idea how long she had lain there. Though the lava channel still flowed beside her, illuminating the cave, she saw that she was no longer at the cave entrance. She had been moved. This cavern was still rough and rocky, but areas of the walls, floor, and ceiling showed signs of being carved. She knew they were. Carved out in a great labyrinth that stretched for many miles beyond the City. The vast city stood at its hub. The sewers, she knew, were just the beginning. She was closer to it now, to

Malifaux. Interesting that she had been lured to one remote and hidden location after another, far beyond the City, only to have that quest return her to the starting point.

She sat up, quickly shaking the foggy stupor that dulled her mind. She couldn't be certain but thought she saw a glowing reflection from several sets of eyes disappearing in the shadows and branching tunnels. They were not natural creatures, she knew at once. She could sense them, like the gentle lure of a large soulstone more than she could see them. These creatures were different though, burning shadows at the edge of her arcane perception rather than the cool defiant spirit that could be captured, chilling the person who harnesses it.

She stood, turning to face the direction of the lava flow. Far above her, the heat and gases poured through holes in the rock face by the earthquake. *It* had done that. Cherufe. Otherwise, she wouldn't have been able to breathe. Those strange creatures she had vaguely perceived belonged to It as well. Creatures of fire and molten rock given life as December had created creatures of ice and snow.

She followed the lava, observing the branches of magma merging into this one as it, too, flowed into yet a wider flow. She crossed natural bridges of flat granite or basalt that had fallen from above, always keeping her on her path.

'It was underground, all along,' she thought. 'Each of the temples, each of the ruins, each of the artifacts I found up there –' She paused, both in her mind and in her pace. "No," she said aloud. "How could I have overlooked that?" She thought of those places where she had made the most important discoveries – the key books or artifacts that gave her more pieces of the puzzle. She quickly unslung a tattered leather bag from her shoulder and withdrew a beaten book with yellowed pages. She thumbed through the familiar journal quickly and found a map scrawled by her own hand. A map of the City and surrounding area. Deeper in the back of the folio she found a much different sketch she had once transcribed of the cage designed to hold Cherufe. Back to the map of the City, with graphite stick in hand, she frantically circled each of the major locations and ruins that guided her every step. In her obsessive pursuit to keep her private research hidden, obfuscated from the probing eyes of the Guild, she had never marked those locations on any map; never before recorded those key locations in any way.

She saw it now, though. The last cave that led her down here – *the buried library that housed not a book, but the gilded necklace that, when outstretched, had formed a map that led her to the fallen temple where she found the record describing the first rise of the Tyrants – of the Kythera ruins where they confronted December and the Grave Spirit, but where she had also found yet more pieces of the puzzle – of the ruins where she had been forced to take Francis, the Governor's son, and she had discovered the dry fragments of one important piece of parchment while he doted over some pretty trinket – of Phillip Tombers' various discoveries –* thinking of those numerous places all at once, she reeled and dropped to one knee, losing her balance. She couldn't focus, not on the cave, not on anything save the great inundation of sudden awareness.

She had crisscrossed the landscape dozens of times. She had thought of the City of Malifaux as the central hub and some of her research took her nearer the City while other locations were further away. The City was *not* the hub. Each of those locations that provided the key instruments of understanding formed a nearly perfect circle that spanned many miles. She hadn't discovered them in sequential order, however. That had added to the confusion. Now she saw it. Putting the artifacts, books, other discoveries in order around that great circle on an imaginary map in her mind, she saw the story unfold so logically, now.

Another image focused within her mind and superimposed itself on the mental map and highlighted locations she had painstakingly explored over the last three years. The new image was of a drawing, an oddly recorded schematic of Neverborn engineers that created the arcane Red Prison to contain Cherufe, the fiery Tyrant determined to consume this world in conflagration. Its shape was a circle. Key points around the cage were marked in glyphs, each drawing power out of the strange being, siphoning it into the very cage that held It. *It* fueled the very device of its long imprisonment. Each of those arcane points aligned perfectly with the forgotten places here, around Malifaux, where she had found more and more of the clues. The image of the mental map had several places missing from that otherwise perfect representation of the Red Cage. 'Places I hadn't even discovered yet,' she thought. It was too late to find them now. What might she have found in those places had she been there? What artifacts or clues could she use to fight for her survival and the survival of all the inhabitants within Malifaux? She regretted not knowing.

No one, so far as she knew, had ever traveled further beyond the City than her, and she had gone no further than those key points along the great circle. Was there anything left out there, across the Northern Mountains, across the dry wasteland to the west beyond the Badlands? Was the City all that remained?

It was a prison.

Of the Tyrants that sought to ascend; to end their imprisonment in Malifaux. The Neverborn that remained – it was their prison, too, she realized. And there were not many remaining; not enough to fill the smallest section of the great city. The settlers? Humans here through the Breach? Were they equally trapped but didn't know it?

She stood and stared down the tunnel toward her destination. She knew where she was going now. In her mind, she saw the center of the great ring that surrounded Malifaux where each of the artifacts and clues had been discovered. The center of the ring was not within the City Malifaux – it was just north of its boarders

It was the Breach.

Sonnia surveyed the expansive chamber that opened beyond the tunnel, which while seemingly natural, had become ever more precise and clearly carved. The floor was now smooth and even, and the walls, too, were cut in sharp angles. The numerous lava flows ran in equally precise channels that were exact replicas of the sewer labyrinth below the City. The lava rivers poured into one wide pool from different channels from the north, west, east, and even several smaller channels from Malifaux, all leading toward the river to the south.

The molten pool, really a small subterranean lake, illuminated the large cavern with warm light. The ceiling of the chamber was far above. Beyond it, directly above the epicenter of the whirlpool at the heart of the burning pool, was the crackling breach -- the gateway bridging this world and Earth. She was deep beneath the ground, but the hill above was just as large. The Breach, Ridley Station, the Governor's Mansion, even the Hanging Tree and innumerable bodies buried beneath it all loomed in the rock and dirt far overhead.

"I'm here!" she called. Her voice echoed above the crackling lava which occasionally erupted in a pyroclastic rush as bubbles rose to the surface of the churning lava, now more quiescent as it moved into the large pool. Only her voice called back to her. "I'm here, you bastard! What do you want of me?" The "me" of her voice bounced back to her in diminishing echoes.

She waited. Much longer than she expected.

"So you've got a sense of humor," she said more naturally.

On the far side of the chamber, she could see the shape of the walls change as columns and funneled into a secondary tunnel extending out beyond her.

The Necropolis, she realized. She was within the vast Necropolis. She had read much about it and had expected it. This place was significant in many of the references to the Tyrants. She realized she had just entered it but expected it ran far throughout the subterranean area below the world they knew. The answers were all below the ground. They were never looking in the right place. Or, perhaps that was their salvation. What dark secrets were buried beneath Malifaux's surface, she wondered. What dark secrets were better left undiscovered?

Despite the sweltering heat within the tunnels, she had kept her coat on throughout her subterranean trek. She didn't perspire. She was never too hot. 'How long have I been its vessel?' she thought. 'Since I crossed the Breach? Before?' She unbuckled the numerous straps holding the long coat tightly fastened around her torso. She removed the greatsword from her back and rested it against the low brick wall encircling the lava pool. The angle upon which it rested was too oblique, and when she sat upon the wall beside it, the sword clattered to the paving stones beneath her.

It glowed dimly blue. 'This is what started it all,' she thought, looking at the thick blade. She shouldn't even be able to swing such a great weapon, much less wield it with any skill. Others found its weight match its size, but to her, it was light. Where others found the metal cool to the touch, it felt warm to Sonnia, like a candle's flame when her fingers drew near it. She no longer remembered whether she had developed her mastery and manipulation of fire before or after finding the sword.

The glow behind her grew more luminous, and she jumped to her feet. She spun to see the form of a giant creature rising from the midst of the pool. It was anthropomorphic, yet reptilian, too, with twin eyes of dark obsidian that reflected her image as it rose. The lava flowed over its great body and cooled to a dark gray in seconds. The dry shell continued to crack and flow down its molten body. Between them, across its form, the cracks glowed white hot from the heat beneath.

Sonnia had come here on her own, fulfilling the desperation to understand her role in the ascension of the tyrants and her clear connection to this creature, the most feared and reviled of them all. She had been unafraid. But now, standing beneath the monster that towered above her, she had only the instinctive need to flee. Her heart beat, and for the first time in several years, she felt the heat as its humid breath washed down upon her.

It took all of her will to stifle the panic rising so quickly within her. She addressed the creature, shouting up at it, "You have physical form! What do you want of me?"

Nothing. Its voice was soft and soothing, but deep, like a fire burning hot but long, near the end of a coal's usefulness.

She was confused.

Its arm reached toward her, the smell of sulfur striking first, stinging her eyes and making her recoil. She turned involuntarily from It, from the fear she could not deny as well as the foulness. Through watering eyes, she saw the sword at her feet. 'You're not here for me,' she thought.

No.

"You want my sword."

It was never yours.

So many clues. They were all so obtusely written, obfuscated so cleverly that she could barely understand the portents and prophecies that were spelled out so long before man ever set foot in Malifaux. And she knew more than any other human in Malifaux about its history and the struggle the Neverborn fought for survival. She possibly had acquired more knowledge than the Neverborn had, themselves.

There was a key and a vessel they each needed. Rasputina was the vessel for December, she knew, and Seamus, too, had been chosen though he doggedly pursued the Grave Spirit. Others she suspected and considered as she uncovered more and more of the truth. But the keys for each were so much more guarded and obscurely referenced. She had arrogantly thought she must be the chosen vessel for Cherufe. It had seemed so logical. But now, she realized that her destiny was not in becoming the living embodiment of the Fire Tyrant, but in delivering the key to open the final lock of Its mortal imprisonment.

Its burning hand, large enough to engulf her torso drew before her.

"You want it?" she growled. "You'll have to take it." Her boot kicked beneath the cross-guard spikes, lifting it easily into the air before her. In the same movement, she grabbed the long hilt with one hand, and as she swung it up and then down toward the arm, her second hand closed around the hilt. She howled as she swung with all of her might, leaping forward beside its outstretched arm of crackling fire and molten rock. The sword slid easily through Its wrist, severing it, and a spray of lava erupted as the hand fell back into the swirling pool below. Where she struck, the lava turned crystalline and blue, snaking up Its arm.

It seemed to groan at first, like a rumbling of rocks just before the ground would split in a quake. But, as the creature pulled back, she wondered if it was laughter.

Cherufe's other arm lunged forward, faster than she could imagine, but she held her sword firm and impaled the blade into the open palm. Pressing forward against her, she could not hold her ground. Her boots dragged and scraped on the stone as she was pushed back, but the heat of its hand quickly cooled as the lava within crystallized, turning deep blue like the sword's glow. She grew confident once more.

She pulled herself up onto Its hand, easily drawing the sword from the cool stone of Its arm. The crystallization within the arm snaked upwards toward Its torso but no more than half way, and she leapt toward that point where the glow beneath the gray plates of Its outer mantle was still burning white. She sank the blade within the arm, and It hissed as the arm grew blue around the impaling weapon.

The "key" was not for them to use to free the final bonds of their mortal prison after all. It was the final tool to hold them at bay. She jerked the sword free from Its arm, standing upon its body above the lava. Ever inquisitive, she studied the sizzling pock-marks burning into Its surface and so never saw the blue stump of Its other arm swinging toward her. It struck violently, knocking her through the air. The sword flew from her, arcing end over end toward the pool. She hit the ground bodily and rolled, the wind knocked from her and several bones cracked, at the least. Sonnia watched as the weapon, her only hope, fell toward the pool.

Cherufe saw both the girl and the sword and surprised her by lunging toward the weapon, as quickly as it could, to strike it in mid-air with the end of its blue hand, frozen by the magical blade for which it was created. It flew beyond the end of the pool, struck the wall, and fell to the ground. Its rocky head turned toward her, the gleaming stone eyes reflecting the lava below.

Cool white vapor enveloped her as the stone in her hand cracked, releasing the spiritual energy within. She drew it in, melding the fragmentary whispers it spoke with her own formidable will, and found immediate relief from the pain. Before the healing was complete, she was up and moving, running around the circumference of the pool toward her sword.

The Tyrant's arm slashed in the air, and a tall spray of fire sliced forth, striking the path before her. But Sonnia Criid was not without similar mastery of the primal forces of nature, and without pausing in her stride, her hand struck the air before her, and the wall of flame exploded before her as her own red fire struck it. She ran through the hole in Cherufe's flame wall even as it closed back around her. Not to have her escape again, Its dark arms lifted quickly above Its head, and the entire pool rose in a wave, rolling quickly toward her. It rose above the short wall around the pool, at least ten feet high. She had little time to prepare for it but had grabbed another soulstone and crushed it just as the wave crested before her. Flame exploded from her outstretched arms as she slid to a halt on the paving stones, facing the lava and attacking it with the full force of the power she commanded. The fire that belched forth was deep red and streaked with cool white from the stone. She howled in defiance and determination as her own fire burst through the thick wave of lava, redirecting it as it washed down upon her. The lava spilled around her, but she was safe. The sword, however, was in the path of the orange liquid from her explosive fire.

The twisting of the fabric of fate and the arcane threads of the aether were something intangible, imperceptible to almost every living thing, even those that had some mastery of the arcane, themselves. Sonnia Criid, however, had acquired her position in the Guild for the almost unique skills she commanded at being able to perceive the very exertion upon those gossamer threads that wove around all things. She saw its twisting of the threads of fate and the aether, wrapping its will about it and manipulating it. The rock beneath the sword bucked in a small but violent tremor. The sword leapt from the ground, spiraling end over end toward Cherufe.

Also unlike so many other beings that could command the twisting of the fabric of fate, she had the power to unravel others' control of it, of the unnatural interference they invoked upon it. Typically, she could only affect another's aetheric manipulation if the spells they cast involved her own spiritual connection with the aether, but the sword was not just a weapon of metal, folded by man in a forge. It was a weapon made for the undoing of Cherufe, and it was intended to be wielded by her. Fate had chosen a purpose and a weapon for her long before she was ever conceived.

She saw the threads of aether twisting in the space between Cherufe and the spiraling sword. They were cool and white, but gaseous and tenuous. Those threads did not envelop her, she knew. How could she unravel them?

Her mind raced. Time seemed to slow as she sought the answer.

It was too powerful. Cherufe had far greater control over self and the arcane than Its fellow Tyrants. She knew her sword was meant to strike down Cherufe, but the Tyrant was keeping it from her, drawing it in. If It held the weapon, consumed or otherwise destroyed it, there would be nothing to stop Its ascent.

The image of December flickered in her mind as she succumbed to failure. But she realized something at the last moment about December. He was a mere shell of His true form. She had read dozens of manuscripts about Him along with the more fragmentary snippets offered of Cherufe. For all of the Fire Tyrant's might and terror, December had occupied more of the ancient Neverborn's attention. Though the Wendigo at Kythera was formidable, nearly unstoppable, He *was* a mere reflection of His true self. They needed a vessel.

Cherufe had lied to her, and she knew it. She felt it. She was sure of it beyond any certainty she had known before. She *was* this creature's vessel. The sword was the key to Its undoing, and possessing it meant It would have nothing again to fear. Nothing would step in Its way, and It would consume her in the fires of Its will and being.

The truth struck her immediately. The sword was *not* the key. She was.

The sword was hers, and she was tied to it. She felt the tendrils of control it had wrapped around the sword, pulling it through space. She screamed, extending her own control through the distance that separated them and severed its control over the sword.

The sword continued through the air, but free from its control.

Sonnia's boot hit the top of the short wall, and she released an explosive blast of concentrating fire that sent her hurling toward the sword, her legs aflame.

Cherufe again tried to manipulate the threads of fate, lashing out in frustration at her unexpected defiance. Its will striking her with the tectonic vibrations at its disposal, hitting her in the side strong enough to again snap her ribs. She could have unraveled the magical manipulations again, even easier than she did with the sword, but she did not try to stop it. Instead, she had

counted on it for the strike sent her straight across the lava, feet above the burning pool. It sent her directly toward the sword hurling across its surface. Despite its strongest attempt to manipulate this outcome, this moment had been established by fate so long before either of them walked that she wondered how any of them, Tyrant, human, Neverborn — how any of them could avoid the great power that sought to right the path that they continued to twist.

The Fire Tyrant could do nothing more as the sword and Sonnia came together in the space above the lava. She certainly did not try to stop it. She knew the truth now. It was in the books, the artifacts, all through the uncovered ancient messages that she found and read over and over. She was the vessel It was destined to consume. Possessing her, It would walk again, heralding the beginning of the end.

The sword arced once more as she flew before it. The tip of the blade struck her in the chest and sank deep, piercing the fabric of her blouse, severing flesh, bone, and the sinews of muscle before bursting through the back of the thick canvas coat. She gasped as the metal burned, unraveling not only the threads of fate that had long entwined her, but the control of the spiritual and arcane bonds that had tied her to It.

Cherufe howled and the ground trembled, splitting and bucking even as the woman and sword tumbled together into the lava.

Fade to Black

December 21

The ground bucked and heaved, rumbling angrily. All throughout the City the inhabitants clutched one another as the quake cracked the foundations of their homes and split the roads. Furniture and decorations were broken. Lives were lost as ceilings and walls fell.

Stepping frantically out of their crumbling homes and businesses, the residents of Malifaux did not find any comfort or hope outside. Steam and fire erupted from the numerous cracks splitting the pavement, and lava spewed from the wider crevasses. Lives were lost as some teetered upon the shaking ground to be thrown into a crack that crushed the victim between two walls.

The temperature of the ground grew warm, and steam rose from its surface as the frost was quickly burned away. But the wind rolled strong and bitter from out of the north where a dark storm raged, the edges stretching and circling from directly overhead and out beyond the mountains and into the unknown regions to the north.

Their bones shook so violently it was difficult to stand, and the tremors sent pain shooting through them, knocking most to the ground. The wind bit into their flesh, slicing into them like daggers. Darkness loomed above, blotting out the pale afternoon sun and bringing darkness upon them. Black fog snaked its way through alleys and narrow streets, up the sloping hills of the City to the more populated region of the Northern Gates. It emanated from the Plague Pit to envelop everyone in its inky opacity so that they struggled against the tumult in near blindness. Almost all believed they wouldn't survive more than a few minutes now, and people clutched desperately at anyone near to avoid loneliness at what they believed was the end of all their lives.

No voice or cry could be heard above the quaking and moaning of the rocks below and the deafening wind attacking from above.

As quickly and violently as it had come upon them, the rumbling ground suddenly calmed, only their bodies continued to shake as they began to recover. The wind silenced, and the gale that pressed against them so violently lost its strength and blew gently against exposed flesh. Still cold, it was so warm in contrast that people gasped, feeling comforted by the calm and gentle breeze upon them. Many were uncertain whether they remained alive or had died and this was their joining lost loved ones in the dark afterlife. But the darkness surrounding them, also dissipated in the span of several quick and frantic breaths. People looked around in shock and confusion as they began to sit up slowly, expecting the reprieve to be temporary, soon returning them to the apocalyptic events that sought to end them. Their wide eyes looked around, and momentarily, light broke through the gray clouds above, bathing them in sudden warmth.

The silence was startling. In the distance, some blocks away, they heard the wailing of a child, the pained moans of the wounded dimly joining some seconds later. They had been spared.

On the edge of the Quarantine Zone, beside the pit of the plagued victims, Samael Hopkins struggled to wake, to dispel the stupor that sought to drag him comatose. He had lost consciousness but could not be certain of the length of the darkness and stupor. Even now, fighting against it, his head lolled, and his eyes were far too heavy to open. They flickered, and he nearly gave in to the weakness that sought to suppress him. But he saw the blurry image of Molly stooping over the gray body of Seamus, the lunatic with the ridiculous top hats. Hopkins had little left, yet his senses came briefly to some clarity, and the image of the girl came slowly into focus.

She might have been lovely in life, but her pallor was grotesque and unnatural and revolting as of old meat, too spoiled to consume. It was a strange analogy to make for a person walking amongst them, but he found her both revolting and alluring at once. Her facial features were slack and emotionless as she regarded Seamus.

The blackness had dissipated, he realized, and the sun glinted off of a green gem she held between her thumb and forefinger. She pressed it against the gray flesh of his forehead and pushed hard, though she gave no visible expression of exertion. Hopkins watched, slipping in and out of lucidity.

The stupor that enveloped Samael's senses dissipated slowly.

Molly pushed her whole weight down upon his forehead. In her hand was the large green gem. She was pressing it into the bullet hole that had ended him.

'What the hell?' Hopkins thought, confusion replacing the last vestiges of fear that lingered at the base of his mind. Strangely, with each pressing upon the gem, he felt a sudden surge of anathema toward Seamus and unreasonable fear of the damnation that surrounded him. A final urging upon the gem sank the green stone through the skull and into the brain beneath. Like a pebble dropped into a still pool, a ripple on the air passed over Samael Hopkins like the resonance of a gong.

Seamus' dead body twitched. Hopkins felt the dissipating fear suddenly return in a deluge, and his fearful gasp caught in his throat. Seamus twitched again, his hand turning over on the cobblestone in the pool of his own blood, blackened by the stain of damnation that consumed him. Abruptly twisting, he sat bolt upright, his eyes wide and confused as he looked about. The flesh of his ghastly wound stretched and pulled to cover the bullet hole, and as it sealed, his dead gray eyes began glowing bright green. They darted about in confusion, making him look briefly normal as anyone in such phenomenal circumstances might feel panic and bewilderment. But then his high arching brows drew angrily down over his unnatural eyes, and his broad maniacal smile returned.

"Ah, no," Seamus said, his voice more or less back to normal, but Hopkins thought he detected a strange and subtle echo in the voice. "Molly! Damn ye. What d'ye think ye're doing?" She said nothing. She had no visible emotion whatsoever, if she were even still capable of feeling anything.

The dark gray of his skin slowly resumed its more pale and pinkish hue as he pulled the dandy's shirt from his back, now just tattered rags from the gargantuan growth that had shredded it to pieces. Seamus pointed to a severed head beside the two, against other bodies slung onto the pit. He accused, "You put 'er up to this, didn't ye? You!"

The head spoke, Samael saw, but he couldn't make out what it said. He was aghast.

Seamus continued, saying, "Now I be doubly damned, Tombers. You said you and the Tear could bring me back but ye didn't say ye'd be sticking it in me damned *head*! Not a lot of room in there for me, the Spirit, and the Gorgon, ye blasted imbecile. I'll be leaving ye here on the pit to think about what ye've done. Both of ye." He turned back to Molly and spat, "And you! I gave ye life! I can take it from ye, too." He stood, sputtering and cursing. He saw Samael, chained to the iron fence. Chained by his own tools, chained and trapped. The Resurrectionist looked quickly around and found the outlandish hat that towered ridiculously above his head. He pushed it down over his head. Still sputtering incoherently, Seamus approached him angrily.

Hopkins struggled against the chains, confused by his own desperately fashioned lashings that made little sense. He had bound himself in the throes of the most unreasonable fear. He'd never be able to get free in time. Seamus was right upon him when Hopkins grabbed the Colt from the ground near him. He lifted it and fired. Seamus flinched. The bullet, however, struck the hat, knocking it once more from his head. Seamus jumped and flailed briefly in surprise, looking back at the hat rolling away from him, a large hole through the center of it. "Damn ye are the lousiest shot with that thing I have ever heard of," he yelled angrily.

Samael leveled it upon him, sure that he'd take the lunatic's head off with the next shot. He pulled the trigger. It clicked, but did not fire. He gasped. Between the two were the rest of his bullets, there on the ground. Both men saw them.

Seamus turned to Molly, standing off behind him. "You emptied the gun, didn't ye?" he called to her. "One in the chamber, too, Molly, Dear." He shook his head, cursing her briefly.

Hopkins lunged toward the bullets, but they were just beyond his reach. He jerked and tugged at the gate, the chains bruising and lacerating his flesh. Desperately he pulled, nearly breaking his hand. He sought to pull free even if it meant tearing his hand off.

Seamus stood above the bullets, then bent to look Hopkins in the face. His eyes glowed green and the skin around them began to turn pale, the ashen pallor moving in a most disturbing manner as it slowly spread. The odd echo returned to Seamus's speech as he growled, "She be not that bright," of Molly. "But she means well. You could 'ave killed me, boyo. You often miss when ye're target's so close?" The gray of his flesh receded once again though his eyes retained the luminescent green.

Hopkins recoiled, pulling himself against the gate upon which he was lashed, preparing for the death that was about to be delivered. "No," he said calmly. "I don't often miss. This close or otherwise."

"Yet ye did. And I didn't do much to stop ye. Didn't even try to get out of the way. I've heard too much of ye to believe I could, either."

"Soulstones," Samael said.

"Did ye see any of the vapor? No need to twist the fates here, boyo. It's strong enough today. We be just poppets to its greater will." He stood and shook his head. Samael expected his death to come at any moment, but Seamus turned and walked away. He stooped to pick up his hat and dusted it off briefly before popping it down upon his head. He winked at Hopkins and walked away.

"That's it?" Hopkins called, surprised. He was happy enough to live but surprised that Seamus didn't kill him. Seamus had a reputation for killing everyone that crossed him, and Hopkins was bound and vulnerable.

Seamus didn't stop, however, but said, just loud enough to be heard, "Ye and that daft girl, Criid, didn't pay attention to anything, did ye? Left all the clues I could, and it's a wonder ye did anything correct at all." He shook his head and then disappeared down an alley, heading toward the more populated areas of the City.

Molly approached him carrying the head Seamus had yelled at beside the mound of bodies. She said, "The Tyrants cannot be stopped."

"Well," the disembodied head added, full of lively animation as though it were just as alive as him, "not by us. Well, you and those like you. I'm not much in the position to try to stop much of anything. Not that I was ever very good at that sort of thing even before I lost my body, if you see what I mean." Molly pulled a dark velvet bag from the belt around her dress. "Now, Molly," the head said, "Just give me a minute!" She said nothing but hesitated before thrusting the head into the pouch.

"Tombers?" Hopkins inquired.

"Yes, well, at your service, as it were," the head of Phillip Tombers said. "The Tyrants cannot be stopped. Not in the way we might understand. Not with the means at our disposal. You see, we don't--" he was interrupted as Molly thrust him into the bag and pulled the drawstring close, cradling it in the crook of her arm.

Molly said, "The vessel must die. Without the vessel, the Tyrant has no means of ascension."

"They'd just find another."

"Yes," she responded emotionlessly. "But if they invest their energy in consuming the host at the time of the death, their power will be greatly dissipated. It would by years, possibly centuries before they might be a threat again. This world was ravaged by them before they could be stilled. Now they rise again. Only a few of the more ambitious have made their presence known, hurrying before the others might awaken. But they stir as well." She stood and walked away. She hesitated and said over her shoulder, "Criid is near. She's beneath the city in long tunnels carved by the ancient people."

"Is she alive?" he asked. Molly didn't respond.

"How can I find her?" he called.

"The Necropolis," Molly said.

"The Necropolis? She's at the Necropolis?" Molly cocked her head, regarding him there upon the ground like a dog seeing something strange and puzzling. She said no more, and the heels of her boots, clearly bound and shod by a master cobbler, clacked on the paving stones. They were dirty. Her dress, too, once very expensive and imported from Europe from the looks of its ornate lacework, bore an unfortunate layer of stains at their length from dragging through city muck and all the strange places Seamus had taken her.

His boots were filthy. Torn and frayed, too.

He and Molly were different than most. They loyally followed a master without question, their loyalty unwavering. He was bound to Criid until death, but often wondered if her cause was true.

He got to work unraveling the chains that bound him. He needed to get below ground, through the twisting and impossible maze of the sewers. He needed to find the Necropolis. Rumor and archaic references in their studies declare it to be somehow more vast than Malifaux – itself a greater city than any standing Earthside. Yet none had found it. That is, if any would-be explorer had discovered it in the depths below, they had not survived to report their findings.

📖 📖 📖

Near the peak of Cold Heart, as the cultists had come to name the mountain they laid claim to, the remaining Silent Ones, priests, and acolytes stood, not quite confident enough to approach the remains of Rasputina, freezing on the ice and snow. The air bore a chill but no longer bit through them with such vehemence. The creamy light from the sun washed across them in broken pools through the dissipating clouds.

The girl, Snow, turned from Rasputina's broken form, unmoving before her. She looked down upon the Wendigo Storm, slain by her own hand. Like Rasputina and December, her bond with the beast was great. His death left her with a tangible void. The weather had bent to her will through him. The wind and cold and snow had been hers to manipulate, though only briefly and in a limited range. Now it was gone. Part of her died with Storm, she realized. Her soul and his were entwined. Rasputina had said it was like a soulstone constantly flooding her with the rapture of another spirit enveloping her own in a strange and comforting embrace. Now that it was gone, Snow could feel nothing at all. She sat upon a rock near the still beast. She wanted to feel remorse if not anguish, anger if not rage. She felt only apathetic and merely stared at it.

Long minutes passed that way in silence. None of the men dared move, and none wanted to be the first to approach Rasputina. They were not afraid, exactly. It was more a question of propriety. They looked to Snow as the natural successor of the order, but she could not speak to direct them and showed no inclination to try.

The thickly muscular shoulders of Storm twitched.

Snow's eyes grew wide. It had been prone, unmoving for long moments. It gave a deep inhale of breath, gurgling around the gaping cut in its throat. It shook as if wrestling something off of its back, rolled over, and stood uncertainly. The long laceration at its throat, cut through to its spine, came slowly together. Muscle and flesh bound together before their disbelieving eyes. Seconds later, its flesh looked undamaged, and it fought off the last of the stupor. Storm bent and howled in rage. There was nothing for him to release his anger upon, so he continued to roar, the sound reverberating far across the valleys separating the mountains.

The others heard only his rage breaking the uncomfortable silence since Rasputina's fall. Snow, however, heard an echo, faint and not from the sides of the mountain, but a subdued whisper beneath Storm's deafening roar. She heard December and He spoke to her.

I will not be undone she heard Him say. invested too much But His voice was weak. So faint she could scarcely be sure she heard it and not simply imagined it. tell her He said in that ghostly whisper, I will come for her again

Storm's howl ceased, and Snow looked upon Rasputina. She jumped, aghast and in revered awe. The Silent Ones and acolytes, too, started. Rasputina sat upright, eyes blinking slowly, weakly, her chest unmarked and whole again and rising and falling with weak breaths. "You will not have me," she said weakly. "You will never have me."

December had been thwarted. He had poured so much of His accumulated might into turning Rasputina into His vessel that *her* death might forever have diminished Him, might have ended the threat of Him forever.

'You couldn't let me die,' she thought, knowing the last bit of His presence was still there. She was weak. He was weaker. 'I am stronger than you. I always will be.'

I will have you. Soon.

'Never. I am willing to do what you cannot. I will die before you will have me.'

He had devoted so much of His will into manifesting His physical incarnation at Kythera, only to be thwarted by the magical Masamune. He had diminished months ago when she had shunted him aside, forming Snow and Storm, weaker facsimiles of *their* hateful symbiotic relationship. It weakened Him again. Losing her at the last moment of his consumption would have been his undoing. She knew He was still there, in her mind, connected to her. But He was weak. He spitefully put her back together with the last vestiges of His aetheric presence. He could not impose a change upon her personality or motivations. However, He could change her physical needs, and for this, she would forever live with a feverish hunger that would never be fully sated.

Samael Hopkins worked his way north as best he could in the subterranean labyrinth of the sewers beneath Malifaux. Typically calm and acutely aware of the most minute detail of his surroundings, he moved frantically, hardly thinking of the details of each stretch of tunnel. He retained his innate sense of direction even as the tunnels twisted upon themselves and ran at length to dead-end in wide drainage pools, forcing him to backtrack cautiously. Still, the tunnels, themselves, seemed to actually *lead* him northward. The less he concentrated on direction and finding the best path, the easier he found it to move forward. Tunnels he thought were wider, or merely seemed a better choice instinctively, led him too far out of his way or even led back upon a former tunnel in his trek.

Giving himself over to Fate, running haphazardly down one narrow tunnel after another, he quickly came to believe the players involved in Malifaux's intricacies were all such pawns to far greater forces beyond them. He gave in to odd impulses to take darker passages that branched away from his supposed destination but that turned around a bend to return northward with more open and easy walkways beside the slowly moving morass of the sewage waste. Tunnels he would swear should better lead him to the north side of the city would have fallen stones and collapsed walls from the violent tremors that had struck the area.

When he came to a narrow channel filled not with sewage but dark lava, crusting over as it cooled, just a dim glow in small cracks across its surface, Samael knew he was close. Seeing the channel of lava not burning hot and moving quickly along the same path caused an uneasy sense of dread that mounted with each continued step. Cherufe, the Fire Tyrant, and Sonnia Criid had no doubt met, and Samael wondered who had succeeded in their goal. With no further thought or hesitation, he followed the lava flow at a dead run.

It was under these conditions that he very accidentally came upon the edge of the Necropolis.

Sonnia had referenced it several times as an important location used by the ancient Neverborn for something essential in their past, though further references of the acts conducted there or its deeper purpose were never articulated within any uncovered text. Moreover, every Guild expedition sent specifically to find the location never met with success. If the explorers resurfaced at all, they were merely covered in grime, exhausted, and deeply afraid they would never have made it out. Those few didn't report sightings of any creature or obstacle of overt danger that inspired their fear. It was the maze that caused the dread. Reports of doubling back, walking the same path over and over again or of simply turning around and retreating without seeming to even realize it was a commonly repeated statement from all of the returnees. The majority of expert trackers and spelunkers sent down to survey the labyrinth and find the fabled Necropolis were never seen again.

Samael, himself, had vowed to lead an expedition to find it, sure he could discover it where none other had been successful. But Sonnia's quest had deferred those plans. Now, without trying, he skirted along the very side of this mysterious region that had eluded trackers specifically seeking it out.

He refused to give in to the unnatural fear emanating from the corridors and alcoves housing stacked sepulchers and ornately carved images that were both beautiful and terrible. As he ran past longer corridors, deeper into the heart of the Necropolis, their depths swallowed all light. Despite his fear, he felt the lure of the secrets around him, wanting to explore this place. Like the fear, he knew the fascination was artificial, planted in his mind by this accursed place, to keep him trapped in its darkness.

More than once he imagined he saw the glint of light from the passage reflected from a set of eyes. Turning to focus upon them, however, revealed nothing save the absolute pitch blackness encompassing the cold passages.

Finally, the gray surface of the lava stream opened upon a vast chamber. Around the perimeter of the great chamber were other passages that ran in every direction, each of them pouring into this cavity a similar stream of lava that was cooling quickly with a dark gray crust and dim glow from below the surface. They all met at this central pool of lava, itself suffering the same hardening due to the dissipating heat.

His heart fell, but he was not surprised to see Sonnia at the center of the pool. She was kneeling. The lava had cooled, dark and hard around her legs and forearms below the surface. Her own sword had impaled her chest, protruding far from her back.

He sighed, wishing he could have been there to protect her. He would have failed, too. She had to die. That's what Seamus had said and Samael now believed him. Sonnia did what she had to do to stop Cherufe. It's why the lava had ceased its burning. Why the quaking had ceased as well.

He stepped gingerly upon the pool, finding the surface strong enough to support him, and walked to her. She was so driven, so focused. Of course she would stop at nothing to end the possible reign of the most dangerous of the Tyrants — even before it could get a foothold in Malifaux once again. He wondered how she had managed it, looking down upon the scene of her body destroyed both by lava and her own sword. It would have been a sight to behold, he knew that.

He also knew that he could not bury her. Not in the way she deserved. He loathed leaving her so unceremoniously out in the open, too. He'd bury her with stones broken from the low wall encircling the pool. Her sword would be left upon the mound to mark her burial. He gripped it for the first time. Even buried within her flesh, held in place through severed bone and sinew, he felt its heft and wondered how she could have wielded it so effortlessly. It was much larger, even, than Lady Justice's. He held it tightly and pulled it from her body. As the end of the blade was about to leave her body, it caught for a second as if in protest. He pulled it free with a jerk.

Sonnia's eyes opened wide as the blade left her body, and she inhaled sharply. A trail of wispy flame followed the sword. She coughed and said, "Sam!" in a voice dry and broken. "Get back!"

The thin fire licking at the end of the greatsword flickered and was gone. As it dissipated, the hardened gray lava rock engulfing Sonnia burst into bright orange liquid magma, flowing away from her, spreading quickly out to engulf the rock all around, turning it back into the burning lava. It spread from her in a ring toward the edge of the round pool.

Samael wasted no time in pondering how she was reawakened from death. He ran. Faster than he had run before, barely letting his boot soles hit the hardened rock as he ran to the low wall, hot lava popping and gurgling just behind him, sizzling upon his pant legs and boots. He dove over the wall just as the lava overtook him, dissolving the rock beneath him, and hit the ground hard, rolling in the accumulated dust. He turned over to see Sonnia lean back, her head facing toward the cavern's ceiling far above, the lava splashing around her. She moaned, barely audible above the roiling pool of glowing magma and suddenly erupted in flame. Her body launched above the pool, the thick liquid dripping from her. Hovering for a moment, head far back and arms outstretched, she clearly suffered no damage from the flames. The wound in her chest glowed as if her blood had turned to the same molten rock that flowed beneath her.

Her head snapped forward, and she looked at him angrily. Her eyes, too, glowed bright yellow, blinding him as he looked upon her.

When she spoke, her voice was gravelly, like metal on stones. "You damned fool! You shouldn't have come. You should have just left me dead." she said. The fire trailing behind her snaked down and bent about the pool. He imagined it even twisted back up and formed the head of a large reptilian beast glaring at him hatefully. But the fire shifted and twisted, and the heat was intense, and everything shimmered and vibrated in his vision as it overwhelmed him. A gout of fire belched forth from her mouth, consuming everything below her. She flew forward on the fire, breathing it down upon everything in her path which, unfortunately, led directly toward him.

He could not run, and there was no shelter to protect him. She was too fast, and the cone of fire too broad. He covered his face with one forearm while the other held the sword he had pulled from her body. When the fire washed down upon him, the sword glimmered and sang a high, sharp note as it glowed blue. The fire bathed him in heat, but he was not burned. Even his clothing was spared from the flames. As she passed above him, the sword's chime dissipated along with the glow down its center. She seemed not to mind that he survived the assault, flying quickly down a larger tunnel toward the southeast of the city, toward the feared Necropolis. The trail of fire behind her formed the head of a draconic beast, he was sure, that snapped at him as it trailed her. The sword struck another high chord as the flaming bite engulfed him, and he heard it growl as it disappeared, glowing brightly down the corridor and around twists and turns in the labyrinth until it was gone. The pool and the channels of lava quickly cooled to dark gray as she left.

Cherufe had won, then, he knew. It had devoured Sonnia, even after she had sacrificed herself to stop It. He, Samael Hopkins, was solely responsible for defying that sacrifice, by making her death moot. He cursed. Now the Tyrant was loosed upon the world to consume far more than the woman chosen as Its vessel. And when It was done with this world, It would move on to the next. Possibly through the Breach into the Old World.

Samael held Sonnia's sword, heavy and cold. It kept him from a fiery death, and he understood now that its arcane purpose was greater than he could have guessed. He would most certainly keep it close.

He did not like the idea of confronting her, but he had an obligation to stop the Tyrant. He particularly did not enjoy the thought of entering the Necropolis. Steeling his resolve, he set out to find her.

Martial Law

Orville Weaver knelt in the dry riverbed. Although mid-January, unseasonable warmth had pushed in from the south, dissipating the thin layer of frost that had settled in the night. Numerous buckles down the front of his gray duster held it wrapped tightly around him, and he began unfastening one after another to afford more freedom of movement as he examined the ashen dirt. His gloved hand broke through the top layer of soil easily, and the clod broke into a loose pile of sand.

Upon his hat, a cross between a gentleman's top hat and the more wide-brimmed hats of the cattlemen working the range, rested a set of mechanical goggles held around the crown by an elastic band. He pulled them over his face, securing them across his brow with the leather side flaps so that no light could interfere with his examination. Glancing quickly to the sky, he worried that he might actually need some additional light due to the thick and ominously dark clouds that had loomed for the past months. They looked ready to unleash a torrent at any moment. Of course, that had been the prevailing thought for weeks, yet the clouds had only released a minute long drizzle several days earlier.

"What do you reckon dried it up?" Louis Hernandez asked as he approached the kneeling investigator.

Orville said nothing. He dialed the clockwork mechanism on the goggles, and the gears protruding from the lenses adjusted to bring the grains of sand into clearer focus. Another button dropped a dark blue filter in front of the convex lenses so that he could see a different spectrum of light upon the grains.

Constance Weber, the commanding Guardsman on site barked, "Step back, Hernandez." A gust of wind picked up, and she held the dark gray hat upon her head lest it blow away, like the sand in Investigator Weaver's open hand. He studied the grains as they blew, the opaque cerulean lenses close to the material as it quickly flew in the breeze.

When his gloved palm was free of the sand, he pulled the goggles away from his face and rested them upon the base of his hat once more. He withdrew a narrow wafer of lead from a pocket on his vest and wrote the findings within his log.

Constance stepped up from behind. They were more escorts to the investigator, but, like Hernandez, she was anxious to have anything to explain the sudden and severe drought. "Same as site three?" she asked.

Orville turned toward her and could not hide his frustration. It was startling to see his emotions, given the typically stoic demeanor of all the investigators. "'Fraid so," he said. "Volcanism so close to the surface dried it right up. Even if water still stood, there's too much sulfur, hydrogen chloride, and other elements that would make it undrinkable." She didn't understand much of the mumbo-jumbo, but "undrinkable" was enough. He stood and brushed the gray dust from his knees. As he walked toward the horses, his feet kicked up small clouds.

Undrinkable. Like the wells that still produced within Malifaux. Too many toxins from the volcanic upheavals that had struck some weeks past. They had, thankfully, subsided, but the damage done was far more outreaching than the accompanying quakes that had brought down some buildings or put cracks in the foundations of many more.

The investigator mounted, and the Guardsmen quickly followed. "We going to site five?" Constance inquired.

Orville nodded. "We'll go to them all. No need to check 'em with the spectrometer, though. They'll all be the same. Let's ride hard and be quick about it. We're looking for water that still runs, now." His spurs dug into the flanks of his mount, and they rode a brisk gallop toward the northern mountains, hoping to find decent water coming down.

Miners were up there again, cutting blocks of snow and ice and shipping them down to Malifaux. But the caravans could not keep up with the demand of Malifaux's population.

Orville Weaver needed to get back to the Enclave by sunset. Lucius Matheson demanded a report.

📖 📖 📖

Rose Crowshaw turned quickly at the alley between the narrow bank and the Hourglass Hotel and Saloon. She stepped lively through the dirt that stuck to her boots from the bog water that permeated the soil in the boomtown of Hope, near the larger swamp region. She didn't take notice. Her boots were well worn, and the layers of dirt and oil were as much a part of their makeup as the original leather beneath. They were not the fashionable women's boots of the day, either. They were men's boots, cut for an adolescent boy most likely, as were her britches. She hadn't considered wearing a dress in a long time. Certainly before she became a steamfitter back home, and she brought none of her more feminine items through the breach some years past. She did still wear the tight corset that had become so fashionable in the day, but it was more because the tight garment offered no loose fabric to get caught in the gears and cogs of the devices she repaired.

Someone was following her, she was certain.

She had felt someone watch her every move ever since that strange confrontation with Kaeris back in November. Even after transferring to Hope, a very remote boomtown far on the outskirts of the Malifaux territories, she hadn't shaken the eyes that always seemed to be upon her every move.

A shadow passed overhead, and she ducked against the side of the Hourglass and looked quickly up but saw nothing. "Just paranoia," she whispered to herself. "Shake it off." But she couldn't. Coming to the end of the narrow alley, she hid in the shadows behind a large barrel, looking back and forth for whoever might be following. She was off the central road, more out of sight, but that might not be a good thing, she realized. Whoever was after her might be more free to act against her without the fear of witnesses. But that wasn't true, either. She had been alone frequently since abandoning her post at the Breach and transferring first to Promise and now Hope. She had been alone in her small shack just outside the town. She had been alone in the mine repairing steam-mining constructs and elevator mechanisms. Looking back down the alley, there was no movement, no sounds. Nothing in the back of the buildings either, save the outhouses.

Paranoia. Nothing was after her. She wondered if it were some odd side-effect of her ability that she felt constantly watched or pursued. Perhaps Kaeris had not done anything out of the ordinary when they met at the Breach, either, but the manifestation of fear was a product of her own out of control imagination.

Rose dismissed the feeling of dread as she stepped out of the shadows. Along the backs of the buildings she'd at least feel more certain that no one else was nearby.

The sound of a scratch upon the roof above her made her freeze, and she looked up in a panic. Only a dark cat. It ran along the edge of the roofline as she chastised herself for irrational fear and continued on. But the cat leapt from the roof before her. As it descended, it changed in midair, shifting in size and shape in the span of a second or two. It was no longer a black cat, but as it landed it had become a woman just as her foot struck the ground. She stood before a very stunned and speechless Rose Crowshaw. The woman's thick blonde hair flowed over her tanned shoulders like a mane.

Rose turned to run. She spun, but behind her stood a powerfully built man, his dark skin, tightly knotted dreadlocks, and thickly muscled torso, exposed to the winter elements made him seem primal. How he snuck up behind her, without a sound and from out in the open, she couldn't understand. Anxiety and the sense of doom turned to outright panic, and she was about to scream when the dark man touched her forehead with the tip of his curved staff. As it touched her skin, she heard a low hum within her mind. Images of running in a pack, of being free of a society that made such demands upon her for behavior and thought. She was bombarded by images of independence.

"Calm," the man said, his voice resonant and commanding. She obeyed, her hammering heart slowed almost instantly, and the fear dissipated as quickly. She would follow any command he gave her. In his presence she felt safe and confident. "I am Marcus," he said. "You will be safe with me." She already knew that. Looking up into the depth of his eyes, she knew she would have nothing more to fear.

"You were following me?" she asked.

"We were not the only ones, but those agents will no longer be a concern to you, or anyone else for that matter." She knew it was true. With him leading her, she was secure that nothing would be a concern for her. With him, she felt free of society and had a strange new sensation to abandon everything she knew of her role as a mechanic. She never fit in, anyway, she thought. Never wanted to belong. She had always sought to be free. She wanted to run. She wanted to run with Marcus and the girl that had been a cat. She wanted to hunt. A strange noise escaped from deep within her throat. Was she purring?

Marcus smiled down upon her. "The strength you feel comes from the primal power unlocked from within. It will dissipate shortly." He touched her again with the tip of his shillelagh. Even more commandingly he said, "You will remember the strength you feel." She would never forget. She didn't need him to command it.

"Where are we going?" she asked. It didn't really matter. She'd follow him anywhere.

"Into hell, most likely," he said. He smiled. The danger he anticipated intoxicated him, and she felt it, too.

"Why have you chosen me?"

"You have a primal skill I need. One that I want, and have sought my whole life. I will study you. In the *hunt*."

The Governor General stood against the railing along the balcony adjoining his private study. A crew was busy within, repairing the damage caused by the recent quake, the epicenter of which seemed directly below the mansion. Repairing it again. Of course, the crew was different than the last repair crew that had worked on his study. Strange happenings seemed to befall any crew that worked within the mansion. The Governor, himself, assured this crew that he would assign his personal guard to them once their work was complete, to escort them to their next assignment. When asked about their next assignment, however, he merely responded that the details were still being worked out.

Various Guild investigators stood behind him, ready to report their findings as he commanded. His secretary, Lucius, remained in the shadow to his right.

Orville Weaver began. "As we suspected, Sir, the volcanic activity did more than shake and batter the city. The release of different chemicals and compounds has poisoned what water might be found in the numerous wells, and the saturation of heat in the soil seems to have quickly dried up the otherwise plentiful running water sources coming into the City from out of the mountains."

"The volcanic drought extends to the mountains?" the Governor inquired.

"Nearly. But the recent sub-zero temperatures have the water there frozen too deeply to melt even at the base of the mountains."

He thought on it for a moment, staring south upon his City. "Mister Clemm," he commanded. "What are your findings on the livestock?"

Investigator Clemm was considerably meeker than Weaver, and he shook far too visibly in the presence of both Lucius Matheson and the Governor General. Even the other investigators made him uncomfortable. He regretted accepting the position as a field agent, not for the first time. He also wondered how he had been assigned the task of investigating the strange occurrences that had befallen the numerous ranches outlying the city. He mustered what courage he could. Speaking quickly to get it over with as soon as possible he said in a squeaky voice, "As Mister Matheson predicted, some ailment has befallen the non-indigenous animal stock brought here from Earthside. They've gone feral. Animals long domesticated and long unthreatening have developed a strange thirst for blood." He thought he was finished. He thought that would be enough.

The Governor General said, "Go on."

Roger Clemm swallowed hard, and the sound carried to them all. "They attack anything in sight. They kick, scratch, bite anything moving. They refuse to eat anything save living flesh."

"Has it spread to each of the ranches?"

"Not yet. I predict it will have infected all of them within weeks. A month at the most."

"Cause?"

"Unknown, Sir. Malifaux, I guess." The joke fell flat. He regretted the attempt.

Investigator Amelia Estremera spoke up, saving the uncomfortable Clemm from any more scrutiny. "This does not bode well for the social climate in Malifaux," she said. The Governor actually turned to face her, irritated that she spoke out of turn without waiting for him to address her. Still, he knew her intent and had all he needed from Roger Clemm as the man was clearly without any new information of any worth. In fact, he only offered what was already known and told to him before setting out on his investigation.

"It's not your job to gauge the demeanor of the city's inhabitants, Ms. Estremera," he said archly. "It's mine."

"Sorry, Sir," she said, suddenly timid.

"Make your report," he commanded.

"The plague continues to spread. It's moved beyond the Quarantine Zone, beyond the slum district as well. Although it's not as potent as the initial outbreak in early fall, there are no known survivors that have contracted the illness."

He turned to the final investigator. Gerald Stevens said, "Several groups have formed various coalitions around the City and have openly engaged in rebellious activities."

"Known affiliations?"

"None, Sir. None that have been discovered, and I interrogated several rigorously. I believe they are independently organized groups raising an insurgence to protest the decline of safety and living conditions."

"There will be connections to the Arcanists. Possibly Resurrectionists as well. Continue probing."

"Of course, Sir," Stevens said, though he did not believe he would find any such connections. "Part of the rhetoric of several of these rebellious groups is to

immediately abandon their homestead here in Malifaux. Hundreds have already done so. Given the casualties of the plague, the death toll of their own violent protests, and the fear of the rising drought and famine, we predict a sharp decline in the population. Save the initial criminals assigned work duty here as well as others refused travel visas, the growth of the rebellious parties seems to have infiltrated most walks of life. If conditions worsen as predicted--"

The Governor had heard enough and cut him off. "Matheson," he barked irritably. "Close the Breach to travel. Effective immediately. Limit the run to soulstone shipment and essential goods import."

"Immigration as well?" Lucius asked.

"No need to add to the discontent. No travel. No immigration. Double the Guardsmen's watch duty. It's time to declare martial law. No one moves within the city save essential duties your office will approve."

"It will require some time to implement such drastic changes."

"You have no time, Mr. Matheson. You'll enact my edict immediately. Spare no time. No manpower. See that it's handled." Lucius nodded. He would get it done. He never failed. "You're all dismissed," he said, and turned back to the city in the valley below him. They each filed out with Lucius at the end.

When they had gone he smiled, and his grip upon the railing tightened. "Even better than planned," he whispered. "Even better than planned." One construction worker just beyond the open door thought he heard the Governor chuckling.

Revelation of the Beast Within

January 19, 115 PF

Doctor Carl Morrow leaned close to the face of his patient, secured to the bed with leather straps a quarter inch thick and metal buckles reinforced beyond what might have been necessary for even the most robust and difficult of his patients. For Perdita, they were significantly thicker and stronger than would ever have been required. Especially now, given her comatose state these past months, unmoving save the subtle trembling of her lower lip as she'd gibber incoherently in the vast depths of her endless dreams.

His eyes, just inches from her flesh, watched a ray of sunlight fall upon the side of her face and gently warm her dark skin. "Ooooh," he whispered in awe as the line of her forehead and nose took on the glow spilling through the narrow window several feet beyond the bed. He ran his index finger down her face, between her eyes and along the bridge of her nose, tracing the sunlight that irradiated her flesh. "Perdita Ortega," he said in a whisper. He had a tendency to over-annunciate his words, and small droplets of spittle struck her earlobe and cheek as he punctuated the sounds. "So much rest time," he said, still gently stroking her facial features with the tip of his finger. It neared the tip of her nose. "Beauty sleep? Rest for the wicked?" He chuckled. His finger slid down the base of her nose and across the depression above her upper lip. "You've had both, dearest. More beautiful than any might desire. More wicked, too." His fingers traced the contour of her lips. "We're all wicked, aren't we?" His fingers tapped their way back up her face, striking with each word as he quietly said, "The monsters hidden here," and with the final word he tapped her forehead. "All those little monsters trapped in here. Busy, busy, busy." *All the monsters in here.*

Time meant nothing to Perdita. To Dr. Morrow, she had been there for over five months. To her, she had just arrived. The voice of a boy, a student lost at Kythera, struggled to speak to her again. But she couldn't hear him well. She was floating in a pool of dark water. Just her nose and lips rose above the surface. Her eyes couldn't see through the dark substance, turning the light from above a strange indigo.

"The truth," she heard the boy say.

"Don't say it," another voice, even more faint, said in the indistinct darkness above her.

An older voice, conveying wisdom in its words, said, "She can handle it. It's why she's here."

"She's here because she's dead."

"They're all dead."

"No, not yet. Not dead."

"There's no escaping Malifaux," another said as Perdita struggled to lift herself from the pool, to hear more clearly.

What's the truth? she asked.

"Don't tell her," the distant voice urged. "She's not ready. Doesn't know where she is."

"None of them do."

Where am I?

"Dead."

"No she's not."

"She's here, isn't she?"

"Not exactly."

"Then where is she?"

"I'm telling you, she's dead."

What's the truth?! she managed to scream in the darkness of her mind.

She couldn't speak to them the way she wanted to. Didn't understand where she was or how she had come to be there. The voices tried to show her what she needed to know, but they didn't know how to speak to her, either. They spoke over each other and contradicted one another. The voice of that young man, a student that went to Kythera on an expedition and never returned, his voice was stronger than the others. It rose above theirs to speak to her more conversationally about what they discovered at Kythera. He explained where she was. He explained *what* she was.

The others were right. She wasn't ready for the truth. It's not that she didn't like it. She couldn't accept it. His words were a revelation to her explaining what he had seen at Kythera – what they had all seen. It's the truth that had driven them mad. It's the madness that had led to them tearing into one another, ripping one another's flesh right off of their bodies.

"The little monsters are dancing in here," Dr. Morrow whispered. "Busy, busy, busy." He inhaled sharply, smelling her hair. It hadn't been washed in weeks. He didn't mind. She was intoxicating. "We all have those monsters we try to hide, don't we Ms. Ortega? Try to keep them out of the public eye. Try to keep them under wraps, as it were. Sometimes our monsters are harder to control than others."

Lucius Matheson stepped out of the shadow behind the doctor. He was silent in his movements and when he said, "Some monsters are more palpable than others," the doctor screeched and knocked his teeth against Perdita's cheek when he jumped. He stood and spun in a movement, and the Governor's Secretary was uncomfortably close. He fidgeted with his lab coat, pulling it taut in the front and buttoning it severely and quickly. "Some are more real than you realize," he added quietly.

Doctor Morrow smiled faintly and laughed uncomfortably.

Sternly, Lucius said, "Leave us." The doctor didn't argue, excusing himself without a word. Matheson loomed above the comatose body of Perdita, staring intently.

"We have need of you," he said to her, his voice dry and wispy. He pressed his open fingers down upon her face, spanning the breadth of her skull. He pressed violently, squeezing painfully. A soulstone was crushed in his other hand, the milky white vapors entwining his arm before he could redirect its powerful influence. "Awaken!" he commanded and his voice boomed.

Her eyes snapped open. The orbs were ashen gray, dull, reflecting no light, though thin bands of silver and purple swirled in their depths as if they were dark pools without end.

Far from the city where the Red Cage had fallen those many months ago, tearing a rift in the fabric separating this world from the aether, releasing the purple wave that had become known as The Event and left her asleep to the world, a cry came up from the unexplored depths of the hole that stretched for miles beyond the point of impact. It was angry and shrill and foreign to all people that had ever walked upon Malifaux's soil. The beast flew out of the pit on wings that stretched wide on thin membranes of flesh stretched between long boney fingers that protruded beyond the reptilian in barbed hooks. Its body stretched longer than a full grown stallion, but it was more like a great panther. It screeched again. Though too far away for her to hear, Perdita jerked upright, pulling at the straps holding her down.

"It's coming for me," she said. Bands of purple and silver swam in the depths of her gray eyes.

The creature shrieked again. Purple and silver bands crisscrossed through its ashen eyes. It knew where she was. It could find her anywhere. With a snap of its wings, it caught a draft, ascending on a course that led straight for Perdita.